AF689457

Progress in Nonlinear Differential Equations and Their Applications
Volume 12

Editor

Haim Brezis
Université Pierre et Marie Curie
Paris
and
Rutgers University
New Brunswick, N.J.

Editorial Board

A. Bahri, Rutgers University, New Brunswick
John Ball, Heriot-Watt University, Edinburgh
Luis Cafarelli, Institute for Advanced Study, Princeton
Michael Crandall, University of California, Santa Barbara
Mariano Giaquinta, University of Florence
David Kinderlehrer, Carnegie-Mellon University, Pittsburgh
Robert Kohn, New York University
P.L. Lions, University of Paris IX
Louis Nirenberg, New York University
Lambertus Peletier, University of Leiden
Paul Rabinowitz, University of Wisconsin, Madison

Seminar on Dynamical Systems

Euler International Mathematical Institute,
St. Petersburg, 1991

S. Kuksin
V. Lazutkin
J. Pöschel
Editors

Birkhäuser
Basel · Boston · Berlin

S. Kuksin
Mathematik
ETH Zentrum
8092 Zürich
Switzerland

V. Lazutkin
Euler International Mathematical Institute
Pesochnaya naber, 10
197022 St. Petersburg
Russia

J. Pöschel
Universität Bonn
Mathematik
Wegelerstr. 10
53115 Bonn
Germany

A CIP catalogue record for this book is available from the Library of Congress, Washington D.C., USA

Deutsche Bibliothek Cataloging-in-Publication Data
Seminar on Dynamical Systems <1991, Sanktpeterburg>:
Seminar on Dynamical Systems / Euler International
Mathematical Institute St. Petersburg, 1991. S. Kuksin ... ed. –
Basel ; Boston ; Berlin : Birkhäuser, 1994
(Progress in nonlinear differential equations and their applications ; Vol. 12)
ISBN 3-7643-2980-7
ISBN 0-8176-2980-7
NE: Kuksin, Sergej B. [Hrsg.]; Meždunarodnyj Matematičeskij Institut Imeni Ejlera <Sanktpeterburg>; GT

This work is subject to copyright. All rights are reserved, whether the whole or part of the material is concerned, specifically the rights of translation, reprinting, re-use of illustrations, broadcasting, reproduction on microfilms or in other ways, and storage in data banks. For any kind of use permission of the copyright owner must be obtained.

© 1994 The Euler International Mathematical Institute, and
Birkhäuser Verlag, P.O. Box 133, CH-4010 Basel
Printed on acid-free paper produced from chlorine-free pulp
Printed in Germany
ISBN 3-7643-2980-7
ISBN 0-8176-2980-7

9 8 7 6 5 4 3 2 1

CONTENTS

Introduction. vii

Part I. KAM theory and related topics. 1

1. Benettin, G., Galgani, L., Giorgilli, A. The dynamical foundation of classical statistical mechanics and the Boltzmann-Jeans conjecture 3
2. Lochak, P., Neishtadt, A.I., Niederman, L. Stability of nearly integrable convex hamiltonian system over exponentially long times 15
3. Chierchia, L. On the stability problem for nearly-integrable hamiltonian systems 35
4. Gelfreich, V.G. Separatrices splitting for the rapidly forced pendulum 47
5. Delshams, A., Seara, T.M. Exponentially small expressions for separatrix splitting 68
6. Moser, J. An unusual variational problem connected with Mather's theory for monotone twist mappings 81
7. Burago, D. Periodic Metrics 90
8. Kuksin, S.B., Pöschel, J. On the inclusion of analytic symplectic maps in analytic hamiltonian flows and its applications 96
9. Delgado, J., Lacomba, E.A., Llibre, J., Pérez, E. Poincaré Compactification of the Kepler and the collinear three body problems 117
10. Martinez, R., Simó, C. A note on the existence of heteroclinic orbits in the planar three-body problem 129
11. Bazzani, A. KAM tori for modulated symplectic maps 140
12. Bazzani, A., Turchetti, G. Analyticity of normalizing transformations for area preserving maps 155
13. Rüssmann, H. On the frequencies of quasi-periodic solutions of analytic nearly integrable hamiltonian systems 160
14. Sevryuk, M.B. New results in the reversible KAM theory 184

Part II. Infinite dimensional dynamical systems. 201

15. Chierchia, L., Perfetti, P. Maximal almost periodic solutions for Lagrangian equations on infinite dimensional tori 203
16. Denzler, J. Nonpersistence of breather solutions under perturbation of the Sine-Gordon equation 213

Part III. Miscellanea. 225

17. Fel'shtyn, A.L. Attractors, integrable hamiltonian systems and the Reidemeister torsion 227
18. Karasev, M., Vorobjev, Yu. Linear connections for hamiltonian dynamics over isotropic submanifold 235
19. Lerman, L.M., Umanskii, Ja.L. Four-dimensional integrable hamiltonian systems with simple singular points 253
20. Osipenko, G. Periodic points and Symbolic Dynamics 261
21. Osipenko, G., Ershov, E. On the perturbation of locally non-unique invariant manifolds 268
22. Veselov, A.P. Complex geometry of the billiard on the ellipsoid and quasicristallic curves 277

Dynamical Systems, Programme. 285

Introduction

The "Dynamical Systems Semester" took place at the Euler International Mathematical Institute in St. Petersburg, Russia, in the autumn of 1991. There were two workshops, October 14–25 and November 18–29, with more than 60 participants giving 70 talks. The titles of all talks are given at the end of this volume. Here we included 22 papers prepared by the authors especially for this volume, while the material of the other talks are published elsewhere.

The semester was sponsored by the Soviet Academy of Sciences and UNESCO. Since the new building of the Euler Institute was not ready at that moment, the sessions were held in the old building of the Steklov Mathematical Institute in the very center of St. Petersburg. Members of the staff of the Euler Institute were doing their best to organize properly the normal processing of the conference—not a simple task at that time because of the complications in the political and economical life in Russia just between the coup d'état in August and the dismantling of the Soviet Union in December. We are thankful to all of them.

* * *

One century ago Henri Poincaré in his famous book "Les méthodes nouvelles de la méchanique céleste" stressed the importance and the difficulty of the problem of three bodies which has been attracting the efforts of *geometricians* for a long time. He also formulated the *main problem of dynamics* as consisting of the investigation of the motions in Hamiltonian systems with a Hamiltonian function of the form

$$H(p,q) = H_0(p) + \mu H_1(p,q), \qquad (*)$$

where p, q are n-vectors, μ is a small parameter, and H_1 is 2π-periodic with respect to q. Many problems in celestial mechanics and in other branches of physics and mathematics can be reduced to $(*)$, and in particular to the problem of the stability of solutions of $(*)$: how fast and how far vary the momenta p for small μ? This question did not loose its importance up to now—see the paper by G. Benettin, L. Galgani and A. Giorgilli which opens the volume.

Was there any progress in studying this problem during the last hundred years?

Yes, of course! The celebrated KAM theory for nondegenerate systems gave rise to invariant KAM tori, which fill the bulk of the phase space of the system $(*)$. Incidentally, two of the three creators of KAM theory, Vladimir Arnol'd and Jürgen Moser, attended the conference, and their talks attracted a large number of people of the St. Petersburg mathematical community. The first creator, Andrei Kolmogorov, died in 1987.

But up to now very little is known about the behavior of trajectories of the system $(*)$ in the gaps between the KAM tori. The best known result by Nikolai Nekhoroshev—who also attended the conference—asserts that in the analytic case, under some generic conditions on H_0, the momenta p vary only over a distance of the order $O(\mu^b)$ during an exponentially long time interval of length $\exp(\mu^{-a})$. Here, a and b are some positive constants. The second paper of these Proceedings by P. Lochak, A.I. Neishtadt and L. Niederman contains a short self-contained proof of this estimate for the case of a convex hamiltonian H_0 with $a = 1/(2n)$ which seems to be optimal.

The drift of the momenta p may be due to the so-called "Arnol'd diffusion" discovered by V. Arnol'd in 1966. Up to now there is no rigorous proof of its existence in general, but the recent paper by L. Chierchia and G. Gallavotti makes a significant step toward that direction. We print here a short and informal account of its results written by the first author, while the original paper is available as a CARR Report in Mathematical Physics 15/92.

One of the difficulties in studying systems like $(*)$ is the exponential smallness of the splitting of separatrices with respect to the small parameter μ in $(*)$ which may arise in the analytic case. Recent progress in establishing asymptotic formulae for this exponentially small splitting in the case of the rapidly forced pendulum is presented in the paper by V. Gelfreich, and for a more general problem in the paper by A. Delshams and T.M. Seara. We hope that these methods will lead to a better understanding of the phenomenon of "Arnol'd diffusion".

Aside from the KAM tori, which represent the "stable" ingredient of motion, and the hypothetical drift of trajectories by Arnol'd diffusion, which represents the "unstable" one, there also exist the so-called cantori, which are the remnants of destroyed tori. The cantori were discovered in the early eighties by Percival, Aubry, and Mather, and Mather gave a rigorous proof of the existence of the cantori using Percival variational principle. The paper by Jürgen Moser in this volume gives a very interesting approach to this variational principle by introducing a small artificial viscosity term in the functional, that smoothens the solutions, which then tend to a Percival-Aubry-Mather set as the viscosity tends to zero.

As it happens, the main problem, which was initially the subject of attention for geometricians as pointed by Poincaré, was developed mainly by mathematicians applying analytical methods. It would be of great interest to restore the geometrical way of approaching the problems in question. We consider the small but substantial paper by Burago as a contribution in this direction.

Returning to the analytical setting, it is important to link two classes of dynamical systems: flows (continuous time) and diffeomorphisms (discrete time). The paper by S. Kuksin and J. Pöschel discusses such a link in the most difficult case of real analytic dynamical systems.

It is fortunate to have in this Proceedings also two papers directly devoted to the three body problem, one by J. Delgado et al., and one by R. Martines and C. Simó. Now one may ascertain that the problem of three bodies remains as unsolved and as rich with new mathematical phenomena as it was one century ago.

In the first Part entitled "KAM theory and related topics" we collected those papers whose topics grew out of Poincaré's treatise. Here we understand KAM theory in the widest possible sense. However, the last four papers of the first Part are devoted to KAM theory directly. These are the paper by A. Bazzani on KAM tori in the presence of time dependent parameter, another paper by A. Bazzani and G. Turchetti on analytic properties of the normalizing transformation near an elliptic point of a diffeomorphism in the complex domain, and a very technical and refined paper by H. Rüssmann which deals with an extension of the famous Kolmogorov theorem which KAM theory started with. The last paper of this Part is by M. Sevryuk and is devoted to so-called reversible systems, which are not Hamiltonian ones but admit a theory which is parallel to the classical KAM theory.

There is another circle of topics developed very recently—"infinite dimensional dynamical systems". Several talks of this circle were given at the workshops, and two of them entered this volume constituting its second Part.

The Theory of Dynamical Systems is a very wide area which spreads to all of mathematics, giving results and absorbing methods. The papers which have no immediate connection with the two areas mentioned before constitute the third Part called "Miscellanea". There we have papers representing both integrable and chaotic areas of modern dynamics.

We hope that this volume gives the reader a true and wide picture of modern developments in Dynamical Systems, especially Hamiltonian ones, as well as that of modern trends in this theory.

Sergei Kuksin *Vladimir Lazutkin* *Jürgen Pöschel*

Part I
KAM theory and related topics

THE DYNAMICAL FOUNDATIONS OF CLASSICAL STATISTICAL MECHANICS AND THE BOLTZMANN–JEANS CONJECTURE

GIANCARLO BENETTIN[1],
LUIGI GALGANI[2] AND ANTONIO GIORGILLI[2]

1. Overview

It is well known that the equipartition principle lies at the very basis of classical statistical mechanics. It is also known that the greatest difficulty with classical statistical mechanics is that some degrees of freedom seem to be frozen, and not to attain the energy expected from that principle. The problem we want to discuss here is whether such a phenomenon can be understood on a dynamical basis.

Usually, the difficulties related to the nonlinear character of the corresponding dynamical problem are just bypassed by making use of the so called ergodic *hypothesis*: essentially, one *assumes* that a typical dynamical system of the kind considered in statistical mechanics evolves towards some sort of equilibrium, well described by the canonical ensemble (see, for instance, the long and detailed discussion in the book of Khinchin [1]). The fact that other dynamical systems, like, e.g., the planetary one, do not present a statistical behaviour is tacitly attributed to the big difference either in the typical time scales or in the number of degrees of freedom between them and, say, a gas.

An old conjecture, going back to Boltzmann [2] and Jeans [3], is that in many cases of interest the equilibrium state, if any, is not reached in a reasonably short time; instead, each degree of freedom should have a characteristic relaxation time greatly increasing with the frequency. Boltzmann considered the model example of a gas of molecules with translational and rotational degrees of freedom. His remark was essentially that, if the molecules were perfectly symmetric, then there would be no energy exchange among the translational and the rotational degrees of freedom, so that the rotational energy would be constant; on the other hand, by the introduction of a small asymmetry one would expect to observe a relaxation to equilibrium after a characteristic relaxation time. In fact he spoke, even if without any definite justification, of relaxation times of the order of "days or years", so that the equilibrium would not occur in many ordinary experiments, and the rotational degrees of freedom would just appear as "frozen". Jeans studied the similar problem of the exchange of energy between translations and internal vibrations during the collisions of molecules. His idea, supported by heuristic considerations, was that there should be general mechanism according to which the energy exchange ΔE per collision could be estimated as

$$\Delta E \sim E_0 e^{-\tau\omega} , \tag{1}$$

where E_0 is a natural energy unit for the system, τ is a typical collision time, and ω is the internal frequency of the molecule; it is assumed that $\tau\omega$ is large. Thus, in order to observe a significant exchange of energy (e.g., of the order of E_0) one would need a number $N \sim e^{\tau\omega}$ of collisions, and so a time $T \sim T_0 e^{\tau\omega}$, where T_0 is the average time between two collisions. He also remarked that, in realistic situations, such a time could be as large as "hundreds of centuries", or even "billions of years". For a detailed discussion including quotations of the original works, see ref. [4].

The point of view of Boltzmann and Jeans was in fact soon forgotten by the scientific community (essentially, after the 1911 Solvay conference): the interest of physicists was captured by the impressive and successful development of quantum mechanics. But more than 40 years later two works caused a renewal of interest around nonlinear problems connected with statistical mechanics. We refer here, on the one hand, to the numerical work of Fermi, Pasta and Ulam on their celebrated model of nonlinear chain [5], and, on the other hand, to the not less celebrated Kolmogorov's theorem on the persistence of conditionally periodic motions under perturbations of nonlinear integrable Hamiltonian systems [6]. Let us briefly recall these results.

The initial purpose of the research of Fermi, Pasta and Ulam was, as claimed by the authors, to observe the rate of thermalization of the system. But they write: "Let us say that the the results of our numerical computations show features which were, from the beginning, surprising to us. Instead of a gradual, continuous flow of energy from the first mode to the higher modes, all of the problems show an entirely different behaviour. (...) Instead of a gradual increase of all the higher modes, the energy is exchanged, essentially, among only a certain few." The relevance of the FPU work for the foundations of Statistical Mechanics was pointed out by Izrailev an Chirikov and their coworkers [7]. In general, it seems that all such authors were suggesting that the dynamics should be consistent with equipartition in the thermodynamic limit, i.e., the limit $n \to \infty$ with finite specific energy E/n. A first clear indication of a result going in the opposite direction was given by Bocchieri, Scotti, Bearzi and Loinger [8], who studied a chain of the FPU type, just replacing the cubic or quartic nonlinearity of the original model with the more realistic Lennard–Jones potential. They observed the existence of a kind of energy "threshold" above which a statistical behaviour (in the classical sense) sets up, the threshold in specific energy E/n being largely independent of n (in the range $10 < n < 100$). It is interesting here to remark that the existence of a threshold was also discovered (before Bocchieri et al.) by Hénon and Heiles [9] in a very simple model with two degrees of freedom, thus contradicting the idea that the statistical behaviour should be due just to the large number of degrees of freedom. Subsequent studies, most of them performed in Italy, confirmed these pioneering results, also adding a number of new informations of phenomenological character [10]. But an analytical understanding of the problem was still completely lacking; the only exceptions were some rather awkward estimates provided by Izrailev and Chirikov, where reference was made for the first time to the mathematical works related to what is now called KAM theory.

The theorem of Kolmogorov, and the related theorems of Moser and Arnold, deal with small perturbations of integrable systems, like, e.g., the planetary system. As is known, they are concerned with an analytic Hamiltonian of the type

$$H(p,q) = H_0(p) + \varepsilon H_1(p,q,\varepsilon), \tag{2}$$

where $p \in \mathbf{R}^n$ are the action variables, $q \in \mathbf{T}^n$ are angle variables and ε is a small parameter controlling the size of the perturbation due to H_1; this problem was referred to by Poincaré as "the fundamental problem of dynamics". For $\varepsilon = 0$ the phase space is foliated into invariant tori p =const, carrying either periodic or quasi periodic motions. The KAM theory states, in rough terms, that for ε small enough most (in the sense of the Lebesgue measure) of the invariant tori are not destroyed by the perturbation. The possible interest of such a result for statistical mechanics is due to the fact that the ergodic hypothesis is incompatible with the existence of a set of invariant tori of positive measure. However, there is a common objection, that we summarize in a few sentences. "The KAM theorem applies *if ε is small enough*". Although nothing is stated for large values of ε, this can be interpreted as a claim that if the perturbation is larger than some critical value, ε_* say, then the arguments of classical statistical mechanics should be applied (by the way, this agrees with the existence of a threshold, as observed by Hénon and by Bocchieri et al). But, according to the available analytical estimates, ε_* is a rapidly decreasing function of the number n of degrees of freedom. Thus, the KAM theorem is meaningless in the thermodynamic limit." Although some recent works have established the existence of invariant tori (but nothing is said about their measure) in infinite systems, the question should be considered, in the best case, as still open.

Even if we disregard the latter question, the KAM theory, despite its invaluable mathematical beauty and interest, seems not to be suited for application to physical systems. Indeed, the invariant tori form a nowhere dense set in the phase space. Moreover, their complement is connected for systems with more than two degrees of freedom. Thus, an orbit could in principle go anywhere in the complement of the invariant tori. This possible phenomenon has been named "Arnold diffusion" because Arnold illustrated it in a simple, although non "generic", example [11] (a proof of the existence of diffusion in typical Hamiltonian systems has been recently found by Chierchia and Gallavotti [12]). This state of affairs could be hardly compatible, e.g., with an approximate knowledge of the initial conditions. In this respect the less famous Nekhoroshev's theorem is more relevant, in our opinion [13]. In its original formulation the theorem can be stated, roughly, as follows: for the Hamiltonian system [14] the actions p satisfy

$$|p(t) - p(0)| < C\varepsilon^b \quad \text{for} \quad |t| < T_0 \exp\left(\frac{\varepsilon_*}{\varepsilon}\right)^a , \tag{3}$$

provided ε is small enough (say, less than ε_*) and the unperturbed Hamiltonian H_0 satisfies some steepness (or convexity) conditions. Here, C, T_0, b, a and ε_* are constants depending on the number n of degrees of freedom. The interesting point is the exponential dependence of the time on the perturbation parameter ε: in realistic situations, such a time could be as large as the estimated age of the universe (see also refs. [14]).

The similarity between Nekhoroshev's result and the conjecture of Boltzmann and Jeans is evident. However, making explicit the connection is not easy at all. The main difficulty is that in the formulation of the theorem there are constants which, according to the original estimates, vanish when the number n of degrees of freedom increases to infinity. Typical estimates are $a \sim 1/n$, and that ε_* and T_0 decrease as fast as some power of $1/n$. Thus, the theorem seems not to be applicable to the large systems of interest for statistical mechanics, its relevance being limited to systems with only few degrees of freedom (e.g., the planetary system).

Despite this difficulty, we maintain that the Nekhoroshev theory can be used to give the conjectures of Boltzmann and Jeans a strong support. In this spirit we started a long investigation, both from a numerical and an analytical viewpoint. Our aim here is to give a short but comprehensive report on the state of our research. For a discussion of the possible relevance for the foundations of quantum mechanics see [15]. The results we are presenting here are the fruit of a long collaboration among the authors, and more recently with younger coworkers, namely Dario Bambusi, Andrea Carati, Alessandra Celletti, Francesco Fassò, Alessandro Morbidelli, Andrea Martinoli, Paolo Sempio and Stefano Vanzini.

2. Models, and numerical results

We consider here two classes of models: molecular collisions, and FPU type models. The underlying idea in all these investigations is just the conjecture of Boltzmann and Jeans: we bring into evidence the fundamental role played by the frequencies of the system, and the existence of exponential laws of Nekhoroshev type.

2.1 One–dimensional model of a diatomic gas

We consider n identical molecules moving on a segment of length L with fixed end points; each molecule consists of two atoms connected by a linear spring; one of the atoms is neutral, the other one has a charge; the charged atoms interact through a smooth, short range potential, like

$$V(r) = V_0 \frac{\sigma}{r} \exp\left[-\left(\frac{r}{\sigma}\right)^2 \right] , \tag{4}$$

where r is the distance and V_0 and σ are constants. This model was proposed and studied in ref. [16]. Denoting by x_j the coordinate of the center of mass of a molecule, by ξ_j the length of the molecule, by p_j and π_j the corresponding momenta, by $m/2$ the mass of an atom and by ω the internal frequency of the molecule, the Hamiltonian of the system can be written as

$$H = h_\omega(\pi, \xi) + \sum_{j=1}^{n} \frac{p_j^2}{m} + \sum_{j=0}^{n} V\big((x_{j+1} + \xi_{j+1}) - (x_j + \xi_j)\big) \ . \tag{5}$$

where

$$h_\omega(\pi, \xi) = \frac{1}{2} \sum_{j=1}^{n} \left(\frac{\pi_j^2}{m} + m\omega^2 \xi_j^2 \right) \ . \tag{6}$$

Our idea was to consider the system h_ω, describing the internal vibrations, as essentially decoupled from the translations. Indeed, the coupling term coming from V can be proven to decrease as $1/\omega$. We computed the auto–correlation function $\varrho(\tau)$, for $\tau \geq 0$ of the total vibrational energy h_ω. In case of a statistical behaviour, $\varrho(\tau)$ is expected to decay from the value 1 at $\tau = 0$ to zero. However, since we are interested in observing the relaxation time to equilibrium, we consider as a good indication the time τ_c at which $\varrho(\tau)$ attains the value 1/2. The numerical experiment was performed for different values of the internal frequency ω and for $n = 16$ and $n = 64$. In both cases we found that τ_c as a function of ω is consistent with the law

$$\tau_c(\omega) = A e^{\alpha\omega} , \tag{7}$$

with suitable constants A and α. A comparison with the Nekhoroshev exponential law (3) shows immediately that the exponent a should have here the value 1, and not $1/n$ as in the best theoretical estimates. We shall come back to this point in discussing the analytical results.

Recently the same system was considered also by Erpenbeck and Cohen [17], with the aim of proving that the relaxation time is actually short, so that the conclusions of statistical mechanics do apply. They replaced the analytical potential (4) by a hard core interaction, and found relaxation to equilibrium in short times. In our opinion, this should be expected a priori. Indeed, the typical interaction time of the hard core potential is zero; on the other hand, as will be discussed below, the exponential bound has to be expected only for frequencies higher than the inverse of the typical interaction time.

2.2 Molecular collisions

A second set of numerical experiments is more strictly connected with the verification of the Jeans law (1). This can be heuristically justified as follows. The exchange of energy in a gas between the translational degrees of freedom and the rotational or the vibrational ones is due to the collisions between molecules. Now, one has to expect that the most efficient mechanism is the two body collision, while the contribution due to collisions of more than two molecules should be irrelevant. Thus, in order to show that the relaxation time to equilibrium for a gas can exceed any physically realistic time scale, it should be sufficient to prove that the exchange of energy in a single collision is actually exponentially small with the frequency.

The model studied is either a purely rotating or a purely vibrating molecule which collides with a wall. The system is described by the Hamiltonian

$$H(\pi,\varphi,p,x) = \frac{\pi^2}{2I} + \frac{p^2}{2m} + V(\varphi,x) \ , \tag{8}$$

in the case of the rotating molecule, and by

$$H(\pi,\xi,p,x) = \frac{1}{2}(\pi^2+\omega^2\xi^2) + \frac{p^2}{2m} + V(\xi,x) \ , \tag{9}$$

for the vibrating molecule. Here, p, x are canonical variables associated with the translation, π,φ and π,ξ are associated with the rotation and the vibration respectively, and V is the potential describing the interaction with the wall. The potentials used have the form

$$V(r) = U\frac{e^{-(r/d)^2}}{r/d}$$

with $r = x + a\cos\varphi$ and $r = \xi - x$ in the rotational and in the vibrational cases respectively; U, d and a are constants. These models have been proposed and studied in refs. [18] and [19].

Denoting by v and ω the initial velocity and angular velocity respectively of the molecule, and by Φ the initial value of the phase φ (either of the rotator or of the oscillator representing the internal vibration), one computes the energy exchange ΔE between the translational and the rotational energy after one collision. Clearly, ΔE depends on v, ω and Φ. The results can be summarized as follows.

i. For not too small ω the dependence of ΔE on Φ follows quite closely a sinusoidal law like

$$\Delta E = E_0(v, \omega) + E_1(v, \omega) \sin(\Phi - \Phi_0) .$$

ii. Both the average E_0 and the coefficient E_1 of the zero–average term follow an exponential law of Jeans type, precisely

$$E_0 = \mathcal{E}_0 e^{-\tau_0 \omega} , \quad E_1 = \mathcal{E}_1 e^{-\tau_1 \omega} , \quad \tau_0 = 2\tau_1 ;$$

moreover, the ratio $\mathcal{E}_0/\mathcal{E}_1$ is independent of v.

iii. Finally, τ_0 and τ_1 are decreasing functions of v, apparently faster than v^{-1}.

2.3 Systems of FPU type

As is well known, the FPU system is a chain of $n+2$ identical mass point on a line connected by identical nonlinear springs; the ends of the chain are fixed, so that the system has n degrees of freedom. The system considered here is a modification of the FPU original system, in the sense that the chain is composed by an even number of alternating light and heavy masses. The Hamiltonian of the system can be written as

$$H(x, y) = \frac{1}{2} \sum_{j=0}^{n} \left[\frac{y_j^2}{m_j} + (x_{j+1} - x_j)^2 \right] + \frac{\alpha}{3} \sum_{j=0}^{n} (x_{j+1} - x_j)^3 + \frac{\beta}{4} \sum_{j=0}^{n} (x_{j+1} - x_j)^4 , \tag{10}$$

where $m_j = 1$ for j odd and $m_j = m < 1$ for j even; for $m = 1$ one recovers the original FPU model. Here, x, y are canonically conjugate coordinates, and α, β are constants.

The interesting feature of this model is the frequency spectrum, which is given by

$$(\omega_l^{\pm})^2 = \frac{1 + m \pm \sqrt{1 + m^2 + 2m \cos 2k_l}}{m} , \quad k_l = \frac{l\pi}{n+1} , \quad 1 \le l \le \frac{n}{2} . \tag{11}$$

Here, the signs $\pm$ refer to the two possible choices of the sign in computing the square root. For $m \ll 1$ the spectrum splits into two well separated components:

the set of frequencies ω^- constitute the so called acoustic modes, while the frequencies ω^+ characterize the so called optical modes. Thus, the system can be considered as composed of two well defined subsystems, namely the acoustic and the optical ones, with a small coupling between them; moreover, the frequencies of the optical modes are very close to each other, so that they can be considered essentially as equal. The results reported here were published in ref. [20].

The results for the FPU model ($m = 1$) can be summarized in a few words: the harmonic actions of the system behave as predicted by the Nekhoroshev estimate (3), but it seems quite evident that the freezing disappears with increasing n. Indeed, a fitting of the experimental data for values of n ranging from 6 to 120 shows that the constants T_0 and ε^* go to zero roughly as $1/n^2$, and a goes to zero roughly as $1/n$. These results agree with the best analytical estimates available.

Things are very different for the FPU model with alternating masses, namely with $m \ll 1$. The relevant parameter here is $\lambda = \omega/\omega^-_{\rm max}$, where ω is the average frequency of the optical modes, and $\omega^-_{\rm max}$ is the maximal frequency of the acoustic modes. The quantity of interest is the harmonic energy of the optical subsystem, that we shall denote by E^+, or, more precisely, the maximal absolute value of its time derivative $|\dot{E}^+|$. All the experiments refer to initial data with the whole energy initially concentrated on the subsystem of the acoustic modes, with *specific* energy E/n constant as n is varied. The value of n ranged form 6 to 200, and the value of λ from 10 to 400. The results can be summarized as follows.

i. The two subsystems go rapidly to separate equilibria.

ii. Only a very small amount of the energy flows toward the subsystem of the optical modes, according to the Nekhoroshev type law

$$\lambda |\dot{E}^+| < A e^{-B\lambda} , \tag{12}$$

with A and B constants.

iii. The constant B is apparently independent of n, while the behaviour of A is not well established; however, A appears to grow less than $\log n$.

3. Analytical results

As explained in Section 1, the greatest problem in dealing with the analytical apparatus of perturbation theory, and in particular with Nekhoroshev like results, is the dependence of the estimates on the number n of degrees of freedom.

Looking at the exponential law (3), it is immediately seen that the most dangerous constant is the exponent a. Now, some recent analytical works [21] show that the behaviour $a \sim 1/n$ is essentially optimal, as is also indicated by the numerical experiment on the FPU model discussed in Sect. 2.3. At first sight, this seem to confirm the idea that the exponential relaxation time of the Nekhoroshev theorem is not relevant for statistical mechanics. However, in our opinion, this means only that in the ordinary formulation of Nekhoroshev's theorem one is still referring to a too strong property: the separate conservation of *all* the actions. On the other hand, the numerical experiment illustrated in Sect. 2.1 suggest the possibility that there are only a few conserved quantities. This is the basis of the analytical approach that we now illustrate.

The general idea is to consider a system with an Hamiltonian of the form

$$H(\pi, \xi, p, x) = h_\omega(\pi, \xi) + \hat{h}(p, x) + f(\xi, x) \ , \tag{13}$$

where

$$h_\omega(\pi, \xi) = \frac{1}{2} \sum_{j=1}^{\nu} \left(\pi_j^2 + \omega_j^2 \xi_j^2 \right) \ . \tag{14}$$

Here, $h_\omega(\pi, \xi)$ describes a system of harmonic oscillators with an n-vector of frequencies $\omega = (\omega_1, \dots, \omega_n)$; $\hat{h}(p, x)$ is the Hamiltonian of a generic system with n degrees of freedom, and $f(\pi, \xi, p, x)$ is a coupling term, which is assumed to vanish for $\xi = 0$. Remark that the hamiltonian $\hat{h}(p, x)$ is not assumed to be integrable; one just needs some hypothesis meaning essentially that the typical frequencies characterizing that system are small with respect to the frequencies ω. Thus, one can say that the system actually considered is composed of two subsystems characterized by well separated proper frequencies. The interesting fact is that all the models illustrated in Sect. 2, with the only exception of the original FPU model (i.e., with $m = 1$) can be given this form. This system was investigated analytically, in the light of Nekhoroshev theorem, in refs. [22], which refer to the simpler case $\nu = 1$ and in ref. [23] for arbitrary ν.

Under quite general hypotheses one proves the following: if there are s independent resonance relations between the frequencies (i.e., there are s independent vectors $k \in \mathbf{Z}^\nu$ such that $k \cdot \omega = 0$), then one can find $\nu - s$ quantities the time derivatives of which are exponentially small with the frequencies ω. More precisely, denoting by Φ any of these quantities, and introducing a parameter λ by $\omega = \lambda\Omega$ in such a way that Ω is of the same size as the proper frequencies of $\hat{h}(p, x)$, one has the estimate

$$|\dot{\Phi}| < A \exp\left[-\left(\frac{\lambda}{\lambda_*} \right)^{1/(\nu - s)} \right] \tag{15}$$

with suitable constants A and λ_*. This formula can be used to conclude that $\Delta\Phi = |\Phi(t) - \Phi(0)|$ is either exponentially small for a short time, or of the order, say, $1/\lambda$ for an exponentially large time.

Comparing (15) with the exponential law (3) one immediately sees that the constant a appearing there is $1/(\nu - s)$. This fact is particularly interesting when h_ω is a completely resonant system, which means $s = \nu - 1$, and so $a = 1$. This is exactly the case for the one–dimensional model of gas illustrated in Sect. 2.1, and also for the FPU model with alternating masses of Sect. 2.3 (in the latter case the optical frequencies are not exactly equal, but the small difference can be considered as a perturbation). This removes the worst dependence on n in the exponential, and gives full theoretical support to the numerical result $a = 1$. Remark however that in this case there is *only one* conserved quantity, which is nothing but the harmonic energy h_ω. Thus, the system of oscillators behaves essentially as if it were isolated from $\hat{h}$, but nothing can be said about its internal dynamics, which could be expected to be chaotic, as was observed in the case of the optical frequencies in the modified FPU model.

A very recent analytical result for infinite systems was published in ref.[24]. The theorem is quite general, but let us discuss only its relations with the modified FPU model. In this case one proves that if the *total* energy of the system is small enough, then the harmonic energy satisfies the estimate (15), with *all* the constants independent of n. This gives an almost complete support to the numerical results of Sect. 2.3. The support is not complete, because the numerical experiment refers to the case of fixed *specific* energy, which is the interesting one for statistical mechanics. However, we think that such a result cannot be improved on a purely dynamical basis. The reason, roughly speaking, is the following: one can not exclude by dynamical considerations that the whole energy of the optical system gets concentrated for a long time on a single optical mode, while in working out the analytical estimates one has to take into account also such an unlikely situation. A full result useful for statistical mechanics could perhaps be obtained by adding statistical considerations on the initial data (see also [25]).

4. Conclusions

Let us now summarize the whole discussion about the problem of the dynamical foundations of Classical Statistical Mechanics. Usually one mentions the problem of proving ergodicity, or rather mixing, in order to justify the use of the traditional equilibrium ensembles. Now, the definition of ergodicity or mixing makes reference to infinite times. In the present paper we have made reference to a somehow complementary problem, namely that of the time necessary for each subsystem to reach equilibrium. Indeed, as first suggested by Boltzmann and Jeans and then supported by modern mathematical theorems it can occur that the relaxation times might be exponentially large with some parameter, typically a characteristic frequency, of a subsystem. Thus, the ergodicity or mixing of the whole system might be compatible with a freezing of a subsystem (i.e., essentially a nonequilibrium situation) over time scales which from a physical point of view are incommensurable (a considerable slice of eternity, in the words of Littlewood).

The problem of giving a rigorous proof of the existence of nonequilibrium situations of such a type for systems of interest for Statistical Mechanics should be considered, as we have tried to show here, still undecided. However, things seem to have changed a lot with respect to twenty years ago, when in the scientific community it was considered as almost obvious that the freezing phenomena discussed above should not occur in Classical Statistical Mechanics; it seems to us that the opposite conjecture, supported especially by the Italian school, is today in rather good shape.

References

1. A. I. Khinchin: *Mathematical foundations of Statistical Mechanics*, Dover, New York (1949).

2. L. Boltzmann: Nature **51**, 413–415 (1895).

3. J. H. Jeans: Phil. Magazine **6**, 279 (1903) and Phil. Magazine **10**, 91 (1905).

4. L. Galgani: *Relaxation Times and the Foundations of Classical Statistical Mechanics in the Light of Modern Perturbation Theory,* in *Non-Linear Evolution and Chaotic Phenomena*, G. Gallavotti and A.M. Anile Editors, Plenum Press, New York (1988).

5. E. Fermi, J. Pasta and S. Ulam: *Los Alamos report No. LA–1940*, later published in Lect. Appl. Math. **15**, 143 (1955).

6. A. N. Kolmogorov: Dokl. Akad. Nauk SSSR **98**, 527–530 (1954);

   J. Moser: Nachr. Akad. Wiss. Göttingen Math. Phys. Kl. II, 1–20 (1962);

   V. I. Arnold: Russ. Math. Surv., **18**, 9 (1963) and Russ. Math. Surv. **18** N.6, 85 (1963).

7. F. M. Izrailev and B. V. Chirikov: Sov. Phys. Dokl. **11**, 30 (1966).

8. P. Bocchieri, A. Scotti, B. Bearzi and A. Loinger: Phys. Rev. A **2**, 2013 (1970).

9. M. Hénon and C. Heiles: Astron. J. **69** (1964).

10. E. Diana, L. Galgani, M. Casartelli, G. Casati and A. Scotti: Teor. Mat. Fiz. **29**, 213 (1976) [Theor. Math. Phys. **29**, 1022 (1976)];

    M. Casartelli, E. Diana, L. Galgani and A. Scotti: Phys. Rev. A **13**, 1921 (1976);

    R. Livi, M. Pettini, S. Ruffo, M. Sparpaglione and A. Vulpiani: Phys. Rev. A **28**, 3544 (1983);

    R. Livi, M. Pettini, S. Ruffo and A. Vulpiani: Phys. Rev. A **31**, 2740 (1985).

11. V. I. Arnold: Sov. Math. Dokl. **5**, 581–585 (1964).

12. L. Chierchia and G. Gallavotti: *Drift and diffusion in phase space*, preprint CARR (1992).

13. N. N. Nekhoroshev: Russ. Math. Surveys **32** N.6, 1–65 (1977); Trudy Sem. Petrovs. N.5, 5–50 (1979);

G. Benettin, L. Galgani and A. Giorgilli: Cel. Mech **37**, 1-25 (1985).

14. J. K. Moser: Nachr. Akad. Wiss. Göttingen, Math. Phys. K1 IIa, nr.6, 87–120 (1955);

J. E. Littlewood: Proc. London Math. Soc.(3), **9**, 343–372 and 525–543 (1959).

15. L. Galgani: *The quest for Planck's constant in classical physics,* in F. Guerra, M. Loffredo and C. Marchioro eds., *Probabilistic methods in mathematical physics,* World Scientific, Singapore (1992).

16. G. Benettin, L. Galgani and A. Giorgilli: Phys. Lett. A, **120** N.1, 23–27 (1987).

17. J. J. Erpenbeck and E.D.G. Cohen: Phys. Rev. A **38**, 3058 (1988).

E. G. D. Cohen and A. Monge: *Statistical mechanical behaviour of dynamical systems: a one–dimensional model of diatomic molecules*, in *Fundamental problems in Statistical Mechanics* VII, H. van Beijeren ed., Elsevier Sc. Publ. B.V. (1990).

18. O. Baldan and G. Benettin: J. Stat. Phys. **62**, 201 (1991).

19. P. Sempio: Ph.D. thesis, in preparation.

20. L. Galgani, A. Giorgilli, A. Martinoli, and S. Vanzini: *On the problem of energy equipartition for large systems of the Fermi–Pasta–Ulam type: analytical and numerical estimates,* Physica D, to appear.

21. P. Lochak: Uspekhi Math. Nauk. (1992), to be translated in Russian Math. Surv.; Russian Math. Surv.;

P. Lochak and A. Neishtadt: Chaos, (1992);

J. Pöschel: Math. Zeitschrift, to appear.

22. A. I. Neishtadt: Prikl. Matem. Mekan. **45**, 80 (1981) and PMM U.S.S.R. **45**, 58 (1982);

G. Benettin, L. Galgani and A. Giorgilli: Comm. Math. Phys., **113**, 87–103, (1987).

23. G. Benettin, L. Galgani and A. Giorgilli: Comm. Math. Phys., **121**, 557–601, (1989).

24. D. Bambusi and A. Giorgilli: *Exponential stability of states close to resonance in infinite dimensional Hamiltonian systems,* J. Stat. Phys., to appear.

25. D. Escande, H. Kantz, R. Livi and S. Ruffo: *Gibbsian check of the validity of Gibbsian calculations through dynamical observables,* preprint.

[1] Universit à di Padova, Dipartimento di Matematica Pura e applicata, Via G. Belzoni 7, 35131 Padova, Italy

[2] Dipartimento di Matematica dell' Universit à di Milano Via Saldini 50, 20133 Milano, Italy

STABILITY OF NEARLY INTEGRABLE CONVEX HAMILTONIAN SYSTEMS OVER EXPONENTIALLY LONG TIMES

P. LOCHAK[1], A. I. NEISTADT[2] AND L. NIEDERMAN[3]

I INTRODUCTION

In the present paper, we shall study the stability of a near integrable Hamiltonian system over finite but very long intervals of times. So we look at the system governed by the Hamiltonian:

$$H(p,q) = h(p) + f(p,q) \text{ with } (p,q) \in R^n \times T^n,\ T = R/Z,$$

where (p,q) are action-angle variables of the integrable Hamiltonian h. We assume that H is **analytic** over some domain $G \times T^n$ ($G \subset R^n$ a "nice" domain say convex open) and that h is a **convex** function ($\nabla^2 h(p)$ is a sign definite symmetric matrix). The perturbation f is of size ε (see below).

We prove that for initial conditions $(p(0), q(0))$ with $p(0) \in G$ not too close from the boundary, one has:

$$||p(t) - p(0)|| \leq R(\epsilon) \text{ for } |t| \leq \mathcal{T}(\epsilon)\ , \tag{1}$$

provided $\varepsilon \leq \varepsilon_0$, with $R(\varepsilon)$ of order ε^b, $\mathcal{T}(\varepsilon)$ of order $\exp(c/\varepsilon^a)$.

For the *stability exponents* (a,b) one may take: $a = b = 1/(2n)$. Such estimates as (1) were first obtained by N. N. Nekhorochev ([2]) in the case where h is assumed to be *steep*, a weaker requirement than convexity, but with different values of the exponents a and b. Recently P. Lochak ([1]) introduced a very different proof method which in particular allowed him to reach the value $a = 1/(2n+2)$ in the convex case for the exponent which governs the time of stability $\mathcal{T}(\varepsilon)$. Our purpose here is to present a short self-contained proof leading to the value $a = 1/(2n)$; we follow [1] closely, except for an improvement of an analytic lemma (see below II.a) which originates in Neistadt ([3]) .

The value of this improvement lies mainly in that $1/(2n)$ is likely to be **optimal** in the sense that on longer timescales, Arnold's diffusion should switch on, leading to a drift of the action variables of order 1; this is predicted by heuristic reasonnings and computations to be found in papers of B. V. Chirikov ([5]) and, under a different guise, in [1].

We refer once and for all to [1] for background informations, corollaries and further applications of the method we use.

We notice that this value of the exponent has been recently obtained by Pöschel (Preprint [7]) where he uses the original proof method of N. N. Nekhorochev. But we stress that the method developped here (from [1]) suggests a rather different picture than the usual one and draws a sharp qualitative distinction between convex systems which are encountered frequently in nature and other strictly non linear (steep) systems. The most striking qualitative new feature that emerges is probably the role of the resonance phenomenon over finite but exponentially long times.

The scheme of the proof is as follows. Let $\omega(p) = \nabla h(p) \in R^n$ be the frequency vector; if $\omega_0 = \omega(p_0)$ is rational (i.e. multiple of an integer one) then the torus $p = p_0$ is filled with closed orbits of the unperturbed system with common period T such that $T\omega_0 \in Z^n$. We shall first study stability properties of the system in the neighbourhood of such a periodic torus (Part II) where we will reach the exponents $a = b = 1/2$. Then we use Dirichlet's theorem which prescribes a minimal rate of approximation of the vectors of R^n by rational ones; it allows here to approach an arbitrary point in the space of the action variables by points corresponding to periodic tori and apply to the latter the stability results of Part II in order to obtain (1) for an arbitrary initial condition.

II Stability in the neighbourhood of a periodic torus

The Hamiltonian H is supposed to be defined and *analytic* in a neighbourhood of the origin, more precisely on a complex domain $\mathcal{D} = D(R, \rho, \sigma)$, $(\rho > 0, \sigma > 0)$ defined as follows: let B_R be the ball of radius R around the origin, then:

$$\mathcal{D} = D(R, \rho, \sigma) = \left\{(p, q) \in C^{2n},\ \text{dist}\,(p, B_R) \leq \rho\ ;\ \Re(q) \in T^n\ ;\ |\Im(q)| \leq \sigma\right\}\ , \tag{2}$$

with $|\Im(q)| = \text{Sup}_i(|\Im(q_i)|)$; H is supposed to be continuous on the boundary of $\mathcal{D}$. Note that the real part of $\mathcal{D}$ is $B_{R+\rho} \times T^n$. When $0 \leq \delta \leq \rho$ and $0 \leq \xi \leq \sigma$ we denote by $\mathcal{D} - (\delta, \xi)$ the domain $D(R, \rho - \delta, \sigma - \xi)$.

The norm $||.||_{\mathcal{D}}$ is the sup norm (L^∞) over $\mathcal{D}$ and we define E and ε by:

$$||H||_{\mathcal{D}} = E\ ,\ ||f||_{\mathcal{D}} = \varepsilon E\ ,\ \varepsilon \geq 0\ . \tag{3}$$

The euclidian norm is denoted $||.||$, and $||.||_{\mathcal{D}}$ for a vector valued function on $\mathcal{D}$ is defined as the supremum over $\mathcal{D}$ of the euclidian norm of its value.

Let $\omega(p) = \nabla h(p) \in R^n$ and $A(p) = \nabla^2 h(p) \in \mathcal{M}_n(R)$ be the frequency vector and the hessian matrix. In this section $\omega_0 = \omega(0)$ is supposed to be

rational of (minimal) period T, i.e. $T\omega_0 \in Z^n$; so the unperturbed flow is periodic of period T on the torus $p = 0$. We denote $\Omega = ||\omega_0||$ (euclidian norm). Since h is supposed here to be convex so that $A(p)$ is sign definite – say – positive. More precisely if m is a lower bound of the spectrum of A over the real part of the domain, then:

$$\forall p \in B_{R+\rho} \subset R^n,\ \forall v \in R^n\ :\ A(p)v.v \geq m||v||^2\ , \tag{4}$$

where $m > 0$ and $u.v$ denotes the scalar product of two vectors u, v. We will denote M the operator norm of A on $\mathcal{D}$ (the complex domain): $||A(p)v|| \leq M||v||$.

All the constants will be explicitely computed as simple functions of the parameters Ω, m, M, ρ, σ, E, T.

a) Analytic part of the proof:

For $g(q)$ a function defined on the torus, we denote $< g >$ its *time average* along the orbits of the flow directed along ω_0, i.e.:

$$< g > (q) = \frac{1}{T}\int_0^T g(q + \omega_0 t)\,dt.$$

We shall say that g is *resonant* (with respect to ω_0) if $g =< g >$, which means that g is constant along the orbits of the flow directed along ω_0. We say that g is *non resonant* if $< g >= 0$.

Viewing p as a parameter, the Hamiltonian can be decomposed as:

$$H(p,q) = h(p) + Z(p,q) + N(p,q) \tag{5}$$

with:

- $Z(p,q)$ resonant with respect to ω_0,
- $N(p,q)$ non resonant with respect to ω_0.

Using an averaging procedure we will construct a near-identity canonical transformation which permits to reduce the size of the non resonant part of H. This analytic lemma will first be used in a preliminary transformation to reduce significantly this non resonant part. It will then be used iteratively to define a sequence of transformations which permit at each step to reduce geometrically the size of the non resonant part of the perturbation. In the end the composition of all the previous transformations gives a Hamiltonian with an exponentially small non resonant part (in the new variables).

We have $||Z+N||_{\mathcal{D}} = ||f||_{\mathcal{D}} = \varepsilon E$ and define η by $||N||_{\mathcal{D}} = \eta E$, with $\eta \leq 2\varepsilon$ because $N = f- < f >$ and $|| < f > ||_{\mathcal{D}} \leq ||f||_{\mathcal{D}}$ ($< . >$ is an orthogonal projection operator).

Let $\mu > 0$ and $\nu > 0$ be such that:

$$\left\|\frac{\partial Z}{\partial p}\right\|_{\mathcal{D}-(\delta/4,\xi/4)} \leq \mu \,, \quad \left\|\frac{\partial Z}{\partial q}\right\|_{\mathcal{D}-(\delta/4,\xi/4)} \leq \nu. \tag{6}$$

In this setting, the following obtains:

Analytic lemma:

Let δ and ξ be two real numbers satisfying:

$$0 < \delta < \rho \; ; \; 0 < \xi < \sigma \text{ and } \; 2\eta T E < \xi\delta. \tag{7}$$

Then there exists a canonical transformation $\mathcal{C} : \mathcal{D}' \to \mathcal{D}$ with $\mathcal{D}' = \mathcal{D}-(\delta,\xi)$ such that $\mathcal{C}$ is one-to-one and its image $\mathcal{C}(\mathcal{D}')$ satisfies:

$$\mathcal{D} - \left(\frac{3\delta}{2};\frac{3\xi}{2}\right) \subseteq \mathcal{C}(\mathcal{D}') \subseteq \mathcal{D} - \left(\frac{\delta}{2};\frac{\xi}{2}\right). \tag{8}$$

If we denote $(p,q) = \mathcal{C}(p',q')$ and $H' = H \circ \mathcal{C}$, then H' can be written as (5) (using primed letters) with:

$$||Z' + N'||_{\mathcal{D}'} = \varepsilon' E \;,\; ||N'||_{\mathcal{D}'} = \eta' E,$$

$$\text{where: } \varepsilon' \leq \varepsilon + \frac{\eta\alpha}{2} \;,\; \eta' \leq \eta\alpha \text{ and } \alpha = 9M(R+\rho)\frac{T}{\xi} + 70\frac{\eta T E}{\xi\delta} + 5\frac{\mu T}{\xi} + 5\frac{\nu T}{\delta}. \tag{9}$$

Finally, let δ' and ξ' such that $0 < \delta' < \rho - \delta$ and $0 < \xi' < \sigma - \xi$ then:

$$\left\|\frac{\partial Z'}{\partial p'}\right\|_{\mathcal{D}'-(\delta'/4,\xi'/4)} \leq \mu' = \mu + \frac{2\eta\alpha E}{\delta'} \,, \quad \left\|\frac{\partial Z'}{\partial q'}\right\|_{\mathcal{D}'-(\delta'/4,\xi'/4)} \leq \nu' = \nu + \frac{2\eta\alpha E}{\xi'}. \tag{10}$$

Proof:

We use the formalism of Lie series, so that the transformation $\mathcal{C}$ will be defined as the time 1 map of an auxiliary Hamiltonian $\chi(p',q')$ on $\mathcal{D}'$ (see e.g.[6] for some information about Lie series). Using the Poisson bracket:

$$L_\chi(f) = \{\chi, f\} = \frac{\partial \chi}{\partial p}.\frac{\partial f}{\partial q} - \frac{\partial \chi}{\partial q}.\frac{\partial f}{\partial p},$$

we have $\mathcal{C} = \exp(L_\chi)$ and $H' = \exp(L_\chi)(H)$.

Let f be analytic on $\mathcal{D}$ (continuous on the boundary), in order to estimate the size of the derivatives of f on $\mathcal{D} - (\delta, \xi)$, one writes that at a given point (p, q)

$$\left|\left|\frac{\partial f}{\partial q}(p,q)\right|\right| = \mathrm{Sup}_{||e||=1}\left|\left|\frac{d}{dt}_{|t=0} f(p, q+te)\right|\right|.$$

One then applies Cauchy formula to the function $t \mapsto f(p, q+te)$ of the complex variable t, defined for $|t| \leq \xi$ and continuous on the boundary when $(p,q) \in \mathcal{D} - (\delta, \xi)$, and obtains

$$\left|\left|\frac{\partial f}{\partial q}(p,q)\right|\right|_{\mathcal{D}-(\delta,\xi)} \leq \frac{1}{\xi}||f||_{\mathcal{D}},$$

the equivalent inequality for $\partial f/\partial p$ is proved in the same way. These inequalities for the Poisson bracket provides:

$$\begin{aligned}||\{f,g\}||_{\mathcal{D}-(\delta,\xi)} &\leq \frac{||f||_{\mathcal{D}-(\delta',\xi')}}{\delta-\delta'}\frac{||g||_{\mathcal{D}-(\delta',\xi')}}{\xi-\xi'} + \frac{||f||_{\mathcal{D}-(\delta',\xi')}}{\xi-\xi'}\frac{||g||_{\mathcal{D}-(\delta',\xi')}}{\delta-\delta'}\\ &\leq \frac{2}{(\delta-\delta')(\xi-\xi')}||f||_{\mathcal{D}-(\delta',\xi')}||g||_{\mathcal{D}-(\delta',\xi')}\end{aligned}$$

for two functions defined on $\mathcal{D}$ (this estimate could be slightly improved).

Then we can write:

$$H' = h + Z + N + \{\chi, h\} + \{\chi, Z+N\} + H' - H - \{\chi, H\} = h + Z + \mathcal{R},$$

with $\mathcal{R} = H' - h - Z$.

The terms of order 1 in $\mathcal{R}$ (w.r.t. ε) are:

$$N(p', q') + \{\chi, h\}(p', q') = N(p', q') + \omega(p', q').\frac{\partial \chi}{\partial q}(p', q').$$

We will choose as χ a solution, on $\mathcal{D}$, of the equation:

$$\omega_0.\frac{\partial \chi}{\partial q}(p,q) = N(p,q). \tag{11}$$

In fact, this equation is satisfied by: $\chi(p,q) = \frac{1}{T}\int_0^T N(p, q+\omega_0 t)t\, dt$. Then:

$$\begin{aligned}\mathcal{R}(p', q') = (\omega_0 - \omega(p'))\frac{\partial \chi}{\partial q}(p', q') + \{\chi, Z+N\}(p', q')\\ + H'(p', q') - H(p', q') - \{\chi, H\}(p', q').\end{aligned}$$

We write:

$$H' = h + Z' + N' \text{ where } Z' = Z + <\mathcal{R}> \,,\; N' = \mathcal{R} - <\mathcal{R}>;$$

one has: $\eta' \leq \dfrac{2||\mathcal{R}||_{\mathcal{D}'}}{E}$, so there only remains to estimate $||\mathcal{R}||_{\mathcal{D}'}$.

From the explicit expression of χ, one immediately obtains: $||\chi||_{\mathcal{D}} < \dfrac{T}{2}||N||_{\mathcal{D}} = \dfrac{\eta TE}{2}$, which implies, taking (7) into account,

$$\left|\left|\frac{\partial\chi}{\partial p}\right|\right|_{\mathcal{D}-(\delta/2;0)} < \frac{\eta TE}{\delta} < \frac{\xi}{2}\,; \quad \left|\left|\frac{\partial\chi}{\partial q}\right|\right|_{\mathcal{D}-(0;\xi/2)} < \frac{\eta TE}{\xi} < \frac{\delta}{2};$$

this in turn ensures the validity of (8).

Using Taylor formula at order two and the fact that $\mathcal{C}(\mathcal{D}') \subset \mathcal{D}-(\delta/2, \xi/2)$, one finds the estimate:

$$||\mathcal{R}||_{\mathcal{D}'} \leq ||\omega_0 - \omega||_{\mathcal{D}'} \left|\left|\frac{\partial\chi}{\partial q}\right|\right|_{\mathcal{D}'} + ||\{\chi, Z+N\}||_{\mathcal{D}'} + \frac{1}{2}||\{\chi,\{\chi,H\}\}||_{\mathcal{D}-(\delta/2,\xi/2)}. \tag{12}$$

Cauchy inequalities and the properties of the hessian matrix imply the following estimates:

$$\bullet||\omega_0 - \omega||_{\mathcal{D}'} \left|\left|\frac{\partial\chi}{\partial q}\right|\right|_{\mathcal{D}'} \leq M(R+\rho)\frac{\eta TE}{2\xi},$$

$$\bullet||\{\chi, N\}||_{\mathcal{D}'} \leq 2\frac{||\chi||_{\mathcal{D}}||N||_{\mathcal{D}}}{\xi\delta} = \frac{\eta^2 TE^2}{\xi\delta};$$

on the other hand, since $\mathcal{D}' \subset \mathcal{D} - (\delta/4, \xi/4)$, we can write:

$$||\{\chi, Z\}||_{\mathcal{D}'} \leq \left|\left|\frac{\partial\chi}{\partial p}\right|\right|_{\mathcal{D}'} \left|\left|\frac{\partial Z}{\partial q}\right|\right|_{\mathcal{D}'} + \left|\left|\frac{\partial\chi}{\partial q}\right|\right|_{\mathcal{D}'} \left|\left|\frac{\partial Z}{\partial p}\right|\right|_{\mathcal{D}'} \leq \frac{\eta\nu TE}{2\delta} + \frac{\eta\mu TE}{2\xi}.$$

To estimate the third term we insert again the definition of χ into the Poisson bracket to get:

$$\{\chi, H\} = -N + (\omega_0 - \omega)\frac{\partial\chi}{\partial q} + \{\chi, N+Z\},$$

so that:

$$\begin{aligned} ||\{\chi,\{\chi,H\}\}||_{\mathcal{D}-(\delta/2,\xi/2)} \leq\; & ||\{\chi, N\}||_{\mathcal{D}-(\delta/2,\xi/2)} \\ & + \left|\left|\left\{\chi, (\omega_0-\omega)\frac{\partial\chi}{\partial q}\right\}\right|\right|_{\mathcal{D}-(\delta/2,\xi/2)} \\ & + ||\{\chi,\{\chi,N\}\}||_{\mathcal{D}-(\delta/2,\xi/2)} \\ & + ||\{\chi,\{\chi,Z\}\}||_{\mathcal{D}-(\delta/2,\xi/2)}. \end{aligned}$$

Using again Cauchy inequalities and (7) we can estimate the previous terms. The sum of these inequalities yields (9) with the given value of α.

To control the derivative of Z', we use $Z'(p',q') - Z(p',q') =< \mathcal{R} >$ and Cauchy inequality gives (10).

At this point we will make a few remarks:

– The first term on (12) represents a frequency shift and comes in because we solve (11) instead of adapting the frequency, that is solve the same equation with $\omega(p)$ substituted for ω_0. Because of this frequency shift which grows with R, we do not work directly on the whole of $\mathcal{D}$, but restrict attention to the smaller domain: $\mathcal{D}' = \mathcal{D}(R(\varepsilon), \rho(\varepsilon), \sigma) \subset \mathcal{D}(R, \rho, \sigma)$, where $R(\varepsilon)$ will be the confinement radius in our theorem. In fact convexity implies that the unperturbed energy increases at least as the square of the distance to the origin; adding a perturbation of order ε, both terms have to be on the same size to ensure confinement. This implies that $R(\varepsilon)$ is at least on the order of $\sqrt{\varepsilon}$, which will be the value chosen here ($b = 1/2$). For a fixed value of the radius of confinement, we cannot improve the frequency shift term, hence we will try to reduce (9) essentially to the first term.

– The analytic lemma will be used $s(\varepsilon)$ times to have a non resonant part in the transformed Hamiltonian of size $\eta' = 2^{-s}\eta$, here $s(\varepsilon)$ will be on the order of $\varepsilon^{-a} = \varepsilon^{-1/2}$. To stay on the domain where H is defined, δ and ξ will be $\mathcal{O}(R(\varepsilon)/s)$ and $\mathcal{O}(\sigma/s)$. If one directly uses Cauchy inequalities to estimate μ and ν (as in [1]), the last two terms in (9) are $\mathcal{O}(\varepsilon^{-1/2}T/\sigma)$ while the frequency shift term is $\mathcal{O}(T/\sigma)$. To obtain terms of the same size in (9), one must first perform a preliminary transformation to have a small enough non resonant part (i.e. η) before using (9) and (10) in the iterative scheme.

– In order to simplify the expression of α we will choose $R(\varepsilon) = \rho(\varepsilon)$; this is an arbitrary but not essential specialisation. We shall often write R and ρ, without making the dependence on ε explicit and rewrite the conditions $R(\varepsilon) \leq R$ and $\rho(\varepsilon) \leq \rho$ at the very end.

b) Preliminary transformation:

As previously said, the iterative scheme must begin with a nonresonant part of size η_0 such that the second term in (9) is on the same order as the frequency shift term (i.e. srT with our value of ξ in the iterative part). Hence, we will first build a preliminary transformation which will be denoted $\mathcal{C}^{(0)}$.

The analytic lemma will be used with: $\delta = R/3$; $\xi = \sigma/3$. Taking into account inequality $\eta < 2\varepsilon$, (7) becomes:

$$\frac{\varepsilon T}{R} \leq \frac{\sigma}{36E}.$$

Also, by Cauchy inequalities:

$$\left\|\frac{\partial Z}{\partial p}\right\|_{\mathcal{D}-(\delta/4,\xi/4)} \leq \frac{12\varepsilon E}{R} \text{ and } \left\|\frac{\partial Z}{\partial q}\right\|_{\mathcal{D}-(\delta/4,\xi/4)} \leq \frac{12\varepsilon E}{\sigma},$$

so (8) becomes:

$$\mathcal{D}-\left(\frac{R}{2},\frac{\sigma}{2}\right) \subset \mathcal{C}^{(0)}\left(\mathcal{D}-\left(\frac{R}{3},\frac{\sigma}{3}\right)\right) \subset \mathcal{D}-\left(\frac{R}{6},\frac{\sigma}{6}\right).$$

The new size of the non resonant part satisfies: $\eta' \leq 54\eta\left(\frac{M}{\sigma}TR + 30\frac{\varepsilon TE}{\sigma R}\right)$.

We suppose that:

$$R = R(\varepsilon) \geq \left(\frac{6E}{M}\right)^{1/2} \varepsilon^{1/2};$$

then (9) yields:

$$\varepsilon' \leq \varepsilon\left(1 + 162\frac{M}{\sigma}TR\right) = \varepsilon_0 \text{ and } \eta' \leq 324\frac{M}{\sigma}\varepsilon TR = \eta_0.$$

c) Main transformation:

We will now define the intermediate transformations: $\mathcal{C}^{(j)} : \mathcal{D}^{(j)} \longrightarrow \mathcal{D}^{(j-1)}$ for $j \in \{1,\dots,s\}$. The initial Hamiltonian, $H = H^{(0)}$ is the one obtained after the preliminary transformation; it is defined on:

$$\mathcal{D}^{(0)} = \mathcal{D}-\left(\frac{R}{3},\frac{\sigma}{3}\right);$$

the intermediate quantities are denoted $H^{(j)}$, ε_j, η_j, μ_j, ν_j. We shall impose that the sequence (η_j) decrease at least geometrically.

Here we take: $\mathcal{D}^{(j)} = \mathcal{D}^{(j-1)} - (\delta_j, \xi_j)$ with $\delta_j = \delta = \frac{R}{3s}$, $\xi_j = \xi = \frac{\sigma}{3s}$, in order that the image $\mathcal{C}^{(0)} \circ \dots \circ \mathcal{C}^{(n)}\left(\mathcal{D}^{(n)}\right)$ contains the real ball B_R in action space.

Since

$$\left\|\frac{\partial Z}{\partial p}\right\|_{\mathcal{D}-(R/12,\sigma/12)} \leq \frac{12\varepsilon E}{R}, \quad \left\|\frac{\partial Z}{\partial q}\right\|_{\mathcal{D}-(R/12,\sigma/12)} \leq \frac{12\varepsilon E}{\sigma},$$

after the preliminary transformation we get (see (10)):

$$\mu_0 \leq \frac{12\varepsilon E}{R} + \frac{6\eta_0 Es}{R} = \mu_0', \quad \nu_0 \leq \frac{12\varepsilon E}{\sigma} + \frac{6\eta_0 Es}{\sigma} = \frac{R}{\sigma}\mu_0'.$$

With the previous inequalities, our values of δ and ξ at each step of the iterative scheme, and formula (10), we can connect μ_j and ν_j for $j \in \{1, \ldots, s\}$ by the relations:

$$\nu_j = \mu_j \frac{\delta}{\xi} = \mu_j \frac{R}{\sigma}.$$

Assume that for $j \in \{0, \ldots, n\}$, one has $\eta_j \leq 2^{-j}\eta_0$, then:

$$\mu_n - \mu_0 \leq \left(2^{-1} + \ldots + 2^{-n}\right) \frac{2\eta_0 E}{\delta} \leq \frac{6E\eta_0 s}{R}.$$

We can apply the lemma if (see (7)): $18s^2TE\eta_n \leq \sigma R$; since $\eta_n < \eta_0$, the previous inequality is satisfied if one imposes the threshold condition:

$$\frac{s^2T\eta_0}{R} \leq \frac{\sigma}{18E}.$$

Under these assumptions, (9) becomes:

$$\eta_{n+1} \leq 54\eta_n \left[\frac{M}{\sigma}sRT + 7\frac{E}{\sigma}\frac{\varepsilon sT}{R} + 20\frac{\eta_0 TEs^2}{R\sigma}\right].$$

We will now require that the second and third terms in the bracket be smaller than the first, which gives two more threshold conditions to satisfy. Under this condition,

$$\eta_{n+1} \leq 162\,\eta_n\,\frac{M}{\sigma}sRT;$$

in order to get a geometric decrease for the sequence (η_j), we assume that:

$$sRT \leq 3 \cdot 10^{-3}\frac{\sigma}{M}. \tag{13}$$

This relation represents the natural link between the three parameters s, R, T, namely that $s(\varepsilon)$ should be on the order of $(RT)^{-1}$. This implies, $\eta_{n+1} \leq \eta_n/2 \leq 2^{-(n+1)}\eta_0$.

We denote: $(p,q) = \mathcal{C}(p',q') = \left(\mathcal{C}^{(0)} \circ \ldots \circ \mathcal{C}^{(n)}\right)(p',q')$ by composing the transformations built in the two previous parts, $\mathcal{C}$ is defined on $\mathcal{D}-(2R/3, 2\sigma/3)$ and satisfies:

$$c(\varepsilon) = ||p-p'||_{\mathcal{D}-(2R/3,2\sigma/3)} \leq \frac{3sTE}{\sigma}(\eta_0+\ldots+\eta_{s-1})+\frac{6\varepsilon TE}{\sigma} \leq 6(\varepsilon+\eta_0 s)\frac{TE}{\sigma},$$

with the same estimate for $||q-q'||$.

If we assume:

$$36(\varepsilon+\eta_0 s)TE \leq R\sigma,$$

then, one can state:

$$\mathcal{D}-(R,\sigma) \subseteq \mathcal{C}\left(\mathcal{D}-\left(\frac{5R}{6},\frac{5\sigma}{6}\right)\right),$$

so that we can use $\mathcal{C}$ to change variables on the real part of $\mathcal{D}$. The threshold conditions can be simplified if we use (13) and the definition of η_0, which gives $\eta_0 \leq \varepsilon/s$.

Gathering everything together we arrive at the following:

Lemma:

There exists a canonical transformation $\mathcal{C} : \mathcal{D}' \longrightarrow \mathcal{D}$ with $\mathcal{D}' = \mathcal{D} - (5R/6, 5\sigma/6)$, which is one-to-one and satisfies:

$$||p-p'||_{\mathcal{D}'} \leq \frac{R}{6}\ ; \quad ||q-q'||_{\mathcal{D}'} \leq \frac{\sigma}{6}.$$

The transformed Hamiltonian can be decomposed as in (5) (using primed letters) with:

$$\varepsilon' \leq \varepsilon\left(1+324\frac{M}{\sigma}TR\right) \quad \text{and} \quad \eta' \leq 2^{-s}\left(324\frac{M}{\sigma}\varepsilon TR\right),$$

provided the following thresholds are satisfied ($s = s(\varepsilon)$, $R = R(\varepsilon)$):

1) $sRT \leq 3\cdot 10^{-3}\dfrac{\sigma}{M}$; 2) $\dfrac{\varepsilon T}{R} \leq \dfrac{\sigma}{72E}$; 3) $\varepsilon^{1/2} \leq \left(\dfrac{M}{20E}\right)^{1/2} R$.

d) Intermediate statement with free parameters:

In order to obtain a stability result one must complement the above lemma with a simple geometric argument which uses convexity and energy conservation. We are aiming at a statement of the following type: every trajectory with initial condition (in action space) lying in the (real) ball of radius $r(\varepsilon)$ around the origin will stay for $|t| \leq \mathcal{T}(\varepsilon)$ in the ball of radius $R(\varepsilon) \leq R$. One can expand the unperturbed Hamiltonian around the initial condition:

$$h(p'(t)) = h(p'(0)) + \omega(p'(0)).(p'(t)-p'(0)) + \frac{1}{2}A(p^*)(p'(t)-p'(0)).(p'(t)-p'(0)),$$

where p^* is located between $p'(t)$ and $p'(0)$ (the domain is convex). The *convexity* of h then allows to estimate the last term from <u>below</u>; more precisely, (4) implies:

$$\frac{1}{2}m||p'(t) - p'(0)||^2 \leq |h(p'(t)) - h(p'(0))| + |\omega(p'(0)).(p'(t) - p'(0))|.$$

To estimate the first term of the right hand side one uses energy conservation for the (perturbed) system, $H'(p'(t), q'(t)) = H'(p'(0), q'(0))$ which implies:

$$\begin{aligned}|h(p'(t)) - h(p'(0))| &\leq |Z'(p'(t))| + |Z'(p'(0))| + |R'(p'(t))| + |R'(p'(0))| \\ &\leq 2\left[\varepsilon E + \frac{\eta_0 E}{2} + (2^{-1} + \ldots + 2^{-s})\frac{\eta_0 E}{2}\right] \\ &\quad + 2^{-s}\eta_0 E + 2^{-s}\eta_0 E \leq 2(\varepsilon + 2\eta_0)E\ .\end{aligned}$$

To estimate the term $|\omega(p'(0)).(p'(t) - p'(0))|$, one considers the projections of the vectors $\omega(p'(0))$ and $p'(t) - p'(0)$ on ω_0 and the orthogonal complement (we denote Π and $\Pi^\perp$ the corresponding orthogonal projection operators).

First, $||\Pi^\perp(\omega(p'(0))|| \leq ||\omega(p'(0)) - \omega_0|| \leq M||p'(0)|| \leq 2rM$ provided that:

$$c(\varepsilon) \leq 6(\varepsilon + \eta_0 s)\frac{TE}{\sigma} \leq 12\frac{\varepsilon TE}{\sigma} \leq r(\varepsilon)\ . \tag{14}$$

On the other hand, since Z' is resonant with respect to ω_0 we have the crucial fact that:

$$\frac{\partial Z'}{\partial q}\ .\ \omega_0 = 0,$$

and because of the Hamiltonian character of the equation: $\Pi(\dot{p}') = -\Pi\left(\frac{\partial R'}{\partial q}\right)$, which implies:

$$\begin{aligned}||\Pi(p'(t) - p'(0))|| &\leq |t| \left|\left|\frac{\partial R'}{\partial q}\right|\right|_{\mathcal{D}-(5r/6, 5\sigma/6)} \\ &\leq \frac{6}{\sigma}|t| \cdot ||R'||_{\mathcal{D}-(2R/3, 2\sigma/3)} \leq \frac{6}{\sigma}\mathcal{T}(\varepsilon)\eta_s E.\end{aligned}$$

Here $|t| \leq \mathcal{T}(\varepsilon)$ where the later is still to be specified.

Gathering the previous inequalities together we obtain:

$$|\omega(p'(0)).(p'(t) - p'(0))| \leq 2rM||p'(t) - p'(0)|| + \frac{6}{\sigma}\mathcal{T}(\varepsilon)\eta_s E||\omega(p'(0))||.$$

With the threshold (14) we have $p'(0) \in \mathcal{B}_{2r}$ and if we add the hypothesis: $2rM \leq \Omega$, we get: $|\omega(p'(0))| \leq \Omega + 2rM \leq 2\Omega$.

Finally, provided all the previous conditions are satisfied and denoting $a = ||p'(t) - p'(0)||$ we find that:

$$\frac{1}{2}ma^2 \leq 2(\varepsilon + 2\eta_0)E + 12\frac{\Omega}{\sigma}\mathcal{T}(\varepsilon)\eta_s E + 2rMa. \tag{15}$$

This inequality can be simplified if we first impose $s \geq 2$ which ensures $\eta_0 \leq \varepsilon/s \leq \varepsilon/2$.

On the other hand, we also want that: $12\frac{\Omega}{\sigma}\mathcal{T}(\varepsilon)\eta_s E \leq \varepsilon E$, that is satisfied if:

$$\mathcal{T}(\varepsilon) \leq \frac{\sigma}{12\Omega}s2^s,$$

which is the value we finally adopt. Now, solving (15), we find that:

$$a \leq 2r\frac{M}{m} + \left(4r^2\frac{M^2}{m^2} + 10\frac{\varepsilon E}{m}\right)^{1/2}.$$

Let g be an arbitrary positive constant such that:

$$10m\varepsilon E \leq 4gr^2M^2 \quad \text{or} \quad r^2 \geq \frac{5mE}{2M^2g}\varepsilon. \tag{16}$$

Then one gets: $a \leq (4+g)r(\varepsilon)\frac{M}{m}$. Moreover, using (14) we can state:

$$||p(t)|| \leq (7+g)\frac{M}{m}r(\varepsilon) \quad \text{for} \quad t \leq \mathcal{T}(\varepsilon);$$

we will now connect r and R by the relation: $r(\varepsilon) = \frac{m}{(7+g)M}R(\varepsilon)$.

With $s = s(\varepsilon)$ big enough and $R(\varepsilon) = \rho(\varepsilon)$ small enough to stay in the domain where H is defined, we obtain our first statement about stability over exponentially long times.

Model statement:

If the following inequalities are satisfied:

$$1)\ \varepsilon \leq \frac{2M^2 g}{5mE} r^2(\varepsilon)\ ;\quad 2)\ \frac{\varepsilon T}{r(\varepsilon)} \leq \frac{\sigma}{12E}\ ;\quad 3)\ s(\varepsilon) r(\varepsilon) T \leq 3 \cdot 10^{-3} \frac{m\sigma}{(7+g)M^2}\ ;$$

$$4)\ r(\varepsilon) \leq \frac{\Omega}{2M}\ ;\quad 5)\ s(\varepsilon) \geq 2\ ;\quad 6)\ (7+g)\frac{M}{m} r(\varepsilon) \leq \inf(R, \rho)\ ;$$

and the initial conditions are such that $||p(0)|| \leq r(\varepsilon)$, then one has:

$$||p(t)|| \leq R(\varepsilon) = (7+g)\frac{M}{m} r(\varepsilon) \text{ for } |t| \leq \mathcal{T}(\varepsilon) \text{ with } \mathcal{T}(\varepsilon) = \frac{\sigma}{6\Omega} 2^{s(\varepsilon)}\ .$$

e) Stability results in the neighbourhood of the periodic solutions:

In this section, we prove three theorems which follow directly from the above model statement. The first one is not the most natural statement at this point, but it yields a time of validity which is independant of the periodic orbit one considers and this will be crucial in the next part, when we approach an arbitrary initial condition by rational points corresponding to periodic tori. The second theorem is nothing but a particuliar case of the first; it costs a stronger condition on the period T so that in Part III, it will not allow to obtain the best time exponent (i.e. a), but with a better threshold for the size of the perturbation. The last statement in this section gives the best stability theorem around a given, fixed, periodic torus.

Theorem 1.1 :

Let α, $0 < \alpha \leq 1/2$, λ an arbitrary positive constant and assume that:

$$||p(0)|| \leq r(\varepsilon) = \lambda \frac{\varepsilon^\alpha}{T}\ ,\ \text{with } T \text{ satisfing } 1 \leq T < \varepsilon^{\alpha - 1/2}.$$

Then:

$$||p(t)|| \leq R(\varepsilon) = (7 + g(\lambda))\frac{M}{m} r(\varepsilon)\ ,\ \text{when } |t| \leq \mathcal{T}(\varepsilon) = \frac{\sigma}{6\Omega} \exp\left(K(\lambda)\varepsilon^{-\alpha}\right),$$

where the constants are:

$$g(\lambda) = \frac{5mE}{2M^2\lambda^2}\ ,\quad \text{and}\quad K(\lambda) = 10^{-3} \frac{m\sigma}{(7+g(\lambda))M^2\lambda}\ ,$$

provided that ε satisfies the following threshold conditions:

$$i)\ \varepsilon^\alpha < 10^{-3}\frac{m\sigma}{(7+g(\lambda))M^2\lambda}\ ; \qquad ii)\ \varepsilon^\alpha \leq \frac{\sigma\lambda}{12E}\ ;$$

$$iii)\ \varepsilon^\alpha \leq \frac{\Omega}{2M\lambda}\ ;\ iv)\ \varepsilon^\alpha \leq \frac{m\inf(R,\rho)}{(7+g(\lambda))M\lambda}.$$

Proof:

To prove the theorem, we only need to apply the model statement with $r(\varepsilon)$ as in the statement above and

$$s(\varepsilon) = E\left[\frac{K(\lambda)}{\log(2)}\varepsilon^{-\alpha}\right] + 1,$$

where $E[x]$ is the integer part of a real x. In this case inequalities 1) and 3) of the model statement are always satisfied with our values of g and K (we use inequality 5) to check condition 3)) and the other inequalities give the four thresholds of the theorem.

In the following two theorems we set:

$$\lambda_1 = 10^{-4}\frac{m\sigma}{M^2}\ , \quad \text{and} \quad T_1 = 5\cdot 10^{-5}\left(\frac{m}{E}\right)^{1/2}\frac{\sigma}{M}\ ,$$

then the following statement holds:

Theorem 1.2 :

Let $\alpha > 0$, $\alpha < 1/2$ (notice the <u>strict</u> inequality), if $||p(0)|| \leq r(\varepsilon) = \lambda_1\varepsilon^\alpha/T$ with T such that $1 \leq T < T_1\varepsilon^{\alpha 9-1/2}$, then:

$$||p(t)|| \leq R(\varepsilon) = 8\frac{M}{m}r(\varepsilon) \text{ when } |t| \leq \tau(\varepsilon) = \frac{\sigma}{6\Omega}\exp(\varepsilon^{-\alpha}),$$

provided ε satisfies:

$$i)\ \varepsilon^{1/2-\alpha} < T_1\ ;\ \ ii)\ \varepsilon^\alpha \leq 10^3\frac{M}{\sigma}\inf(R,\rho)\ ;\ \ iii)\ \varepsilon^\alpha \leq 5\cdot 10^3\frac{M\Omega}{m\sigma}.$$

Proof:

We apply the model statement with:

$$g = 1\ ,\ R(\varepsilon) = 8\frac{M}{m}r(\varepsilon) \text{ and } s(\varepsilon) = E\left[\frac{\varepsilon^{-\alpha}}{\log(2)}\right] + 1,$$

then conditions 1) and 3) in the model statement are always satisfied with our values of λ_1 and T_1. The other inequalities give the last two threshold conditions of the theorem, and condition $1 < T_1\varepsilon^{\alpha-1/2}$ has to be added separately.

Theorem 1.3 :

If $||p(0)|| \leq r(\varepsilon) = r_0\sqrt{\varepsilon}$, then:

$$||p(t)|| \leq 8\frac{M}{m}r_0\sqrt{\varepsilon}\ ,\ \text{if } |t| \leq \frac{\sigma}{6\Omega}\exp\left(\frac{T_1}{T\sqrt{\varepsilon}}\right),$$

with:

$$r_0 = \left(\frac{5mE}{2M^2}\right)^{1/2}.$$

Provided ε satisfies:

$$i)\quad \varepsilon \leq \frac{\Omega^2}{10mE}\ ;\qquad ii)\quad \varepsilon \leq 6\cdot 10^{-3}\left(\frac{m}{E}\right)(\inf(R,\rho))^2\ ;$$

$$iii)\quad \sqrt{\varepsilon} \leq 5\ 10^{-5}\left(\frac{m}{E}\right)^{1/2}\frac{\sigma}{MT}.$$

Proof:

We apply the model statement with:

$$s(\varepsilon) = E\left[\frac{T_1}{\log(2)T\sqrt{\varepsilon}}\right] + 1\ ,\quad g = 1\ ,\ \text{and}\quad R(\varepsilon) = 8\frac{M}{m}r(\varepsilon)\ .$$

In this case, it follows from the values of r_0 and T_1 that conditions 1) and 3) of the model statement are satisfied; the threshold conditions in the theorem ensure the validity of the remaining ones.

III Stability for arbitrary initial conditions

We now combine Theorems 1.1 and 1.2 with a simple approximation argument to complete the proof of the stability estimates for arbitrary initial conditions. Let us first recall the following elementary approximation theorem (due to Dirichlet):

Let $\alpha \in R^n$ and $Q > 1$; there exists $\zeta \in Z^n$ and an *integer* q with $1 \leq q < Q$ such that $||q\alpha - \zeta|| \leq \sqrt{n}Q^{-1/n}$, $||\ ||$ denotes the usual euclidian norm.

This immediately implies the following

Proposition:

Let $Q > 1$, $q > 1$, $q < Q$ and $\omega^* \in R^n$ with $||\omega^*||_\infty = w$ then there exists a rational vector ω of period $T = q/w$ such that

$$||\omega - \omega^*|| \leq \frac{\sqrt{n-1}}{TQ^{1/(n-1)}} \ .$$

Proof:

Indeed, relabeling the components if necessary, one can write $\omega^* = w\ \omega_1^*$ with $\omega_1^* = (\pm 1, \omega^{*\prime})$. Then, apply Dirichlet theorem with $\alpha = \omega^{*\prime} \in R^{n-1}$ and pick $\omega = w(1, q^{-1}\zeta)$, which is a rational vector of period $T = q/w$ which satisfies the statement (one uses the fact that q is an integer).

Let now $(p(0), q(0))$ be an arbitrary initial condition; we write $p^* = p(0)$, $\omega^* = \omega(p^*)$ and apply the above proposition which yields some rational ω.

Here, we can always be reduced to the case when $w = 1$ (i.e. $T = q$) if one introduces the scalings:

$$t' = wt\ ,\ H' = \frac{H}{w}\ ,\ \omega^{*\prime} = \frac{\omega^*}{w}\ ,\ m' = \frac{m}{w}\ ,\ M' = \frac{M}{w}\ ,\ E' = \frac{E}{w}\ ,\ \varepsilon' = \varepsilon\ . \quad (17)$$

Below, for the sake of clarity, we write everything using the original quantities and shall remember at the very end that one should *first* perform the transformations (1) and change the results accordingly.

We assume that ω is closed enough to ω^* so that the frequency map can be inverted, by an easy application of the implicit function theorem, this is the case over the ball $B\left(\omega^*, m^2/(4|h|_3)\right)$, where $|h|_3$ is an estimate from above of the third derivative of h. So assume:

$$\frac{\sqrt{n-1}}{Q^{1/(n-1)}} < \frac{m^2}{4|h|_3} .$$

Under this condition, there exists an action $p \in R^n$ such that

$$\nabla h(p) = \omega \ \text{ and } \ ||p - p^*|| \le \frac{\sqrt{n-1}}{m} \frac{1}{TQ^{1/(n-1)}} , \tag{18}$$

where the factor $1/m$ estimates from above the norm of the inverse of the frequency map.

In order to apply Theorem 1.1 *around the point* p, which is a rational point of period T thereby obtaining a stability estimate for p^*, the latter point must lie in the "*influence zone*" of p, i.e.one should have (see Theorem 1.1):

$$r(\varepsilon) = \lambda \frac{\varepsilon^\alpha}{T} \ge ||p - p^*||.$$

In turn, from (18), this is ensured if:

$$\lambda = \frac{\sqrt{n-1}}{m} \qquad \text{and} \qquad Q = \varepsilon^{-(n-1)\alpha}.$$

Another important requirement to keep in mind is that the period should not be too long, more precisely, one must require that $T < \varepsilon^{\alpha - 1/2}$; since $T < Q$, we want:

$$Q = \varepsilon^{-(n-1)\alpha} \le \varepsilon^{\alpha-1/2}, \text{ that is } \varepsilon^{1/2 - n\alpha} \le 1,$$

which is satisfied for $\alpha \le \dfrac{1}{2n}$ (and $\varepsilon \le 1$). We set $\alpha = \dfrac{1}{2n}$.

We can then apply Theorem 1.1 and find that: $||p(t) - p(0)|| \le (6 + g(\lambda))\frac{M}{m} r(\varepsilon)$.

When making the threshold conditions, one should beware of the fact that, in the third one (iii) Theorem 1.1), $\Omega = ||\omega(p)||$ refers to p and not p^*. Everything should then be expressed with parameters centered at p^*, this is easy because, denoting $\Omega^* = ||\omega^*||$, one has:

$$|\Omega - \Omega^*| \le M r(\varepsilon) \le \frac{\Omega^*}{2} ,$$

so we need only substitute Ω with Ω^* in the third condition and with $3\Omega^*/2$ in the definition of $\mathcal{T}(\varepsilon)$. We can also simplify the expressions for the parameters $g(\lambda)$ and K. This leads to the following

Theorem 2.1:

Any trajectory starting from the initial point $(p(0), q(0)) \in \mathcal{D} \cap R^{2n}$ satisfies:

$$||p(t) - p(0)|| \le \ 3M \left(E + \frac{2}{m} \right) \varepsilon^{1/(2n)} \quad \text{for} \quad |t| \le \frac{2\sigma}{9\Omega^*} \exp\left(K \varepsilon^{-1/(2n)} \right),$$

with the parameter: $K = 10^{-3}\frac{m^2\sigma}{(7\sqrt{n-1}+3mE)M^2}$, provided ε satisfies the following inequalities:

$$i)\quad \varepsilon^{1/(2n)} < 10^{-3}\frac{m^2\sigma}{(7\sqrt{n-1}+3mE)M^2}\ ;$$

$$ii)\quad \varepsilon^{1/(2n)} \leq \frac{m^2}{(7\sqrt{n-1}+3mE)M^2}\inf(R,\rho)\ ;$$

$$iii)\quad \varepsilon^{1/(2n)} < \frac{m^2}{4|h|_3\sqrt{n-1}}\ ;\quad iv)\quad \varepsilon^{1/(2n)} \leq \frac{m\Omega^*}{2M\sqrt{n-1}}$$

where $|h|_3$ is an estimate (from above) of the third derivative of h on the domain $\mathcal{D}$.

In this statement, all the parameters connected with the Hamiltonian, along with time t, are those which are obtained *after* the rescalings (17) have been performed, i.e. one should use the primed quantities in (17).

This theorem gives the desired "optimal" exponents but the time of validity and the threshold conditions deteriorate strongly when the number of degrees of freedom increases. In fact, for "reasonably" small values of ε, the next theorem may very well provide better estimates in spite of a worse exponent.

In the same way, Theorem 1.2 around p can be applied if $r(\varepsilon) = \lambda_1\frac{\varepsilon^\alpha}{T} \geq ||p-p^*||$ — here we use the constants λ_1 and T_1 defined in the previous part, the inequality is ensured with (18) if

$$Q^{1/(n-1)} = 10^4\sqrt{n-1}\frac{M^2}{m^2\sigma}\varepsilon^{-\alpha}.$$

To apply Theorem 1.2, the period must not be too long, so one wants the inequality:

$$Q = \left(\frac{\sqrt{n-1}}{\lambda_1 m}\right)^{n-1}\varepsilon^{-(n-1)\alpha} \leq T_1\varepsilon^{-(1-2\alpha)/2} \text{ or } \varepsilon^{1/2-n\alpha} \leq T_1\left(\frac{\lambda_1 m}{\sqrt{n-1}}\right)^{n-1}. \tag{19}$$

This defines a threshold condition provided that $1/2-n\alpha > 0$. Consequently the value $\alpha = 1/(2n)$ is not accessible, but any smaller value is. Here we shall take, for example:

$$\alpha = \frac{1}{2(n+1)}\ .$$

Under this condition, Theorem 1.2 may be applied and one gets:

$$||p(t) - p(0)|| \leq 7\frac{M}{m}\lambda_1 \frac{\varepsilon^{1/[2(n+1)]}}{T}.$$

With the same substitution as in 2.1 for the parameter Ω and a simplification of the inequality (19), we arrive at:

Theorem 2.2:

For any initial point $(p(0), q(0))$ a trajectory starting at $(p(0), q(0))$ satisfies:

$$||p(t) - p(0)|| \leq \ 10^{-3}\frac{\sigma}{M}\varepsilon^{1/[2(n+1)]} \text{ when } |t| \leq \frac{2\sigma}{9\Omega^*}\exp(\varepsilon^{-1/[2(n+1)]}) \ ,$$

provided that ε satisfies:

$$i)\ \varepsilon^{1/[2(n+1)]} \leq \ 10^3\frac{M}{\sigma}\inf(R,\rho) \ ; \quad ii)\ \varepsilon^{1/[2(n+1)]} \leq \ 5\ 10^3\frac{M\Omega}{m\sigma}$$

$$iii)\ \varepsilon^{1/[2(n+1)]} < \ 5\ 10^{-5}\left(\frac{m}{E}\right)^{1/2}\frac{\sigma}{M} \ ; \quad iv)\ \varepsilon^{1/[2(n+1)]} \leq \ \frac{m}{4\lambda_1|h|_3} \ ;$$

$$v)\ \varepsilon^{1/[2(n+1)]} \leq \ \left(\sqrt{mE}\right)^{-1}\left(10^{-4}\ \frac{m^2\sigma}{\sqrt{n-1}M^2}\right)^n .$$

This statement also refers to the primed quantities in (17).

So far, we have only used basic approximation results and all the previous theorems may be improved, exactly as in [1], if one restricts attention to certain classes of initial conditions with further arithmetical properties. Among other things, one can prove that *almost all* points in phase space admit, for any $\eta > 0$, the stability exponents:

$$(a,b) = \left(\frac{1}{2n} - \eta, \frac{1}{2} - \eta\right) \ ;$$

we recall that the pair $(1/(2n), 1/2)$ corresponds to B.V. Chirikov's prediction for the maximal speed of Arnold's diffusion.

References

[1] P. Lochak. Canonical Perturbation Theory via Simultaneous Approximation, Uspekhi. Math. Nauk., **6**, 1992, p.59 (English translation in Russian Math. Surveys).

[2] N. N. Nekhorochev, Russian Math. Surveys, **32**, p.1, 1977.

[3] A. I. Neistadt, J. Appl. Math. Mech., **45**, p. 80, 1981.

[4] A. I. Neistadt, J. Appl. Math. Mech., **48**, p. 197, 1981.
[5] B. V. Chirikov, Physics Reports, **52**, p.263, 1979.
[6] G. Benettin, L. Galgani, A. Giorgilli, Celestial Mechanics, **37**, p.1, 1985.
[7] J. Pöschel, Preprint E.T.H., 1992, to appear in Math. Zeitschrift (See also this volume).

[1]D.M.I., Ecole Normale Supérieure 45 rue d'Ulm, F-75230 Paris Cedex 05

[2]Space Research Institute Profsoyuznaya ul. 84/32, 117810, Moscow, Russia

[3]Université P. et M. Curie U.F.R. de Mathématiques, 4 place Jussieu, F-75252 Paris Cedex 05

ON THE STABILITY PROBLEM FOR NEARLY-INTEGRABLE HAMILTONIAN SYSTEMS

LUIGI CHIERCHIA[1]

ABSTRACT. The problem of stability of the action variables in nearly-integrable (real-analytic) Hamiltonian systems is considered. Several results (fully described in [CG2]) are discussed; in particular: (i) a generalization of Arnold's method ([A]) allowing to prove instability (i.e. drift of action variables by an amount of order 1, often called "Arnold's diffusion") for general perturbations of "a-priori unstable integrable systems" (i.e. systems for which the integrable structure carries separatrices); (ii) Examples of perturbations of "a-priori stable sytems" (i.e. systems whose integrable part can be completely described by regular action-angle variables) exhibiting instability. In such examples, inspired by the "D'Alembert problem" in Celestial Mechanics (treated, in full details, in [CG2]), the splitting of the asymptotic manifolds is not exponentially small in the perturbation parameter.

1 A THEOREM AND A CONJECTURE BY V. I. ARNOLD

Consider a Hamiltonian system with N degree of freedom with a Hamiltonian of the form $H_\mu \equiv H_0 + \mu f$, where H_0, f are real-analytic functions on the phase space $V \times T^N$ (V being a bounded region in R^N, $T \equiv R/2\pi Z$) and μ is a real parameter. For $\mu = 0$, H_0 is assumed to be *integrable i.e.* there exist N integrals, $I_1, ..., I_N$, independent and in involution (see [A1] or [G] for the standard terminology). Typically, for $\mu \neq 0$ the system will be no longer integrable, however the time for a possible variation of $\mathcal{O}(|\mu|^c)$ of one of the above integrals is (again: in typical situations) extremely long as dictated by a result of Nekhoroshev [N].

In 1964 V. I. Arnold conjectured that, *in general, for $\mu \neq 0$ small enough, there exist initial data $z \in V \times T^N$ and a time $T > 0$ such that* $|I(\phi_\mu^T(z)) - I(z)| = \mathcal{O}(1)$; here $I \equiv (I_1, ..., I_N)$ and $t \to \phi_\mu^t$ is the flow generated by the Hamiltonian H_μ. The conjecture was based on the following theorem and on its proof:

---

[1] Dip. di Matematica, II^a Università di Roma, "Tor Vergata", via della Ricerca Scientifica, 00133 Roma, Italia. *Lecture delivered at the S. Petersburg Conference "Dynamical Systems", November 1991 describing joint work in collaboration with Giovanni Gallavotti,* Dip. di Fisica, Università di Roma, "La Sapienza", P. Moro 5, 00185 Roma, Italia

Theorem ([A2]). *Fix $\varepsilon > 0$ and let $H_\mu \equiv H_0 + \mu f$ with:*

$$H_0 \equiv \frac{a^2}{2} + b + \frac{p^2}{2} + \varepsilon(\cos q - 1) , \qquad f \equiv \varepsilon(\cos q - 1)(\sin\alpha + \cos\beta) \quad (1.1)$$

where $(a,\alpha), (b,\beta), (p,q) \in (R \times T)^3$ are standard canonical (symplectic) coordinates i.e. the equations of motion are:

$$\begin{aligned} \dot\alpha &= a & \dot a &= \varepsilon\mu(1-\cos q)\cos\alpha \\ \dot\beta &= 1 & \dot b &= \varepsilon\mu(\cos q - 1)\sin\beta \\ \dot q &= p & \dot p &= \varepsilon\sin q[1 + \mu(\sin\alpha + \cos\beta)] \end{aligned}$$

For each $0 < a' < a''$ there exists a motion $(a(t), b(t), p(t), \alpha(t), \beta(t), q(t))$ and a time $T > 0$ such that $a(0) < a'$ while $a(T) > a''$, provided $\mu > 0$ is small enough.

Before discussing the method of proof let us comment on the presence of the *two parameters* ε, μ.

In the theory of nearly-integrable Hamiltonian systems one considers Hamiltonians of the form:

$$H \equiv h_0(J) + \varepsilon F_0(J,\psi)$$

$(J,\psi) \in V \times T^N$ being the so-called action-angle variables and ε a small parameter. Under suitable non-degeneracy assumptions, in a neighborhood of a *simple resonance* (a "simple resonance" is a hypersurface in V of the form $\{J \in V : \partial_J h_0 \cdot \nu_0 = 0$ for some $\nu_0 \in Z^N \backslash \{0\}$ and $\partial_J h_0 \cdot \nu \neq 0$ for all ν not parallel to ν_0 $\})$ one can find, for any $Q > 0$, a canonical transformation $(J,\psi) \to (a,\alpha), (p,q) \in R^{N-1} \times T^{N-1} \times R \times T$ such that in the new variables H takes the form:

$$\tilde h(a;\varepsilon) + P(p,q;a,\varepsilon) + \varepsilon^{Q+1}\tilde F(a,\alpha,p,q;\varepsilon)$$

In general, the integrable Hamiltonian P (*parametrized* by $a \in V \subset R^{N-1}$ and ε) generates a structure similar to that of the standard pendulum (*i.e.* isolated unstable equilibria, separatrices, etc.). The relation of Arnold's Hamiltonian (1.1) to the general problem of nearly-integrable motions near simple resonances is transparent.

The proof of the above Theorem is based on the idea of *transition chains of whiskered tori.*

For $\mu = 0$ the (integrable) system with Hamiltonian H_0 carries a "partially-hyperbolic structure": there are *lower dimensional invariant tori*

$$\mathcal{T}(\omega) \equiv \{p = q = 0\} \times \{a = \omega, b = b_0\} \times \{(\alpha,\beta) \in T^2\}$$

on which the motion is *quasi-periodic*: $(\alpha, \beta) \to (\alpha + \omega t, \beta + t)$. These tori are linearly unstable and admit asymptotic manifolds called by Arnold "whiskers":

$$\begin{aligned} W^{\pm}(\mathcal{T}(\omega)) \equiv \ & \{a = \omega, b = b_0\} \times \{(\alpha, \beta) \in T^2\} \\ & \times \{(p,q) : \frac{p^2}{2} + \varepsilon(\cos q - 1) = 0\} \\ = & \{ \text{ phase points } z : \ \text{dist. } (\phi_0^t(z), \mathcal{T}(\omega)) \to 0 \ \text{ as } t \to \pm\infty\} \end{aligned}$$

The whiskers $W^{\pm}(\mathcal{T}(\omega))$ are 3-dimensional manifolds lying in the same 5-dimensional ambient space (energy level). In general two 3-dimensional surfaces in a 5-dimensional space intersect in a line; however in the integrable (and hence degenerate) situation ($\mu = 0$) it is $W^+ \equiv W^-$. The perturbation f in Arnold's Theorem is taken so that *all whiskered tori $\mathcal{T}(\omega)$ are preserved for $\mu \neq 0$*: this, of course, is a highly non-generic property. The perturbation removes the degeneracy of the integrability and persistent whiskers will, in general, intersect transversally along a curve ζ, which is a trajectory such that dist.$(\zeta(t), \mathcal{T}_\mu(\omega)) \to 0$ as $t \to \pm\infty$, where $\mathcal{T}_\mu$ denotes the continuation in μ of the persistent torus $\mathcal{T}(\omega)$. Trajectories of this type were called by Poincarè *homoclinic.*

Transversality is checked by a first order (in μ) computation by means of "Poincarè [P]-Melnikov [Me]-Arnold [A2] integrals" (we shall come back on this point).

Persistent whiskers are arbitrarly close one to the other, therefore transversality yields *heteroclinic trajectories i.e.* trajectories $\zeta(t) \equiv \zeta(t; \omega, \omega')$ such that $\zeta \equiv \{\zeta(t) : t \in R\} = W^+(\mathcal{T}_\mu(\omega)) \cap W^-(\mathcal{T}_\mu(\omega'))$ with $\omega \neq \omega'$.

Since in Arnold's example *all tori* are preserved, one can construct *long* chains of whiskered tori $\mathcal{T}_i \equiv \mathcal{T}_\mu(\omega_i)$ for which $|\omega_{i+1} - \omega_i| = o(|\mu|)$ (say, $|\omega_{i+1} - \omega_i| = c|\mu|^2$) and $\emptyset \neq W^+(\mathcal{T}_i) \cap W^-(\mathcal{T}_{i+1}) = \zeta_i$; $\omega_1 < a'$, $\omega_M > a''$. Here $M = \mathcal{O}((a'' - a')/c\mu^2)$ and the reason for taking $|\omega_{i+1} - \omega_i| = o(\mu)$ is related to the fact that transversality is measured by a suitable determinant, which is, in general, of $\mathcal{O}(|\mu|)$ (see below).

The idea is now to "shadow" the "pseudo-orbit" $\mathcal{P} \equiv \cup_{i=1}^M \zeta_i$ with a true orbit starting near $\mathcal{T}_1$, staying close for $0 \le t \le T$ to $\mathcal{P}$ and passing at time T near $\mathcal{T}_M$. In [A2] it is claimed that this is possible as long as all ω_i's are irrational. Below we shall sketch the argument under stronger (*i.e.* "Diophantine") assumptions on the frequencies ω_i: the argument will rely upon a "strong" KAM linearization around the whiskered tori.

2 Three classes of model problems

We shall now discuss a few generalizations of the results and methods outlined above. Rather than introducing the general setting to which our theory applies, we shall restrict here on the following three *model problems.*

Consider a *real-analytic* Hamiltonian of the form:

$$H_\mu \equiv H_0(a, p, q; \varepsilon) + \mu \varepsilon^Q f(a, \alpha, p, q)$$

with $(p,q) \in R \times T$, $(a,\alpha) \in R^{N-1} \times T^{N-1}$ standard symplectic coordinates, $Q \geq 0$, and the integrable part H_0 given by:

$$H_0 \equiv h(a) + P(p,q;a,\varepsilon) \ , \qquad P \equiv \frac{p^2}{2J_0} + \varepsilon g_0^2 J_0(\cos q - 1) \tag{2.1}$$

where g_0, J_0 may depend on a. We shall then consider the following three models:

$$h \equiv \sum_{i=1}^{N-1} \frac{a_i^2}{2J_i} \ , \quad \varepsilon > 0 \quad \text{fixed} \ , \quad |\mu| \ll 1 \ , \quad (Q \ \text{arbitrary}) \qquad \textbf{(M1)}$$

$$h \equiv \sum_{i=1}^{N-1} \frac{a_i^2}{2J_i} \ , \quad Q > Q_0, \quad 0 < \varepsilon < \varepsilon_0 \ll 1,$$
$$|\mu| \leq 2, \quad (\text{suitable } Q_0, \varepsilon_0) \qquad \textbf{(M2)}$$

$$h \equiv \omega_1 a_1 + \varepsilon \frac{a_2^2}{2J} \ , \quad Q, \varepsilon, \mu \ \text{as in } \textbf{(M2)} \qquad (N = 3) \qquad \textbf{(M3)}$$

Remarks: (i) To cover Arnold's example one should substitute in **(M1)** h with $\sum_{i=1}^{N-2}(a_i^2/2J_i) + \omega a_{N-1}$, to which, with the due (and well known) modifications all the theory below applies (see [CG2]).

(ii) In the models **(M2)** and **(M3)** μ is just an *auxiliary parameter* as its large domain of definition allows to set it equal to 1.

(iii) The Hamiltonian H_0 in the third model **(M3)** (for which the above comment (ii) holds as well) is an example of *degenerate system*: for $\varepsilon = 0$, H_0 is independent of the action variable a_2. Such systems are important as they are common in Celestial Mechanics. Consider the *D'Alembert model of the Earth precession*: a planet assimilated to a rigid rotational ellipsoid with small "flattness" ε (*i.e.* with "equatorial radius" R and "polar radius" $R/(1+2\varepsilon)^{1/2}$), revolving on a given Keplerian orbit of eccentricity $e \equiv \varepsilon^Q$, around a fixed star and subject only to Newtonian gravitational forces. One can show that the model just described is a suitable generalization of **(M3)** above: see [CG2] where "Arnold's diffusion" for such a model is proved.

(iv) The model **(M1)** will be called *a-priori unstable* as the integrable part ($\mu = 0$) contains separatrices on which the motion is partially hyperbolic as already explained above, The models **(M2)**, **(M3)** are, instead, examples of *a-priori stable systems* as the perturbative (small) parameter is ε [see (ii)] and separatrices may be introduced only at resonances by the perturbation (see also the comment after the Theorem in §1).

(v) In fact the theory sketched below can be extended so as to cover cases where $h(a)$ is a rather arbitrary function verifying standard non-degeneracy conditions and where J_i, g_0 could also depend on p, q (besides depending on the actions a as assumed here): this extensions allow to cover nearly-integrable situations in a neighborhood of a simple resonance (included the D'Alembert model).

3 Instability mechanism

Roughly speaking the mechanism for instability (or "drift" or "diffusion") of the perturbed integrals is based on the following idea.

Fixed a reference energy E, consider a path $\mathcal{L} \subset \{a : H_0(a,0,0;\varepsilon) = E\}$, piecewise analytic. Attached to each $a_0 \in \mathcal{L}$ we shall think a lower dimensional invariant torus

$$\mathcal{T}(\omega) \equiv \{\alpha \in T^{N-1},\ a = a_0,\ p = q = 0\}\ , \quad \omega \equiv \partial_a h(a_0)$$

(which is actually independent of ε) together with its whiskers

$$W^{\pm}(\mathcal{T}(\omega)) \equiv \{\alpha \in T^{N-1}; a = a_0; (p,q) : P(p,q;a_0,\varepsilon) = 0\}$$

According to (partially hyperbolic) KAM theory ([M],[Gr],[Z]), for general $\mathcal{L}$, "most" of the whiskered tori persist for $\mu \neq 0$ but small enough. However, *gaps* of size as big as $\mathcal{O}(\sqrt{|\mu|\varepsilon^Q})$ where none of the above tori persist, have to be expected.

It is therefore clear which are the problems to be overcome:

(P1) Persistence of whiskered tori emerging from the unperturbed ones attached to the path $\mathcal{L}$; smoothness properties of the whiskers (with respect to parameters, smooth interpolation properties, etc.); behaviour of the trajectories around the whiskered tori; analytic continuation for large values of μ for the models **(M2)**, **(M3)**;

(P2) Transversal splitting and creation of homo/heteroclinic orbits;

(P3) Quantitative relation between the size of gaps and the "size of transversality" (location of high-density zones of persistent tori and admissible choises of "diffusion" paths $\mathcal{L}$).

4 Persistence of whiskered tori and their analyticity properties

Regarding problem **(P1)** the following result holds. Let $\mathcal{L} \equiv \{a_\sigma : \sigma \in [0,1]\}$ be a piecewise analytic (in σ) path on a fixed energy level $\mathcal{E}_E \equiv \{a : H_0(a,0,0;\varepsilon) = 0\}$ and, if $\omega_\sigma \equiv \partial_a h(a_\sigma)$, let

$$\tilde{\mathcal{L}} \equiv \{a \equiv a_{\sigma\gamma} : \partial_a h(a) = \omega_\sigma(1+\gamma)\ ,\ \sigma \in [0,1], \gamma \in [-\bar{\gamma},\bar{\gamma}]\}$$

Clearly if $\bar{\gamma}$ is small enough, $\tilde{\mathcal{L}}$ is $|\gamma|$-close to $\mathcal{L}$. Finally, let

$$\Sigma(C,\tau) \equiv \{\sigma \in [0,1] : |\omega_\sigma \cdot \nu|^{-1} \leq C|\nu|^\tau,\ \forall\, \nu \in Z^{N-1}, \nu \neq 0\}$$

and denote by $B^n_r \equiv \{x \in R^n : |x_i| \leq r\ , i = 1,...,n\}$.

Theorem 1 ([CG2]). **(i):** *Consider the model* **(M1)** *and fix* $k > 0$. *There exist* $\mu_0, \kappa_0, \bar{\gamma} > 0$ *and* C^k*-functions*

$$\zeta: \ (\mu, \psi, y, x, \sigma, \gamma) \in B^1_{\mu_0} \times T^{N-1} \times B^2_{\kappa_0} \times [0,1] \times B^1_{\bar{\gamma}} \to \zeta_\mu(\psi, y, x; \sigma, \gamma) \in R^N \times T^N$$

$$g: \ (\mu, z, \sigma, \gamma) \in B^1_{\mu_0} \times B^1_{\kappa_0^2} \times [0,1] \times B^1_{\bar{\gamma}} \to g_\mu(z; \sigma, \gamma) \in R$$

which, for $\sigma \in \Sigma(C, \tau)$ *and* $\gamma \in B^1_{\bar{\gamma}}$ *fixed, are analytic in the remaining arguments, and are such that:*

$$\phi^t_\mu \ \zeta_\mu(\psi, y, x; \sigma, \gamma) = \zeta_\mu(\psi + \omega_\sigma(1+\gamma)t, ye^{-g_\mu t}, xe^{g_\mu t}; \sigma, \gamma)$$
$$(\sigma \in \Sigma(C, \tau), \ |\gamma| \le \bar{\gamma})$$

where ϕ^t_μ *denotes the flow generated by* H_μ. *In particular*

$$\mathcal{T}_{\sigma\gamma} \equiv \ \{\zeta_\mu(\psi, 0, 0; \sigma, \gamma) : \psi \in T^{N-1}\}$$

is a H_μ*-invariant torus with local whiskers given by:*

$$\begin{aligned} W^+_{loc}(\mathcal{T}_{\sigma\gamma}) &\equiv \ \{\zeta_\mu(\psi, y, 0; \sigma, \gamma) : \psi \in T^{N-1}, y \in [-\kappa_0, \kappa_0]\} \\ W^-_{loc}(\mathcal{T}_{\sigma\gamma}) &\equiv \ \{\zeta_\mu(\psi, 0, x; \sigma, \gamma) : \psi \in T^{N-1}, x \in [-\kappa_0, \kappa_0]\} \end{aligned} \tag{4.1}$$

Finally, the value γ *can be chosen to be a smooth function of* μ, σ *and so that the energy* $H_\mu(\zeta_\mu(\psi, 0, 0; \sigma, \gamma))$ *has a preassigned value* E *within the range of the possible unperturbed energy values.*

(ii): *Consider the models* **(M2)**, **(M3)**: *There exist* $Q_0 > 1$, $\varepsilon_0 > 0$ *such that for* $Q > Q_0$, $0 < \varepsilon < \varepsilon_0$ *all the above results hold with* $\mu_0 = 2$. *More precisely: Let* $\Omega \equiv \ \sup_{\sigma,\gamma} |\omega_{\sigma\gamma}|$; *then there exist a (universal) number* $Q_0 > 1$ *and a positive constant* K *(depending on* τ, κ_0 *and other natural parameters associated to the functions* H_0, f*) such that if:*

$$K\mu_0\varepsilon_0^{Q-Q_0} \ (C\Omega)^{14} < 1 \tag{4.2}$$

then the results in **(i)** *hold for all* $|\mu| \le \mu_0$, $0 < \varepsilon \le \varepsilon_0$, $Q > Q_0$.

From (4.2) it follows that the radius of analyticity in μ is in fact proportional to ε_0^{-m} for a suitable m.

Clearly for μ_0 (respectively, ε_0) small enough, the above functions defining the local whiskers can be analytically extended, using the flow, to "long stretches": *e.g.*, if π_q denotes the projection on the q-variable, the y, x-domain of ζ can be extended so as to contain a segment $[-\kappa, \kappa]$ so that $|\pi_q\zeta_\mu(\psi, \pm\kappa, 0; \sigma, \gamma)|$

and $|\pi_q \zeta_\mu(\psi, 0, \pm\kappa; \sigma, \gamma)|$ are larger than $3\pi/2$; of course, in such an extended region, the local whiskers are $\mathcal{O}(\varepsilon^{Q-Q_0}|\mu|)$-close to the unperturbed ones.

The existence of whiskered tori was first established by [M] and [Gr], and, more recently, it has been re-examined by [LW]. For the joint smoothness of the parametric representation (which yields smooth interpolation of the whiskered tori) compare with the analogous results for maximal (N-dimensional) tori by [L1], [S], [Pö], [CG1].

One can show (see §8 of [CG2]) that from the above linearization it follows that the tori $\mathcal{T}_{\sigma\gamma}$ are *transition tori* in the sense of [A2].

Finally, notice that the μ analyticity allows to give a precise meaning to μ-expansions also for the models **(M2)**, **(M3)** and yields an algorithm to compute ("perturbatively") various objects of interest.

5 Transversal homoclinic points

Here we discuss **(P2)**. Consider first the model **(M1)**.

The analyticity properties established in Theorem 1 imply that $W^\pm \cap \{q = \pi\}$ is a *graph* over the angles $\alpha \in T^{N-1}$. By the Implicit Function Theorem there exist real-analytic functions $x_\mu, y_\mu, \psi_\mu^\pm$ such that (dropping the σ, γ parameters in the notation and denoting π_q,...,π_a the projections on the coordinates q,...,a):

$$\pi_q\ \zeta_\mu(\psi_\mu^+(\alpha), y_\mu(\alpha), 0) = \pi = \pi_q\ \zeta_\mu(\psi_\mu^-(\alpha), 0, x_\mu(\alpha)),$$
$$\pi_\alpha\ \zeta_\mu(\psi_\mu^+(\alpha), y_\mu(\alpha), 0) = \alpha = \pi_\alpha\ \zeta_\mu(\psi_\mu^-(\alpha), 0, x_\mu(\alpha)).$$

Define:

$$a_\mu^+(\alpha) \equiv \pi_a\ \zeta_\mu(\psi_\mu^+, y_\mu, 0)\ , \qquad p_\mu^+(\alpha) \equiv \pi_p\ \zeta_\mu(\psi_\mu^+, y_\mu, 0),$$
$$a_\mu^-(\alpha) \equiv \pi_a\ \zeta_\mu(\psi_\mu^-, 0, x_\mu)\ , \qquad p_\mu^-(\alpha) \equiv \pi_p\ \zeta_\mu(\psi_\mu^-, 0, x_\mu).$$

Then:

$$W^\pm \cap \{q = \pi\} = \{(a_\mu^\pm(\alpha), \alpha, p_\mu^\pm(\alpha), \pi) : \alpha \in T^{N-1}\}.$$

Since the p-variable can be eliminated by conservation of energy, we see that finding non-degenerate homoclinic intersections is equivalent to find α_0 such that:

$$\Delta(\alpha_0; \mu) \equiv\ a_\mu^+(\alpha_0) - a_\mu^-(\alpha_0) = 0\ , \quad D(\alpha_0; \mu) \equiv\ \det[\partial_\alpha \Delta(\alpha_0)] \neq 0. \quad (5.1)$$

The quantity $D(\alpha_0; \mu)$ is *a measure of the transversality* of the intersection between W^+ and W^-; in fact, the eigenvalues of $\partial_\alpha \Delta$ are related to the geometric angles between $W^+ \cap \{q = \pi\}$ and $W^- \cap \{q = \pi\}$ (of course such geometry depends upon our coordinates). Notice that $\Delta(\alpha_0; 0) \equiv\ 0$ by the degeneracy of the unperturbed system.

Theorem 1 and a perturbative study of the linearized (in μ) Hamiltonian equations yield easily the following first-order evaluation of Δ (compare [P], [Me], [A2]):

Proposition 1. *In all the above model* **(M1)** $\div$ **(M3)**, Δ *is analytic both in* α *and* μ *and if* $\Delta \equiv \mu\Delta_1(\alpha) + \mu^2\Delta_2(\alpha) + \ldots$ *then:*

$$\Delta_1(\alpha) = \partial_\alpha m_f$$

with

$$m_f(\alpha;\sigma,\gamma) \equiv - \sum_{0\neq\nu\in Z^{N-1}} e^{i\nu\cdot\alpha} \int_{-\infty}^{+\infty} \frac{e^{i\omega_{\sigma\gamma}\cdot\nu t}}{i\omega_{\sigma\gamma}\cdot\nu} \partial_t[e^{i\nu\cdot\vartheta_t} \hat{f}_\nu(a_{\sigma\gamma}, p_t, q_t)]dt \quad (5.2)$$

where $\hat{f}_\nu$ *are the Fourier coefficients of* $\alpha \to f(a,\alpha,p,q)$, (p_t,q_t) *is the unperturbed separatrix motion starting at* $q=\pi$ *and* ϑ_t *is such that*

$$\pi_q\ \phi_0^t(a_{\sigma\gamma},\alpha,p_0,\pi) = \alpha + \omega_{\sigma\gamma}t + \vartheta_t.$$

Thus, for the model **(M1)** (where μ is small), by the standard Implicit Function Theorem, *homoclinic points* (in the transversal section $\{q=\pi\}$) correspond to *non-degenerate critical points* of the periodic function $\alpha \to m_f(\alpha)$. And it is easy to see that, *generically*, m_f has at least 2^{N-1} non-degenerate critical points. The determinant D will be (again: in general) of $O(|\mu|)$ and therefore in order to establish *drift along a path* $\bar{\mathcal{L}} \equiv \{\bar{a}_\sigma : \sigma \in [0,1]\}$ one will have to check that such a path has a density of persistent whiskered tori of $o(|\mu|)$; see next section. Here and below $\bar{\mathcal{L}}$ will denote a path $\{a_{\sigma\gamma(\sigma)} : \sigma \in [0,1]\}$ where the value $\gamma(\sigma)$ has been fixed so that $\bar{\mathcal{L}}$ belongs to the same energy level (compare **(i)** in Theorem 1).

For **(M2)** the situation is more delicate as, in general, $\partial_\alpha\Delta_1$ is *exponentially small in* ε. More precisely, assume (for simplicity) that f is a *trigonometric polynomial* in the angular variables α, q and recall the analyticity properties of the unperturbed separatrix motion:

$$p_t = \pm 2\sqrt{\varepsilon}\bar{J}\bar{g}(\cosh\sqrt{\varepsilon\bar{g}}t)^{-1}\ , \quad q_t = 4\arctan e^{\pm\sqrt{\varepsilon\bar{g}}t}\ ,$$
$$\vartheta_t = -2\partial_a(\sqrt{\varepsilon\bar{g}}\bar{J})\tanh\sqrt{\varepsilon\bar{g}}t$$

where $\bar{J} \equiv J_0(\bar{a}_\sigma)$, $\bar{g} \equiv g_0(\bar{a}_\sigma)$. In particular, the integrand in (5.2) is holomorphic in t in a strip $|\ \mathrm{Im}\ t| < \pi/(2\sqrt{\varepsilon\bar{g}})$. Therefore, shifting the contour of integration to

$$\mathrm{Im}\ t = \ \mathrm{sign}(\omega_{\sigma\gamma}\cdot\nu)\left(\frac{\pi}{2\sqrt{\varepsilon\bar{g}}} - r\right)$$

(with any $r>0$) one obtains the estimate:

$$\sup_{\alpha\in T^{N-1}} |\partial_\alpha^j m_f| \leq k_j \sup_{\nu\neq 0}[e^{-|\omega_{\sigma\gamma}\cdot\nu|\pi/(2\sqrt{\varepsilon\bar{g}})}e^{-|\nu|}] \quad (5.3)$$

where k_j is a suitable constant. Under our Diophantine assumption on the frequencies $\omega_{\sigma\gamma}$ the supremum in the right hand side of (5.3) can be bounded by (or, better: is essentially equal to) $c_1 \exp(-c_2/\varepsilon^{\frac{(\tau+1)}{2}})$, for suitable positive constants c_1, c_2.

In the case **(M3)** the frequency vector has the form $\omega = (\omega_1, \varepsilon\bar{\omega}_2)$, for a suitable $\bar{\omega}_2(a)$; thus the *supremum in* (5.3) *is of order* 1. However what is really important here is to estimate from below $D \equiv \det \Delta$ and one can show that, even in the case **(M3)**, $D|_{\mu=1}$ is *exponentially small in* ε. But this phenomenon is an *accident*: indeed, in general, a second order (in μ) computation shows that $D|_{\mu=1} = \mathcal{O}(\varepsilon^M)$ for a suitable $M > 1$; see §7 below for a precise statement.

6 Density of whiskered tori

The strategy at this point is clear: it remains to find , on the energy surface $\mathcal{E}_E$, "diffusion paths" where the gaps ($\equiv$ "intervals of non-persistent whiskered tori") are smaller than the size of D (*i.e.* intuitively, of the "smallest" non-trivial angle formed by vectors tangent to the whiskers).

High-density zone of persistent tori may be detected by using the theory of normal forms in the way it is used in Nekhoroshev's Theorem ([N], [BG]). Then, choosing suitably the Diophantine constant C (recall the definition of $\Sigma(C,\tau)$ in §4) as a function of μ or ε, one can prove the following results concerning **(M1)** and **(M3)**.

Before we need a **definition**: *we say that a path* $\bar{\mathcal{L}} \subset \mathcal{E}_E$ *has "residual measure"* ρ *if the Lebesgue measure of* $[0,1] \setminus \Sigma_{\text{ persistent}}$*, with* $\Sigma_{\text{ persistent}} \equiv \{\sigma \in [0,1]$ *s.t. to* a_σ *it can be associated a persistent whisker (2.1) with the properties described in Theorem 1* $\}$*, is bounded above by* ρ. The residual measure gives an upper bound on the maximal size of gaps in $\bar{\mathcal{L}}$.

Now, assume (for simplicity) that f is a trigonometric polynomial in the angle variables α, q.

Proposition 2. [*Case* **(M1)**] *Let* $m > 1$. *There exist a* $\mu_1 < \mu_0$, *a* $\tau_0 \geq N-1$, *an open* $(N-2)$*-dimensional set* $\mathcal{A}_{f,m} \subset \mathcal{E}_E$ *and a function* $C = C_{\mu,m}$ *such that* $\forall\ |\mu| < \mu_1$, $\tau \geq \tau_0$ *any two points of* $\mathcal{A}_{f,m}$ *can be joined by a path* $\bar{\mathcal{L}}$ *with* $\Sigma(C_{\mu,m}, \tau_0) \subset \Sigma_{\text{ persistent}}$ *and residual measure of* $\mathcal{O}(|\mu|^m)$. *Furthermore, the set* $\mathcal{E}_E \setminus \mathcal{A}_{f,m}$ *itself has* $(N-2$ *dimensional) measure of* $\mathcal{O}(|\mu|^m)$.

Proposition 3. [*Case* **(M3)**] *There exist* a_2*-intervals* (a,b) *of order* $\mathcal{O}(1)$, *constants* Q_1, ε_1 *with* $Q_1 > Q_0$, $0 < \varepsilon_1 < \varepsilon_0$ *and a function* $C = C_\varepsilon$ *such that* $\forall$ $0 < \varepsilon < \varepsilon_1$, $|\mu| \leq 2$ *the path* $\bar{\mathcal{L}} \equiv \{(a_1(\sigma), a + \sigma(b-a))\}$ *(*a_1 *being determined by* $\bar{\mathcal{L}} \subset \mathcal{E}_E$*) has* $\Sigma(C_\varepsilon, 1) \subset \Sigma_{\text{ persistent}}$ *and residual measure of* $\mathcal{O}(\exp(-c/\sqrt{\varepsilon}))$, *c being a suitable positive constant.*

While Proposition 2 is easily obtained by performing a *finite number* of "classical perturbative steps", Proposition 3 involves the use of high order normal forms as in the "analytic part" of Nekhoroshev theory (see [N] and [BG]).

We also remark that the sentence "there exist" in the above propositions really means "one can construct", *i.e.* it is possibly to decide wether a certain region of phase space has a high density of persistent tori.

It is clear that the above results are sufficient in order to get for **(M1)** and **(M3)** the so-called Arnold's diffusion *i.e.* a drift of order 1 in action variables no matter how small the perturbation is (as long as certain non-degeneracies are verified; see also next section). The model **(M2)** is more difficult as indeed the size of $D|_{\mu=1}$ is smaller than any power in ε (see [L2], [GLT], [HMS], [DS] for lower dimensional discussions) and we refrain to formulate a density result as further analysis is needed.

7 Instabilities and Arnold's diffusion

From Proposition 2 and the results of §5, it follows easily, for the model **(M1)**, the existence of "diffusion paths" *i.e.* of paths having a density of persistent whiskered tori higher than the measure of the splitting of the whiskers; genericity being related to the condition:

$$\inf_{\sigma\in\Sigma} |\det \partial_\alpha^2 m_f| \geq \delta > 0. \tag{6.1}$$

If such a condition (easily checked on explicit examples including Arnold's one, at least for subintervals of $\mathcal{O}(1)$) holds, any two points of $\mathcal{A}_f$ can be joined by a path $\bar{a}_\sigma$. Then using the linearization of Theorem 1, one can prove that the time T_μ needed for the a-variable to *drift along the path* $\bar{\mathcal{L}}$ can be *bounded below* by:

$$T_\mu \leq c_3 e^{c_4/|\mu|^2}$$

for suitable positive constants c_3, c_4; such constants depends of course on ε (which for **(M1)** is fixed) and indeed c_3 is exponentially small in ε.

We collect now the above results for the model **(M3)** with

$$f \equiv \cos(\alpha_1 + q) + \cos(\alpha_2 + q) \tag{7.1}$$

in the following

Theorem 2. *Consider the model* **(M3)** *and set* $\mu = 1$ *i.e. consider* $H_1 \equiv H_0(a_1, a_2, p, q; \varepsilon) + \varepsilon^Q f$ *with* f *as in (7.1). Then the above Theorem 1 and Proposition 3 apply for* $Q > Q_1$ *and* $0 < \varepsilon < \varepsilon_1$*. Furthermore* $\alpha_0 \equiv (0,0)$ *(at* $\phi = \pi$*) is a "transversal homoclinic point" i.e. a non-degenerate solution of (5.1) and* $D(\alpha_0; 1) = \mathcal{O}(\varepsilon^m)$ *for a suitable* $m > 1$*. Along any* $\mathcal{O}(1)$*-path* $\bar{\mathcal{L}}$ *as in Proposition 3 "Arnold's drift or diffusion" takes place i.e. there exist initial* *data $z_\varepsilon(0)$ generating a trajectory $z_\varepsilon(t)$ which for $t = 0$ has a_2-coordinate ε-close to one extreme of $\bar{\mathcal{L}}$ while for a suitable $t = T_\varepsilon$ it has a_2-coordinate ε-close to the other extreme of $\bar{\mathcal{L}}$ [recall that* length *of $\bar{\mathcal{L}} = \mathcal{O}(1)$]. The time T_ε can be bounded below by $c_5 \exp(1/\varepsilon^{c_6})$ for suitable constants c_5, c_6.*

As already mentioned above this theorem is a consequence of Theorem 1, Proposition 3 and of a second order (in μ) analysis of the Melnikov integrals showing that the "homoclinic angles" (better: D) are *polynomially small in* ε (the higher μ-orders being easily controlled because of the large radius of μ-convergence).

References

[A1] Arnold, V. I.: *Mathematical methods of classical mechanics*, Springer Verlag, 1978.

A2] Arnold, V.: *Instability of dynamical sistems with several degrees of freedom*, Sov. Mathematical Dokl., 5, 581–585, 1966.

BG] Benettin, G., Gallavotti, G.: *Stability of motionions near resonances in quasi-integrable hamiltonian systems*, J. Statistical Physics, 44, 293–338, 1986.

G1] Chierchia, L., Gallavotti, G.: *Smooth prime integrals for quasi-integrable Hamiltonian systems* Il Nuovo Cimento, 67 B, 277–295, 1982.

G2] Chierchia, L., Gallavotti, G.: *Drift and Diffusion in Phase Space* Preprint 1992, 1–135

[DS] Delshams, A., Seara, M.T.: *An asymptotic expression for the splitting of separatrices of rapidly forced pendulum*, preprint 1991.

[G] Gallavotti, G.: *The elements of Mechanics*, Springer, 1983.

LT] Gelfreich, V. G., Lazutkin, V.F., Tabanov, M.B.:*Exponentially small splitting in Hamiltonian systems*, Chaos, 1 (2), 1991.

Gr] Graff, S.M.: *On the conservation for hyperbolic invariant tori for Hamiltonian systems*, J. Differential Equations 15, 1–69, 1974.

MS] Holmes, P., Marsden, J., Scheurle,J: *Exponentially Small Splittings of Separatrices in KAM Theory and Degenerate Bifurcations*, Preprint, 1989.

La1] Lazutkin, V. F.: *The existence of caustics for a billiard problem in a convex domain*, Izv. Akad. Nauk. SSSR, 37 (1), 1973

.a2] Lazutkin, V.F.: *Separatrices splitting for standard and semistandard mappings*, Preprint, 1989.

LW] de la Llave, R., Wayne, E.: *Whiskered Tori*, preprint 1990

[M] Moser, J.: *Convergent series expansions for quasi-periodic motions*, Mathematische Annalen, 169, 136–176, 1967.

Me] Melnikov, V.K.: *On the stability of the center for time periodic perturbations*, Trans. Moscow Math Math. Soc., 12, 1–57, 1963.

[N] Nekhorossev, N.: An exponential estimate of the time of stability of nearly integrable hamiltonian systems, Russian Mathematical Surveys, 32, 1–65, 1975.

[P] Poincarè, H.: *Les Méthodes nouvelles de la mécanique céleste*, 1892, reprinted by Blanchard, Paris, 1987.

[Pö] Pöschel, J.: *Integrability of Hamiltonian systems on Cantor sets*, Communications Pure Appl. Math, 35, 653–696, 1982.

[Sv] Svanidze, N.V.: *Small perturbations of an integrable dynamical system with an integral invariant*, Proceed. Steklov Institute of Math., 2, 1981

[Z] Zehnder, E.: *Generalized implicit function theorems with applications to some small divisors problems* I, II, Communications Pure Applied Mathematics, 28, 91–140, 1975.

SEPARATRICES SPLITTING FOR THE RAPIDLY FORCED PENDULUM

V. G. Gelfreich

Abstract. The equation of the rapidly forced pendulum

$$\ddot{x} + \sin(x) = \delta\varepsilon^p \sin(t/\varepsilon),$$

$p > 5$, is considered. It is proven that Poincaré–Arnold–Melnikov method gives the right asymptotic formula for the separatrices splitting angle for the case of a small ε.

1. Introduction. Formula for the separatrices splitting

We know from Poincaré's famous paper [1] that splitting of separatrices gives rise to complicated behaviour of trajectories in hamiltonian dynamical systems. The simplest equation which provides an example of separatrix splitting is the pendulum equation with periodic forcing

$$\ddot{x} + \sin x = \delta\varepsilon^p \sin(t/\varepsilon)\,, \tag{1}$$

where ε, δ and p are parameters. This equation became a paradigm problem and everyone applies methods of separatrices splitting investigation to it.

If $\delta = 0$ the equation (1) is a pendulum equation. A homoclinic solution

$$\begin{aligned} x_0(t) &= 2\arctan\sinh(t)\,, \\ y_0(t) - \dot{x}_0(t) &= \frac{2}{\cosh(t)}\,, \end{aligned} \tag{2}$$

connects a saddle point $(x, y) = (-\pi, 0)$ to itself on a cylinder with coordinates $(x, y) = (x, \dot{x})$.

The author thanks prof.Lazutkin and prof.Neishtadt for helpful discussions and remarks. The author thanks for the hospitality the Universitá degli Studi di Milano, where the final part of the work on this paper was carried out, and especially prof.Luigi Galgani. This work was partially supported by the grant of the State Comity of Science, Higher Education and Technical Politics of Russia

It is convenient to consider the full equation (1) as a system

$$\begin{aligned} \dot{x} &= y \\ \dot{y} &= -\sin x + \delta\varepsilon^p \sin(\tau) \\ \dot{\tau} &= \varepsilon^{-1} \end{aligned} \tag{3}$$

in a 3-dimensional space with coordinates $(x, y, \tau) = (x, \dot{x}, t/\varepsilon) \in S \times \mathbb{R} \times S$, where S is a circle.

For $\delta\varepsilon^{p+2}$ being small there exists a $2\pi\varepsilon$-periodic trajectory Γ in a neighborhood of the line $x = -\pi$, $y = 0$. There exist 2-dimensional invariant surfaces W^u and W^s called unstable and stable separatrices respectively, which are formed by points approaching Γ in the past (W^u) and in the future (W^s).

If we fix ε and consider small δ, than the simple application of Poincaré–Arnold–Melnikov theory [2] shows that the separatrices intersect transversely with intersection angle being $O(\delta)$.

The difficult problem arises when $\varepsilon > 0$ is small, since the splitting of separatrices becomes $O\big(\exp(-\text{const}/\varepsilon)\big)$ in systems with fast perturbation [3]. It was shown in the papers [4,5] that one can take any number less than $\pi/2$ as the constant in the exponent.

We fix a point of intersection of the separatrices using the symmetry of the equation (1). Note that if $x(t)$ satisfies the equation (1) then $-x(-t)$ also is a solution of the same equation. If $x(t)$ is close to a periodic trajectory in the past then $-x(-t)$ approaches a periodic trajectory (generally not the same) in the future. The periodic trajectory Γ is invariant with respect to the considered involution. Consequently if $(x, y, t) \in W^u$ then $(-x, y, -t) \in W^s$ and vice versa. Thus any point of intersection of W^u with the line $x = 0$, $\tau = 0$ is homoclinic. Let $\vec{z}_h$ denote the "first" intersection of W^u with this line in the upper half space $y > 0$.

Main Result. Provided $p > 5$ the angle of separatrices splitting in $\vec{z}_h$ is given by

$$\alpha = \pi\delta\varepsilon^{p-1} \exp\left(-\frac{\pi}{2\varepsilon}\right)\left(1 + O(\varepsilon^{p-5})\right). \tag{4}$$

The main term in (4) coincides with the prediction given by the Poincaré–Arnold–Melnikov theory.

The two sided estimates of the angle were previously obtained in the paper [4] for $p > 8$. It was announced in the paper [9] that similar results remain valid for some class of differential equations. The equation (1) with $p \geq 0$ belongs to this class.

The remaining part of the paper contains the proof of the formula (4). The proof is based on an approximation of analytical continuation of the separatrices and its main idea is related to the papers [6,7].

2. Periodic trajectory

If $\delta\varepsilon^{p+2}$ is small enough there exist the periodic trajectory Γ of the system (3) with the components $(-\pi + x_{per}(t), y_{per}(t), t)$, where

$$\begin{aligned} x_{per}(t) &= -\frac{\delta\varepsilon^{p+2}}{1+\varepsilon^2}\sin\frac{t}{\varepsilon} + O(\delta^3\varepsilon^{3p+8}), \\ y_{per}(t) &= -\frac{\delta\varepsilon^{p+1}}{1+\varepsilon^2}\cos\frac{t}{\varepsilon} + O(\delta^3\varepsilon^{3p+7}). \end{aligned} \tag{5}$$

The function $x_{per}(t)$ is odd. The second order linear differential equation with periodical coefficients

$$\ddot{u} - \cos(x_{per}(t))u = 0 \tag{6}$$

plays the important role in the proof. According to Floquet theory it has two linear independent solutions of the form

$$u_+(t) = e^{\omega t}\phi_+(t), \quad u_-(t) = e^{-\omega t}\phi_-(t), \tag{7}$$

where $\phi_\pm$ are $2\pi\varepsilon$ periodic functions. The Floquet exponent is defined uniquely and has the following asymptotic

$$\omega = 1 - \frac{\delta^2\varepsilon^{2p+4}}{8} + \text{h.o.t.} \tag{8}$$

(h.o.t.=higher order terms in ε and δ). The functions $\phi_\pm$ are defined up to a multiplicand independent of time. It is convenient to choose them in such a way that

$$\phi_+(t) = 2 + \frac{\delta^2\varepsilon^{2p+6}}{8}\sin\frac{2t}{\varepsilon} + \text{h.o.t.} \tag{9}$$

The coefficients in the equation (6) are even so we can choose $\phi_-(t) = \phi_+(-t)$.

3. Separatrices in the complex space

The stable W^s and unstable W^u separatrices of the periodic orbit Γ are two dimensional surfaces in the 3-dimensional phase space of the system (3). It is convenient to represent W^u in a parametric form

$$\begin{aligned} x &= x^u(t,t_0), \\ y &= y^u(t,t_0) = \dot{x}^u(t,t_0), \\ \tau &= t/\varepsilon. \end{aligned} \tag{10}$$

The parametrization of W^s can be defined by

$$\begin{aligned} x &= x^s(t,t_0) = -x^u(-t,-t_0), \\ y &= y^s(t,t_0) = y^u(-t,-t_0), \\ \tau &= t/\varepsilon \end{aligned} \tag{11}$$

due to the symmetry of the system (3). Thus we can construct approximation of only one separatrix instead of two. In the equations (10) the first parameter is time and there is some freedom in the definition of the second one. It is important to choose the definition of this parameter properly since we are going to study analytical continuation of W^u in this parameter. The following lemma states the existence of the suitable parametrization and its properties.

Let denote

$$D_1 = \Big\{(t,t_0) \in \mathbb{R}\times\mathbb{C} : t+\Re t_0 < -1\Big\} \cup \Big\{(t,t_0) \in \mathbb{R}\times\mathbb{C} : |t+\Re t_0| < 3,\ |\Im t_0| < 1\Big\}.$$

Lemma 1. *Given $p > -2$, for $\delta\varepsilon^{p+2}$ sufficiently small there exists a one parameter family $x^u(t,t_0)$ of solutions of the equation (1) such that*

$$x^u(t,t_0) \underset{t_0\to-\infty}{\longrightarrow} -\pi + x_{per}(t)\,, \tag{12}$$

$$x^u(t+2\pi\varepsilon, t_0) = x^u(t, t_0 + 2\pi\varepsilon)\,, \tag{13}$$

$x^u(t,t_0)$ is smooth in the first argument and analytical in the second one. It is estimated in D_1 by

$$\begin{aligned} &\left|\left(1+\frac{\partial}{\partial t_0}+\frac{\partial^2}{\partial t_0^2}\right)\Big(x^u(t,t_0) - x_0(t+t_0)\Big)\right| < \mathrm{const}\cdot\delta\varepsilon^{p+2}\,,\\ &\left|\left(1+\frac{\partial}{\partial t_0}+\frac{\partial^2}{\partial t_0^2}\right)\Big(\dot x^u(t,t_0) - y_0(t+t_0) - y_{per}(t)\Big)\right| < \mathrm{const}\cdot\delta\varepsilon^{p+2}\,. \end{aligned} \tag{14}$$

The proofs of Lemmas 1 and 2 are placed in Appendix A.

Lemma 1 defines the segment of W^u. In order to detect separatrices splitting we construct approximation of $x^u(t,t_0)$ in the vicinity of the pendulum separatrix singularity ($t + t_0 = \pm i\pi/2$). Let denote

$$D_2 = \Big\{(t,t_0) \in \mathbb{R}\times\mathbb{C} : |t+\Re t_0| < 3\,, |\Im t_0| < \frac{\pi}{2} - \varepsilon\Big\}.$$

Lemma 2. *Given $p > 5$, if $\varepsilon > 0$ is sufficiently small, then there exists an analytical continuation in t_0 of $x^u(t,t_0)$ into D_2 and it has in D_2 the following estimates*

$$|x^u(t,t_0) - x_0(t+t_0)| < \mathrm{const}\cdot\delta\varepsilon^{p-2} \tag{15}$$

and

$$\begin{aligned} x^u(t,t_0) - x^s(t,t_0) &= x^u(t,t_0) + x^u(-t,-t_0)\\ &= 4\pi\delta\varepsilon^p \frac{\sinh 2(t+t_0) + 2(t+t_0)}{8\cosh(t+t_0)}\,\frac{2}{\cosh\left(-\frac{\pi}{2\varepsilon}\right)}\sin\frac{t_0}{\varepsilon} + O(\delta^2\varepsilon^{2p-5})\,. \end{aligned} \tag{16}$$

The estimates (15) and (16) can be differentiated with respect to t, the error term being multiplied by $\mathrm{const}\cdot\varepsilon^{-1}$. Fix $r > 0$. If $|t + \Re t_0| > r$ then the error term in the estimate of the derivatieve has the same order in δ and ε as in (16).

Corollary. *The distance between points of W^u and W^s can be estimated by*

$$|x^u(t,t_0) - x^s(t,t_0)| + |y^u(t,t_0) - y^s(t,t_0)| < \text{const}\cdot\delta\varepsilon^p\,, \tag{17}$$

where $(t,t_0) \in D_2$, $|t + \Re t_0| > r > 0$.

If $|\Im t_0| = \pi/2 - \varepsilon$ then the first term in the formula (16) is bigger then the error term and so we detected the splitting of separatrices. Unfortunately we cannot use (16) immediately for obtaining the desired formula (4), since the error term $O(\delta\varepsilon^{2p-5})$ remains of the same order being considered in the real line, while the main one becomes exponentially small there. In order to get rid of this unpleasant circumstance, it is necessary to construct an analytical integral in a neighborhood of the unstable separatrix, and evaluate it at points belonging to the stable one. The dependence on the variable t will disappear. The function will became periodic with respect to t_0 with a period $2\pi\varepsilon$, and finally this will yield an appropriate exponential estimate for the error term too.

4. Analytical integral and the estimates with exponentially small error

We construct an analytical integral of the system (3) defined in some neighborhood of a complex segment of W^u. Let denote

$$D_3 = \left\{(t,t_0) \in \mathbb{R}\times\mathbb{C} : -1 < t + \Re t_0 < -2\,,\ |\Im t_0| < \frac{\pi}{2}\right\}$$

and

$$M_r = \left\{(x,y,t) : |x - x^u(t,t_0)|^2 + |y - y^u(t,t_0)|^2 < r^2,\ (t,t_0) \in D_2\right\}.$$

Lemma 3. *Given $p \geq -1$. If ε is sufficiently small there exist a number $r > 0$ (independent from ε and δ) and analytical in x and y functions $E(x,y,t)$ and $T(x,y,t)$ defined in M_r, such that*

E is constant on trajectories of the system (3);

$$E(x,y,t+2\pi\varepsilon) = E(x,y,t)\,,\quad T(x,y,t+2\pi\varepsilon) = T(x,y,t) + 2\pi\varepsilon\,; \tag{18}$$

$$E(x^u(t,t_0), y^u(t,t_0), t) = 0\,,\quad T(x^u(t,t_0), y^u(t,t_0), t) = t_0\,; \tag{19}$$

the map $(x,y) \mapsto (E,T)$ is symplectic for any fixed t, i.e.

$$dx\wedge dy = dE\wedge dT\,; \tag{20}$$

all derivatives of E with respect to x and y of the first and second order and derivatives of T of the first order are bounded by a constant independent from δ and ε.

The proof of Lemma 3 is placed in the appendix B.

The separation between W^u and W^s can be characterized by the integral E evaluated on the stable separatrix:

$$\theta(t_0) = E(x^s(t,t_0), y^s(t,t_0), t)\,. \tag{21}$$

It follows from the estimate (17) that $(x^s(t,t_0), y^s(t,t_0), t) \in M_r$ for $|\Im t_0| < \pi/2 - 2\varepsilon$, $-2 < t + \Re t_0 < -1$. Since E is an integral of motion, the right hand side of the equation (21) is an analytical function of one variable t_0. The function θ is $2\pi\varepsilon$-periodic:

$$\begin{aligned}\theta(t_0 + 2\pi\varepsilon) &= E(x^s(t, t_0 + 2\pi\varepsilon), y^s(t, t_0 + 2\pi\varepsilon), t)\\ &= E(x^s(t + 2\pi\varepsilon, t_0), y^s(t + 2\pi\varepsilon, t_0), t + 2\pi\varepsilon) = \theta(t_0)\,,\end{aligned}$$

where we used the property (13) of x^s and periodicity of E in t.

In order to estimate $\theta(t_0)$ in the complex strip $\Pi = \{|\Im t_0| < \pi/2 - 2\varepsilon\}$ we develop E in Taylor series in a neighborhood of a point $(x^u(t,t_0), y^u(t,t_0), t)$ with some fixed value of t such that $(t, t_0) \in D_3$:

$$\begin{aligned}\theta(t_0) = {}& \frac{\partial E}{\partial x}(x^u(t,t_0), y^u(t,t_0), t)\Big(x^s(t,t_0) - x^u(t,t_0)\Big)\\ &+ \frac{\partial E}{\partial y}(x^u(t,t_0), y^u(t,t_0), t)\Big(y^s(t,t_0) - y^u(t,t_0)\Big)\\ &+ O\left(\left|x^s(t,t_0) - x^u(t,t_0)\right|^2 + \left|y^s(t,t_0) - y^u(t,t_0)\right|^2\right).\end{aligned} \tag{22}$$

We can differentiate the equalities (19) in respect to t_0 and obtain the linear system on $\frac{\partial x^u}{\partial t_0}$, $\frac{\partial y^u}{\partial t_0}$:

$$\begin{aligned}&\frac{\partial E}{\partial x}(x^u(t,t_0), y^u(t,t_0), t)\frac{\partial x^u}{\partial t_0}(t,t_0) + \frac{\partial E}{\partial y}(x^u(t,t_0), y^u(t,t_0), t)\frac{\partial y^u}{\partial t_0}(t,t_0) = 0\,,\\ &\frac{\partial T}{\partial x}(x^u(t,t_0), y^u(t,t_0), t)\frac{\partial x^u}{\partial t_0}(t,t_0) + \frac{\partial T}{\partial y}(x^u(t,t_0), y^u(t,t_0), t)\frac{\partial y^u}{\partial t_0}(t,t_0) = 1\,.\end{aligned}$$

The determinant of the system is equal to 1 due to (20). The solution of this system is given by

$$\begin{aligned}\frac{\partial x^u}{\partial t_0}(t,t_0) &= -\frac{\partial E}{\partial y}(x^u(t,t_0), y^u(t,t_0), t)\,,\\ \frac{\partial y^u}{\partial t_0}(t,t_0) &= \frac{\partial E}{\partial x}(x^u(t,t_0), y^u(t,t_0), t)\,.\end{aligned} \tag{23}$$

Thus we obtain

$$\theta(t_0) = \frac{\partial y^u}{\partial t_0}(t,t_0)\big(x^s(t,t_0)-x^u(t,t_0)\big)-\frac{\partial x^u}{\partial t_0}(t,t_0)\big(y^s(t,t_0)-y^u(t,t_0)\big)+O(\delta^2\varepsilon^{2p}), \tag{24}$$

where we used (17) to estimate the error term. Then we substitute the estimates (14) and (16) in (24) to obtain the final estimate of the function $\theta(t_0)$ in the strip Π:

$$\theta(t_0) = 4\pi\delta\varepsilon^p \exp\left(-\frac{\pi}{\varepsilon}\right)\sin\frac{t_0}{\varepsilon} + O(\varepsilon^{2p-5}). \tag{25}$$

The following simple proposition provides an instrument for obtaining estimates with exponentially small error term.

Proposition 1. *Given ε, $0 < \varepsilon < 0.5$. If an analytic $2\pi\varepsilon$-periodic function $\psi(\zeta)$ is bounded by some value A, $|\psi(\zeta)| < A$ in the complex strip $\Pi = \{|\Im\zeta| < \frac{\pi}{2} - 2\varepsilon\}$, and has a zero mean value, then on the real axis*

$$|\psi(\zeta)| < 30A\exp\left(-\frac{\pi}{2\varepsilon}\right)$$

and

$$|\psi'(\zeta)| < \frac{300A}{\varepsilon}\exp\left(-\frac{\pi}{2\varepsilon}\right).$$

Proof. We denote by d the half width of the strip Π, $d = \pi/2 - 2\varepsilon$. The Fourier coefficients of the function ψ can be estimated in the following way:

$$|\psi_k| = \frac{1}{2\pi\varepsilon}\left|\int_0^{2\pi\varepsilon}\psi(\zeta)e^{-ik\zeta/\varepsilon}d\zeta\right| = \frac{1}{2\pi\varepsilon}\left|\int_{i\,sign(k)\,d}^{2\pi\varepsilon+i\,sign(k)\,d}\psi(\zeta)e^{-ik\zeta/\varepsilon}d\zeta\right|$$

$$= \frac{e^{-|k|d/\varepsilon}}{2\pi\varepsilon}\left|\int_0^{2\pi\varepsilon}\psi(\zeta+i\,sign(k)\,d)e^{-ik\zeta/\varepsilon}d\zeta\right| \le Ae^{-|k|d/\varepsilon}.$$

On the real line this estimate leads to

$$|\psi(\zeta)| \le \sum_{k\neq 0}|\psi_k| \le 2A\sum_{k>0}e^{-|k|d/\varepsilon} = \frac{2Ac^{-d/\varepsilon}}{1-e^{-d/\varepsilon}}.$$

We insert the definition of d in the last estimate and obtain

$$|\psi(\zeta)| \le \frac{2Ae^2e^{-\pi/(2\varepsilon)}}{1-e^2e^{-\pi/(2\varepsilon)}} < 30A\exp\left(-\frac{\pi}{2\varepsilon}\right)$$

for the given values of ε. To obtain the estimate of ψ' we have to estimate $\varepsilon^{-1}\sum_{k\neq 0}|k||\psi_k|$. This can be done in the similar way. □

In order to apply Proposition 1 we have to estimate the mean value $<\theta> = \frac{1}{2\pi\varepsilon}\int_0^{2\pi\varepsilon}\theta(t_0)dt_0$ of the function θ. Let $\vec{z}_1 = (x_1, y_1, 0)$ and $\vec{z}_2 = (x_2, y_2, 0)$ be two different point belonging to one real homoclinic trajectory, $\vec{z}_1,\ \vec{z}_2 \in W^u \cap W^s$. The algebraic value of the area between segments of W^u and W^s defined by these points in the plain $t = 0$ is equal to zero. The substitution $(x, y) \mapsto (E, T)$ is area preserving. The equation of W^u is $E = 0$ and the equation of W^s is given in a parametric form by $(E, T) = (E(x^s(0, t_0), y^s(0, t_0), 0), T(x^s(0, t_0), y^s(0, t_0), 0)) \equiv (\theta(t_0), t_0 + \psi(t_0))$, $(0, t_0) \in D_3$. the function $\psi(t_0)$ is the difference between the coordinate T calculated in the points of W^u and W^s corresponding to $(0, t_0)$. It is $2\pi\varepsilon$-periodic and bounded by $O(\delta\varepsilon^p)$.

The algebraic value of the area is given by the integration over one period of θ

$$I = \int_0^{2\pi\varepsilon} \theta(t_0)d(t_0 + \psi(t_0)) \equiv 0\,, \tag{26}$$

since t_0 and $t_0 + 2\pi\varepsilon$ always correspond to one trajectory. On the other hand we have

$$I = \int_0^{2\pi\varepsilon} \theta(t_0)\big(1 + \psi'(t_0)\big)dt_0$$

$$= <\theta> \left(2\pi\varepsilon + \int_0^{2\pi\varepsilon} \psi'(t_0)dt_0\right) + \int_0^{2\pi\varepsilon} (\theta(t_0) - <\theta>)\psi'(t_0)dt_0\,. \tag{27}$$

The function $\theta(t_0) - <\theta>$ and $\psi'(t_0)$ are analytic $2\pi\varepsilon$ periodic functions in the strip Π with zero mean value. They are $O(\delta\varepsilon^p)$ in Π. Thus we can apply Proposition 1 to obtain from (26) and (27) the exponential estimate

$$|<\theta>| < \text{const}\cdot\delta^2\varepsilon^{2p}\exp\left(-\frac{\pi}{\varepsilon}\right). \tag{28}$$

The application of Proposition 1 to the function $\theta(t_0) - <\theta> - 4\pi\delta\varepsilon^p e^{-\frac{\pi}{2\varepsilon}}\sin\frac{t_0}{\varepsilon}$ together with the estimates (25) and (28) lead to estimates

$$\theta(t_0) = 4\pi\delta\varepsilon^p \exp\left(-\frac{\pi}{2\varepsilon}\right)\sin\frac{t_0}{\varepsilon} + O\left(\varepsilon^{2p-5}\exp\left(-\frac{\pi}{2\varepsilon}\right)\right) \tag{29}$$

and

$$\theta'(t_0) = 4\pi\delta\varepsilon^{p-1} \exp\left(-\frac{\pi}{2\varepsilon}\right)\cos\frac{t_0}{\varepsilon} + O\left(\varepsilon^{2p-6}\exp\left(-\frac{\pi}{2\varepsilon}\right)\right), \tag{30}$$

where $t_0 \in \mathbb{R}$. The function θ has zeros at the points $t_{h,k} = \pi k\varepsilon + O(\varepsilon^{p-5})$, $k \in \mathbb{Z}$. Let t_h denote one of these zeros. Let t be any moment of time such that $-2 < t + \Re t_h < -1$. In the coordinate system (E, T) the point $(x^s(t, t_h), y^s(t, t_h), t)$ is $(\theta(t_h), t_h + \psi(t_h)) \equiv (0, \tilde{t}_h)$. Due to the property (19) this point corresponds also to $(x^u(t,\tilde{t}_h), y^u(t,\tilde{t}_h), t)$. This fact allow us to calculate the derivative of θ in the following way

$$\theta'(t_h) = \frac{\partial E}{\partial x}(x^s(t,t_h), y^s(t,t_h), t)\frac{\partial x^s}{\partial t_0}(t,t_h) + \frac{\partial E}{\partial y}(x^s(t,t_h), y^s(t,t_h), t)\frac{\partial y^s}{\partial t_0}(t,t_h)$$

$$= \frac{\partial E}{\partial x}(x^u(t,\tilde{t}_h), y^u(t,\tilde{t}_h), t)\frac{\partial x^s}{\partial t_0}(t,t_h) + \frac{\partial E}{\partial y}(x^u(t,\tilde{t}_h), y^u(t,\tilde{t}_h), t)\frac{\partial y^s}{\partial t_0}(t,t_h).$$

We can use the formulae (23) for the derivatives of E to obtain

$$\theta'(t_h) = \frac{\partial y^u}{\partial t_0}(t,\tilde{t}_h)\frac{\partial x^s}{\partial t_0}(t,t_h) - \frac{\partial x^u}{\partial t_0}(t,\tilde{t}_h)\frac{\partial y^s}{\partial t_0}(t,t_h). \tag{31}$$

The right hand side of (31) coincides with the value of the symplectic form $\Omega = dx \wedge dy$ on a pair of vectors tangent to W^u and W^s in the corresponding homoclinic point, namely

$$\vec{e}_u(t,\tilde{t}_h) = \left(\frac{\partial x^u}{\partial t_0}(t,\tilde{t}_h), \frac{\partial y^u}{\partial t_0}(t,\tilde{t}_h), 0\right) \tag{32}$$

and

$$\vec{e}_s(t,t_h) = \left(\frac{\partial x^s}{\partial t_0}(t,t_h), \frac{\partial y^s}{\partial t_0}(t,t_h), 0\right). \tag{33}$$

Although the vectors $\vec{e}_{u,s}$ depend on time the value

$$\omega = \Omega(\vec{e}_s, \vec{e}_u) = \theta'(t_h) \tag{34}$$

does not depend on time since the right hand side of the equation (31) coincides with a Wronskian of two solutions of the variational equation in the neighborhood of the homoclinic trajectory. The estimate (30) leads to the following estimate

$$\omega = 4\pi\varepsilon^{p-1}\exp\left(-\frac{\pi}{2\varepsilon}\right)\left(1 + O(\varepsilon^{p-5})\right) \tag{35}$$

for the homoclinic trajectory corresponding to the value $t_{h,0}$ of the parameter t_0. The value of ω provides a good characteristic of the separatrices splitting due to its invariance. It is closely related to the separatrices splitting angle:

$$\omega = \|\vec{e}_u\| \cdot \|\vec{e}_s\| \sin\alpha\,, \tag{36}$$

where α is the angle between the vectors $\vec{e}_u$ and $\vec{e}_s$. Since ω does not depend on time we can use (36) to calculate the angle for any value of t. We choose $t = 0$. The approximation of W^u given by lemma 1 provides that $x^u(0,0) = O(\delta\varepsilon^{p+2})$ and $\frac{\partial x^u}{\partial t_0}(0,0) = 2 + O(\delta\varepsilon^{p+2})$. Thus there exist a unique solution of the equation $x^u(0,\hat{t}_h) = 0$ in a neighborhood of zero, namely $\hat{t}_h = O(\delta\varepsilon^{p+2})$. As it was shown in the section 1 the point of the form $(0, y^u(0,\tilde{t}_h), 0)$ must belong also to W^s (be a homoclinic point). The homoclinic point corresponds to $\tilde{t}_h$ and thus $\hat{t}_h = \tilde{t}_h$. This fact allows as to use estimate (14) to obtain that $\|\vec{e}_u(0,\tilde{t}_h)\| = 2 + O(\delta\varepsilon^{p+2})$ and $\|\vec{e}_s(0,t_h)\| = 2 + O(\delta\varepsilon^{p+2})$. The last two estimates together with (35) and (36) give the desired asymptotical formula (4) for the separatrices splitting angle.

Appendix A. Proof of Lemmas 1 and 2.

Since the proofs of Lemmas 1 and 2 are quite similar we do them in parallel. The proof is based on the stable point theorem for the integral operator in properly chosen Banach spaces. The estimate (16) appears as a first iterate of a convergent iteration procedure.

The difference between Lemma 1 and Lemma 2 is due to the fact that D_1 does not contain points closed to the singularities $\pm i\pi/2$ of the unperturbed separatrix $x_0(t+t_0)$ and D_2 contains points which are ε-close.

We take an initial approximation of the separatrix W^u suitable in $D_1 \cup D_2$:

$$x_{in}(t,t_0) = x_{per}(t) + \tilde{x}_0(t,t_0)\,, \tag{A1}$$

where

$$\tilde{x}_0(t,t_0) = 2\arctan\left(\frac{e^{\omega(t+t_0)}}{\phi_-(t)} - \frac{e^{-\omega(t+t_0)}}{\phi_+(t)}\right). \tag{A2}$$

The functions $\phi_\pm(t)$ and the Floquet exponent ω were defined in Section 2. The following propositions provide necessary estimates of the function $\tilde{x}_0(t,t_0)$.

Proposition A1. *Let $(t,t_0) \in D_1$, then $\tilde{x}_0(t,t_0)$ is bounded by a constant independent from δ and ε and*

$$|\tilde{x}_0(t,t_0) - x_0\big(\omega(t+t_0)\big)| \le \text{const}\cdot\delta^2\varepsilon^{2p+4}e^{\omega(t+\Re t_0)}\,. \tag{A3}$$

The function $\tilde{x}_0(t,t_0)$ is an approximate solution of the following equation

$$\ddot{\tilde{x}}_0(t,t_0) - \cos(x_{per}(t))\sin\tilde{x}_0(t,t_0) = O(\delta^2\varepsilon^{2p+4}e^{3\omega(t+\Re t_0)})\,. \tag{A4}$$

Proposition A2. *Let $(t,t_0) \in D_2$, then the following estimates hold*

$$|\tilde{x}_0(t,t_0) - x_0(\omega(t+t_0))| < \text{const}\cdot\delta^2\varepsilon^{2p+2}\,, \tag{A5}$$

$$|\sin\tilde{x}_0(t,t_0)| + |\cos\tilde{x}_0(t,t_0)| < \text{const}\cdot\varepsilon^{-2}\,, \tag{A6}$$

$$\begin{aligned}|\ddot{\tilde{x}}_0(t,t_0) - \ddot{x}_0(\omega(t+t_0))| + |\sin\tilde{x}_0(t,t_0) - \sin x_0(\omega(t+t_0))|\\ + |\cos\tilde{x}_0(t,t_0) - \cos x_0(\omega(t+t_0))| < \text{const}\cdot\delta^2\varepsilon^{2p}\,.\end{aligned} \tag{A7}$$

The proofs of Propositions A1 and A2 are quite straightforward and are based on the asymptotics (8) and (9).

We look for the solution of the equation (1) in the form

$$x^u(t,t_0) = x_{in}(t,t_0) + u(t,t_0)\,. \tag{A8}$$

We insert (A8) in (1) and rewrite it as

$$\ddot{u} + \omega^2 \cos x_0(\omega(t+t_0)) \cdot u = g_0(t,t_0) + g_1(u,t,t_0)\,, \tag{A9}$$

where we introduce the notations

$$g_0(t,t_0) = -\ddot{x}_{in}(t,t_0) - \sin x_{in}(t,t_0) + \delta\varepsilon^p \sin\frac{t}{\varepsilon} \tag{A10}$$

and

$$g_1(u,t,t_0) = \omega^2 \cos x_0(\omega(t+t_0)) \cdot u + \sin x_{in}(t,t_0) - \sin(x_{in}(t,t_0)+u)\,. \tag{A11}$$

We invert the linear operator in the right hand side of the equation (A9) and obtain the following integral equation

$$u(t,t_0) = L[g_0](t,t_0) + L[g_1(u)](t,t_0) \equiv \Psi[u](t,t_0)\,, \tag{A12}$$

where L is a linear integral operator in the variable t defined by

$$L[g](t,t_0) = \int_{-\infty}^{t} K(t+t_0, s+t_0)g(s,t_0)ds\,, \tag{A13}$$

$$K(t,s) = \frac{\sinh(2\omega t) + 2\omega t - \sinh(2\omega s) - 2\omega s}{4\omega\cosh(\omega t)\cosh(\omega s)}\,. \tag{A14}$$

Let $D = D_1$ or $D = D_1 \cup D_2$. We denote by $\mathfrak{X}(D)$ a Banach space of functions continuous in $\bar{D}$, analytical in t_0 for any fixed t and satisfying the condition

$$u(t+2\pi\varepsilon, t_0) = u(t, t_0+2\pi\varepsilon)\,. \tag{A15}$$

We introduce the norm in $\mathfrak{X}(D)$ by

$$\|u\|_D = \sup_{(t,t_0)\in D} |e^{-2\omega(t+t_0)}u(t,t_0)|\,.$$

Proposition A3. *Given $p > -2$, the formular (A13) defines the linear operator $L : \mathfrak{X}(D) \to \mathfrak{X}(D)$ with the norm bounded by a constant independed from δ and ε in the case $D = D_1$ and $\|L\| < \mathrm{const}\cdot\varepsilon^{-1}$ in the case $D = D_1 \cup D_2$.*

Now we show that a ball B_{a_D} in $\mathfrak{X}(D)$ of sufficiently small radius a_D and with the center in zero is invariant under the operator $\Psi[u]$ and the restriction of the operator on the ball is contraction.

We have to estimate the norm of $L[g_0]$. It follows from (A10) and (A1) that

$$g_0(t,t_0) = -\ddot{x}_{per}(t) - \ddot{\tilde{x}}_0(t,t_0) - \sin(x_{per}(t) + \tilde{x}_0(t,t_0)) + \delta\varepsilon^p \sin\frac{t}{\varepsilon}$$
$$= -\ddot{\tilde{x}}_0(t,t_0) - \sin(x_{per}(t) + \tilde{x}_0(t,t_0)) - \sin x_{per}(t)$$
$$= -\left[\ddot{\tilde{x}}_0(t,t_0) + \cos x_{per}(t)\cdot\sin\tilde{x}_0(t,t_0)\right] - \left[\sin x_{per}(t)(1+\cos\tilde{x}_0(t,t_0))\right]. \tag{A16}$$

The estimate of the first bracket in D_1 is given by (A4). If $(t,t_0)\in D_2$ then it is estimated from above by the following value

$$|\ddot{\tilde{x}}_0(t,t_0) - \ddot{x}_0(\omega(t+t_0))| + |\ddot{x}_0(\omega(t+t_0)) - \omega^2\sin x_0(\omega(t+t_0))|$$

$$+|\omega^2\sin x_0(\omega(t+t_0)) - \sin\tilde{x}_0(t,t_0)| + |\sin\tilde{x}_0(t,t_0)(1-\cos x_{per}(t))| < \mathrm{const}\cdot\delta^2\varepsilon^{2p},$$

where we used estimates (A5–A7) and (8). The module of the second bracket in (A16) is not lager than $\mathrm{const}\cdot\delta\varepsilon^{p+2}e^{2\omega(t+\Re t_0)}$ for $(t,t_0)\in D_1$ and than $\mathrm{const}\cdot\delta\varepsilon^p$ for $(t,t_0)\in D_2$. We arrive to the estimate

$$|g_0(t,t_0)| \le \mathrm{const}\cdot\begin{cases}\delta\varepsilon^{p+2}e^{2\omega(t+\Re t_0)} & ,\ (t,t_0)\in D_1\,,\\ \delta\varepsilon^p & ,\ (t,t_0)\in D_2\,.\end{cases} \tag{A17}$$

We obtain the following estimate

$$\left\|L[g_0]\right\|_D \le \left\|L\right\|_D\cdot\|g_0\|_D \le a_1\begin{cases}\delta\varepsilon^{p+2}, & D=D_1\\ \delta\varepsilon^{p-1}, & D=D_1\cup D_2\,,\end{cases} \tag{A18}$$

where we used Proposition A3. If $|u|<1$, then

$$|g_1(u,t,t_0)| = |\omega^2\cos x_0(\omega(t+t_0))\cdot u + \sin x_{in}(t,t_0)$$
$$-\sin(x_{in}(t,t_0)+u)| \le |\cos x_{in}(t,t_0)\cdot u + \sin x_{in}(t,t_0)$$
$$-\sin(x_{in}(t,t_0)+u)| + |\omega^2\cos x_0(\omega(t+t_0)) - \cos x_{in}(t,t_0)|\cdot|u|$$
$$\le \mathrm{const}\cdot\begin{cases}|u|^2+\delta\varepsilon^{p+2}|u|\,, & (t,t_0)\in D_1\,,\\ \varepsilon^{-2}|u|^2+\delta\varepsilon^p|u|\,, & (t,t_0)\in D_2\,.\end{cases}$$

We let

$$a_{D_1} = 2a_1\delta\varepsilon^{p+2}\,,\quad a_{D_1\cup D_2} = 2a_1\delta\varepsilon^{p-1}\,. \tag{A19}$$

If $\|u\|_D < a_D$, then

$$\left\|L[g_1(u)]\right\|_D \le \left\|L\right\|_D\cdot\|g_1(u)\|_D \le a_2\begin{cases}\delta^2\varepsilon^{2p+4}, & D=D_1\,,\\ \delta^2\varepsilon^{2p-5}, & D=D_1\cup D_2\,.\end{cases} \tag{A20}$$

It follows from the estimates (A18) and (A20) that

$$\left\|\Psi[u]\right\|_D \leq \left\|L[g_0]\right\|_D + \left\|L[g_1(u)]\right\|_D \leq \begin{cases} a_1\delta\varepsilon^{p+2} + a_2\delta^2\varepsilon^{2p+4}\,, & D = D_1\,, \\ a_1\delta\varepsilon^{p-1} + a_2\delta^2\varepsilon^{2p-5}\,, & D = D_1 \cup D_2\,. \end{cases} \tag{A21}$$

The right hand side of the equation (A21) is less then a_D if $\delta\varepsilon^{p+2}$ ($D = D_1$) or $\delta\varepsilon^{p-5}$ ($D = D_1 \cup D_2$) are suffitiently small. That means that the balls B_{a_D} are invariant with respect to the operator Ψ. Now we prove that the restriction of the operator Ψ on B_{a_D} is contraction. Let $|u|$, $|v| < a$ for some small positive a, then

$$\begin{aligned} \left|g_1(u,t,t_0) - g_1(v,t,t_0)\right| &\leq \sup_{|u|<a}\left|\frac{\partial g_1}{\partial u}(u,t,t_0)\right| \cdot |u-v| \\ &= \sup_{|u|<a}\left|\omega^2\cos x_0(\omega(t+t_0)) - \cos(x_{in}(t,t_0)+u)\right| \cdot |u-v| \\ &\leq \text{const}\cdot|u-v|\cdot\Big[\left|\omega^2\cos x_0(\omega(t+t_0)) - \cos x_{in}(t,t_0)\right| \\ &\quad + \sup_{|u|<a}\left|\cos x_{in}(t,t_0) - \cos(x_{in}(t,t_0)+u)\right|\Big] \\ &\leq \text{const}\cdot|u-v|\cdot\begin{cases} \delta\varepsilon^{p+2} + a\,, & (t,t_0)\in D_1\,, \\ \delta\varepsilon^{p} + \varepsilon^{-2}a\,, & (t,t_0)\in D_2\,. \end{cases} \end{aligned} \tag{A22}$$

If we take two functions $\|u\|_D$, $\|v\|_D < a_D$ then the following estimate follows from (A22) and (A19)

$$\begin{aligned} \left\|\Psi[u] - \Psi[v]\right\|_D &= \left\|L[g_1(u)] - L[g_1(v)]\right\|_D \\ \leq \left\|L\right\|_D \cdot \|g_1(u) - g_1(v)\|_D &\leq a_2\|u-v\|_D \begin{cases} \delta\varepsilon^{p+2}\,, & D = D_1\,, \\ \delta\varepsilon^{p-5}\,, & D = D_1\cup D_2\,. \end{cases} \end{aligned} \tag{A23}$$

Thus the operator Ψ has a unique fixed point in the ball B_{a_D}. That means

$$\|x^u - x_{in}\|_D = \|x^u - \tilde{x}_0 - x_{per}\|_D \leq a_D\,. \tag{A24}$$

This yelds the estimates (14) and (15) due to the estimates of Propositions A1 and A2. To obtain the estimate (16) we note that

$$\left\|u - L[g_0]\right\|_{D_1\cup D_2} = \left\|L[g_1(u)]\right\|_{D_1\cup D_2} \leq a_2\delta^2\varepsilon^{2p-5}\,. \tag{A25}$$

For the difference between separatrices we have

$$\begin{aligned} x^u(t,t_0) - x^s(t,t_0) &= x^u(t,t_0) + x^u(-t,-t_0) \\ &= x_{in}(t,t_0) + u(t,t_0) + x_{in}(-t,-t_0) + u(-t,-t_0) = u(t,t_0) + u(-t,-t_0)\,. \end{aligned} \tag{A26}$$

If $(t,t_0) \in D_2$ then $(-t,-t_0) \in D_2$ and we can use the estimate (A25) to obtain that

$$u(t,t_0) + u(-t,-t_0) = L[g_0](t,t_0) + L[g_0](-t,-t_0) + O(\delta^2 \varepsilon^{2p-5}) . \qquad \text{(A27)}$$

In order to estimate the right hand side of (A27) we use the representation (A16) of g_0 to obtain

$$\left\| g_0(t,t_0) - \Big(\cos x_0(\omega(t+t_0)) + 1\Big) \frac{\delta\varepsilon^{p+2}}{1+\varepsilon^2} \sin\frac{t}{\varepsilon} \right\|_{D_1 \cup D_2} < \text{const} \cdot \delta^2 \varepsilon^{2p} . \quad \text{(A28)}$$

Finally we obtain the following formula

$$\begin{aligned} &x^u(t,t_0) - x^s(t,t_0) \\ &= \int_{-\infty}^{\infty} K(t+t_0, s+t_0) \Big(\cos x_0(\omega(s+t_0)) + 1\Big) \frac{\delta\varepsilon^{p+2}}{1+\varepsilon^2} \sin\frac{s}{\varepsilon} ds + O(\delta^2\varepsilon^{2p-5}) , \end{aligned} \qquad \text{(A29)}$$

The integral in the formula above can be calculated by residues and we obtain the estimate (16).

Appendix B. Proof of Lemma 3.

Linear theory. In order to prove the existence of the functions E and T we have to study a family of the second order differential equations

$$\ddot{u} + \cos(x^u(t,t_0))u = f(t,t_0) . \qquad \text{(B1)}$$

In this subsection we study the properties of solutions of the equation (B1) in a specially chosen Banach space $\mathfrak{X}$. Namely, we suppose $\mathfrak{X}$ to be a set of functions

a) analytical in t_0 for any fixed t, $(t,t_0) \in D_3$;

b) continuous in $\bar{D}_3$;

c) $u(t+2\pi\varepsilon, t_0) = u(t, t_0 + 2\pi\varepsilon)$

with the supremum norm

The method of variation of constants reduces the stated problem to one of solving in $\mathfrak{X}$ an equation

$$\dot{u} - f(t,t_0) . \qquad \text{(B2)}$$

The equation (B2) is not quite trivial since we look for the solutions with specific dependence on the parameter t_0.

Lemma B1. *There exists a linear operator $Q : \mathfrak{X} \to \mathfrak{X}$, such that for any $f \in \mathfrak{X}$ the function $u = Q[f]$ is a solution of the equation (B2). The norm of the operator Q is bounded by a constant independent from ε.*

The proof of Lemma B1 is based on the properties of the following Cauchy type integral.

Let a,b, c be any real numbers, such that $10 > b - a > 1$, $5 > c > 1$. We consider a complex domain

$$\Omega = \left\{a < \Re z < b,\ |\Im z| < c\right\}.$$

We denote by $\chi_+(t)$ a smooth (C^∞) real function of one real argument t, such that a) $0 \le \chi_+(t) \le 1$, $t \in \mathbb{R}$; b) $\chi_+(t) = 1$, $t < a+0.1$; c) $\chi_+(t) = 0$, $t > b-0.1$. Let $\chi_-(t) = 1 - \chi_+(t)$.

Lemma B2. *Let $\chi(z) = \chi_+(\Re z)$ or $\chi(z) = \chi_-(\Re z)$. Let $g(z)$ be an analytic in Ω and continuous in $\bar{\Omega}$ function. Then the integral*

$$h(z) = \frac{1}{2\pi i}\int_{\partial\Omega} \frac{\chi(\zeta)g(\zeta)}{\zeta - z} d\zeta \tag{B3}$$

defines an analytical functions in $\bar{\mathbb{C}} \setminus (\partial\Omega \cap \operatorname{supp}\chi)$. The restrictions of $h(z)$ on Ω and $\bar{\mathbb{C}} \setminus \bar{\Omega}$ have continuous prolongations on the closure of these sets, and

$$|h(z)| < \left(1 + 10 \sup_{\mathbb{R}} |\chi'|\right) \sup_{\Omega} |g|, \tag{B4}$$

for all $z \in \mathbb{C}$.

Lemma B2 and its proof are obtained by a modification of "Lemma on Cauchy integral" of the paper [7].

Proof. The integral (B3) defines an analytical function in $\bar{\mathbb{C}} \setminus (\partial\Omega \cap \operatorname{supp}\chi)$. Consider the function $\tilde{h}(z_0)$ defined on $\partial\Omega$ by the following integral

$$\tilde{h}(z_0) = \frac{1}{2\pi i}\int_{\partial\Omega} \frac{\chi(\zeta) - \chi(z_0)}{\zeta - \zeta_0} g(\zeta) d\zeta\,. \tag{B5}$$

The function $\tilde{h}(z_0)$ is bounded since

$$|\tilde{h}(z_0)| \le \frac{1}{2\pi}\int_{\partial\Omega} \left|\frac{\chi(\zeta) - \chi(z_0)}{\zeta - z_0}\right| \cdot |g(\zeta)|\,|d\zeta| \le \frac{|\partial\Omega|}{2\pi} \sup_{\mathbb{R}} |\chi'| \sup_{\Omega} |g|\,, \tag{B6}$$

where $|\partial\Omega|$ denotes the length of $\partial\Omega$, $|\partial\Omega| < 40$.

The function $\tilde{h}(z_0)$ is continuous in $\partial\Omega$. In order to demonstrate it we denote by d_μ a μ-neighborhood of the point z_0 in $\partial\Omega$. We have

$$\tilde{h}(z_1) - \tilde{h}(z_0) = \frac{1}{2\pi i}\int_{\partial\Omega}\left(\frac{\chi(\zeta)-\chi(z_0)}{\zeta - z_0} - \frac{\chi(\zeta)-\chi(z_1)}{\zeta - z_1}\right) g(\zeta)d\zeta$$

$$= \frac{1}{2\pi i}\int_{d_\mu} + \int_{\partial\Omega\setminus d_\mu}\left(\frac{\chi(\zeta)-\chi(z_0)}{\zeta - z_0} - \frac{\chi(\zeta)-\chi(z_1)}{\zeta - z_1}\right) g(\zeta)d\zeta\,,$$

where $z_1 \in \partial\Omega$. The expression in the brackets can be evaluated by $2\sup_{\mathbb{R}}|\chi'|$. So the module of the first integral is not bigger than

$$\frac{2\mu}{\pi}\sup_{\mathbb{R}}|\chi'|\sup_{\Omega}|g|\,.$$

For given positive μ' take μ small enough so that the first integral becomes less then $\mu'/2$. For this value of μ let $|z_0 - z_1| < \mu/2$. We note that

$$\left|\frac{\chi(\zeta)-\chi(z_0)}{\zeta - z_0} - \frac{\chi(\zeta)-\chi(z_1)}{\zeta - z_1}\right| \le \sup_{z\in d_{\mu/2},\,\zeta\in\partial\Omega\setminus d_\mu}\left|\frac{\partial}{\partial z}\left(\frac{\chi(\zeta)-\chi(z)}{\zeta - z}\right)\right|\cdot|z_0 - z_1|$$

$$\le \sup_{z\in d_{\mu/2},\,\zeta\in\partial\Omega\setminus d_\mu}\left(\left|\frac{\chi'(z)}{\zeta - z}\right| + \left|\frac{\chi(\zeta)-\chi(z)}{(\zeta - z)^2}\right|\right)\cdot|z_0 - z_1| \le \frac{4\sup_{\mathbb{R}}|\chi'|}{\mu}\cdot|z_0 - z_1|\,.$$

Taking z_1 close to z_0 so that the right part of the last inequality becomes less then $\mu'/2$, yields

$$|\tilde{h}(z_1) - \tilde{h}(z_0)| < \mu'\,.$$

Now we prove that

$$\lim_{z\to z_0} h(z) = \begin{cases} \tilde{h}(z_0)\,, & z \in \mathbb{C}\setminus\bar{\Omega}\,,\\ \tilde{h}(z_0) + g(z_0)\chi(z_0)\,, & z\in\Omega\,. \end{cases} \tag{B7}$$

We have for $z\in\Omega$, $z_0 \in \partial\Omega$

$$h(z) - \tilde{h}(z_0) - g(z)\chi(z_0) = \frac{1}{2\pi i}\int_{\partial\Omega}\frac{\chi(\zeta)g(\zeta)}{\zeta - z}d\zeta$$

$$-\frac{1}{2\pi i}\int_{\partial\Omega}\frac{\chi(\zeta)-\chi(z_0)}{\zeta - z_0}g(\zeta)d\zeta - \frac{1}{2\pi i}\int_{\partial\Omega}\frac{\chi(\zeta_0)g(\zeta)}{\zeta - z}d\zeta$$

$$= \frac{1}{2\pi i}\int_{\partial\Omega}\left(\frac{1}{\zeta - z} - \frac{1}{\zeta - z_0}\right)(\chi(\zeta)-\chi(z_0))g(\zeta)d\zeta$$

$$= \frac{1}{2\pi i}\int_{\partial\Omega}\frac{(z - z_0)(\chi(\zeta)-\chi(z_0))}{(\zeta - z)(\zeta - z_0)}g(\zeta)d\zeta\,.$$

The last integral can be estimated from above by

$$\frac{|z-z_0|}{2\pi}\sup_{\mathbb{R}}|\chi'|\sup_{\Omega}|g|\int_{\partial\Omega}\frac{|d\zeta|}{|\zeta-z|}\le \text{const}\cdot|z-z_0|\ln\big(\text{dist}(z,\partial\Omega)\big)\,.$$

Due to continuity of $\tilde{h}$ we can suppose that the strait line defined by z and z_0 is ortogonal to $\partial\Omega$ in z_0. Then $\lim_{z\to z_0}\Big(|z-z_0|\ln\big(\text{dist}\,z,\partial\Omega)\big)\Big)=0$.

The estimate (B4) follows from (B6) and (B7). □

Proof of Lemma B1. We write an explicit formula for the solution of the equation (B2). We define two operators I_+ and I_- by the formula

$$I_{\pm}[f](t,t_0)=\frac{1}{(t+t_0)^2+10}\frac{1}{2\pi i}\int_{\partial\Omega_t}\frac{\chi_{\pm}(t+\Re\zeta)f(t,\zeta)((t+\zeta)^2+10)}{\zeta-t_0}d\zeta\,, \tag{B8}$$

where $\Omega_t=\Big\{t_0\in\mathbb{C}:-2-t<\Re t_0<-1-t,\,|\Im t_0|<\pi/2\Big\}$ is a section of D_3 by a plane of constant t.

From Cauchy theorem we obtain the identity

$$f(t,t_0)=I_-[f](t,t_0)+I_+[f](t,t_0)\,,\quad (t,t_0)\in D_3\,, \tag{B9}$$

since $\chi_+(t)+\chi_-(t)=1$ for all $t\in\mathbb{R}$. It follows from the lemma B2 that (B8) defines the functions which have analytical continuations into $\mathbb{C}\setminus(\partial\Omega_t\cup\text{supp}(\chi_{\pm}(t+\Re t_0))$ with the following estimate

$$|I_{\pm}[f](t,t_0)|<\frac{\text{const}\cdot\|f\|}{|(t+t_0)^2+10|}\,. \tag{B10}$$

The domain of analyticity of the function $I_+[f](t,t_0)$ contains the half strip $\{t_0\in\mathbb{C}:\Re t_0>-2-t\,,\,|\Im t_0|<\pi/2\}$ and the one of $I_-[f](t,t_0)$ contains $\{t_0\in\mathbb{C}:\Re t_0<-1-t\,,\,|\Im t_0|<\pi/2\}$. If $f(t+2\pi\varepsilon,t_0)=f(t,t_0+2\pi\varepsilon)$ then $I_{\pm}[f]$ also possess this property. This fact provides the continuous prolongation of $I_{\pm}[f](t,t_0)$ in t from the point $(t,t_0)\in D_3$ up to $\pm\infty$ respectively for any fixed value of t_0 with the estimates (B10).

The desired solution of the equation (B2) can be defined by

$$u(t,t_0)=Q[f](t,t_0)=\int_{-\infty}^{t}I_-[f](s,t_0)ds-\int_{t}^{+\infty}I_+[f](s,t_0)ds\,. \tag{B11}$$

□

Lemma B3. *Given $p > -1$, there exist two solutions w_1, $w_2 \in \mathfrak{X}$ of the homogeneous equation*

$$\ddot{w}_k + \cos(x^u(t,t_0))w_k = 0, \quad k = 1,2, \tag{B12}$$

such that

$$w_1\dot{w}_2 - w_2\dot{w}_1 = 1 \tag{B13}$$

and for ε small

$$w_1(t,t_0) = \frac{2}{\cosh(t+t_0)} + O(\delta\varepsilon^{p+2}), \tag{B14}$$

$$w_2(t,t_0) = \frac{\sinh 2(t+t_0) + 2(t+t_0)}{8\cosh(t+t_0)} + O(\delta\varepsilon^{p+2}). \tag{B15}$$

The estimates (B14) and (B15) can be differentiated with respect to t and t_0 at least twice with no change in the error term.

Proof. The first solution of the equation (B12) is given by

$$w_1(t,t_0) = \frac{\partial x^u}{\partial t_0}(t,t_0). \tag{B16}$$

The asymptotic formula (B14) follows from (2) and (14). The second solution we can find solving the equation (B13) with respect to w_2:

$$w_2(t,t_0) = w_1(t,t_0)\Big(Q[1/w_1^2](t,t_0) - Q[\dot{\tilde{f}}](t,t_0) + \tilde{f}(t,t_0)\Big), \tag{B17}$$

where $\tilde{f}(t,t_0) = \frac{\sinh 2(t+t_0)+2(t+t_0)}{16}$. The last two terms in the equation (B17) are the solution of the homogeneous equation and are chosen to provide the suitable asymptotic of w_2. Note that $\dot{\tilde{f}}(t,t_0) = \frac{\cosh^2(t+t_0)}{4} = \frac{1}{w_1^2(t,t_0)} + O(\delta\varepsilon^{p+2})$ and take into account the asymptotic (B14) to obtain (B15). □

Lemma B4. *Given $p > -1$, there exist a linear operator $B : \mathfrak{X} \to \mathfrak{X}$, such that $u = B[f]$ is a solution of the equation (B1) for any $f \in \mathfrak{X}$. The norm of the operator B is bounded by a constant independent from ε and δ.*

Proof. According to the method of variation of constants we look for the solution of the equation (B1) in the form

$$u(t,t_0) = c_1(t,t_0)w_1(t,t_0) + c_2(t,t_0)w_2(t,t_0), \tag{B18}$$

where $c_k(t,t_0)$, $k = 1,2$, satisfy the first order linear equations

$$\dot{c}_1(t,t_0) = -w_2(t,t_0)f(t,t_0), \quad \dot{c}_2(t,t_0) = w_1(t,t_0)f(t,t_0). \tag{B19}$$

We have

$$u(t,t_0) = B[f](t,t_0) = -Q[fw_2](t,t_0)w_1(t,t_0) + Q[fw_1](t,t_0)w_2(t,t_0). \tag{B20}$$

The estimates of the norm of B follows directly from Lemmas B1 and B2. □

Nonlinear equation.

Instead of looking for the functions E and T directly, we look for the two parameter family $x(t, E, T)$ of solution of the equation (1) and use the implicit function theorem.

Lemma B5. *Given $p > -1$, there exist a two parametric family $x(t, E, T)$ of solutions of the equation (1) and a positive number b, such that*

a) $x(t, E, t_0) \in \mathfrak{X}$ for any E, $|E| < b$; $x(t, E, T)$ is analytical function of E and T;

b) $x(t, 0, t_0) = x^u(t, t_0)$, $\frac{\partial x}{\partial E}(t, 0, t_0) = w_2(t, t_0)$;

c) the map $(E, T) \mapsto (x(t, E, T), \dot{x}(t, E, T))$ is symplectic for any fixed t;

d) all derivatives of $x(t, t_0, E)$ with respect to E and t_0 up to second order are bounded by a constant independent from δ and ε.

Proof. We search the family $x(t, E, t_0)$ in the form

$$x(t, E, t_0) = x^u(t, t_0) + u(t, E, t_0) \tag{B21}$$

and write the equation for u in the form

$$\ddot{u}+\cos(x^u(t, t_0))u = \sin(x^u(t, t_0))+\cos(x^u(t, t_0))u-\sin(x^u(t, t_0)+u) \equiv g_u(t, t_0)\,. \tag{B22}$$

We invert the linear operator in the right hand side of the equation (B22):

$$u(t, E, t_0) = w_2(t, t_0)E + B[g_u](t, t_0) \equiv \Phi[u](t, t_0)\,, \tag{B23}$$

where we add a solution of the homogeneous equation w_2E. The operator B is defined by (B20).

We prove that the ball $B_a \subset \mathfrak{X}$ of the sufficiently small radius a and with the center in the zero is invariant with respect to the operator Φ. Let $\|u\| < a$, then we have

$$\|\Phi[u]\| \le \|w_2\|\cdot|E|+\|B\| \sup_{|u|<a,\,(t,t_0)\in D_3} \left|\frac{\partial^2 g_u}{\partial u^2}(t, t_0)\right| \|u\|^2 < a_1b+a_2a^2\,, \tag{B24}$$

where a_1 and a_2 are some positive numbers. If we choose $a = 2a_1b$ and $b < 1/(4a_1a_2)$ then the right hand side of (B24) is less then a.

The restriction of Φ on B_a is a contracting operator provided b is sufficiently small. Let u, $v \in B_a$, then

$$\begin{aligned}\|\Phi[u] - \Phi[v]\| = \|B[g_u - g_v]\| &\le \|B\| \sup_{|u|<a,\,(t,t_0)\in D_3} \left|\frac{\partial g_u}{\partial u}(t, t_0)\right| \cdot \|u - v\|\\ &\le \|B\| \sup_{|u|<a,\,(t,t_0)\in D_3} |\cos(x^u(t, t_0)) - \cos(x^u(t, t_0) + u)| \cdot \|u - v\|\\ &< a_3a\|u - v\| = 2a_1a_3b\|u - v\|\,,\end{aligned} \tag{B25}$$

where a_3 is a positive number. If we choose b, such that

$$0 < b < b_0 = \min(1/(4a_1a_2), 1/(2a_1a_3)), \tag{B26}$$

then the restriction of Φ on B_a is contraction. Thus there exists the unique solution of the equation (B22) in B_a, $a = 2a_1b$.

In order to prove the assertion b) we do the following estimate

$$\|u(t, E, t_0) - w_2(t, t_0)E\| = \|\Phi[g_u]\| \le a_2\|u\|^2 \le a_2a^2 . \tag{B27}$$

If we consider $|E| = b$ than we have $a = 2a_1b = 2a_1|E|$ and the right hand side is the value $O(|E|^2)$. It immediately yields the assertion b).

We note that the operator B is defined by the equations (B8), (B11) and (B20) and if the function $f(t, E, t_0)$ depends analyticaly from the parameter E and $f(t, E, t_0) \in \mathfrak{X}$ for $|E| < b$, then $B[f]$ possesses the same properties. The estimates (B24) and (B25) are uniform in E, $|E| < b$ and consequently the function $u(t, E, t_0)$ depends analyticaly from parameter E. In order to prove the boundness of derivatives in E ans T we can do all estimates in a slightly wide region of these parameters and then use the Caucy theorem.

The map $(E, T) \mapsto (x(t, E, T), \dot{x}(t, E, T))$ is almost symplectic, since its Jacobian

$$J(E, t_0) = \frac{\partial x}{\partial E}\frac{\partial \dot{x}}{\partial t_0} - \frac{\partial \dot{x}}{\partial E}\frac{\partial x}{\partial t_0} = 1 + O(E) \tag{B28}$$

due to the assertion b) and the estimates of Lemma B3. We make a small correction of the parameter E in order to obtain the symplectic map. Let define the knew parameter $\tilde{E}(E, T)$ as a solution of equation $\int_0^{\tilde{E}} J(E', T)dE' = E$, obviously $\tilde{E} = E + O(E^2)$. We define the desired parametrisation by $\tilde{x}(t, E, T) = x(t, \tilde{E}(E, T), T)$. This family posses all properties stated in the formulation of the lemma. □

Lemma 3 follows from Lemma B5 due to the implicit function theorem. The independence of r from δ and ε follows from the ordinary proof of this theorem and the estimates of the derivatives of $x(t, E, T)$. The property (18) follows from the property $x(t + 2\pi\varepsilon, E, T) = x(t, E, T + 2\pi\varepsilon)$ and the property (19) from the statement b) of Lemma B5.

References

1. Poincaré H., *Sur la problèm de trois corps et les équations de la dinamique*, Acta Math. **13** (1890), 1–271.

2. Melnikov V. K., Trudy moskovskogo matematicheskogo obshchestva **12** (1963), 3–52. (Russian)

3. Neishtadt A. I., PMM (USSR) **48 (2)** (1984), 197–204. (Russian)

4. Holmes P., Marsden J., Scheurle J., *Exponentially Small Splitting of Separatrices with Applications to KAM Theory and degenerate Bifurcations*, Contemporary Mathematics **81** (1988), 213–244.

5. Fontich E., *Exponentially small upper bounds for the splitting of separatrices for high frequency periodic perturbations*, preprint no. 93 (1991).

6. Gelfreich V. G., Lazutkin V. F., Tabanov M. B., *Exponentially small splitting in hamiltonian systems*, Chaos **1, no.2** (1991), 137–142.

7. Lazutkin V. F., *Exponential splitting of separatrices and an analytical integral for the semistandard map*, Preprint no.7, Université Paris VII (1991), 53 p.

8. Lazutkin V. F., Tabanov M. B., Schachmannski I. G., *Splitting of separatrices for standard and semistandard mappings*, Physica D **40** (1989), 235–248.

9. Delshams A. and Tere M. Seara, *Exponentially small expressions for separatrix splittings*, this volume.

St.-Petersburg Institution of Aviation Instrument Making, Hertzen str. 67, St.-Petersburg, 190000, Russia.

EXPONENTIALLY SMALL EXPRESSIONS FOR SEPARATRIX SPLITTINGS

Amadeu Delshams and Tere M. Seara

Abstract. Exponentially small expressions for the splitting of separatrices are provided for second order equations with a rapidly forced perturbation term

$$\ddot{x} + f(x) = \mu\varepsilon^p g\left(\frac{t}{\varepsilon}\right),$$

where μ and ε are independent small parameters. These asymptotical expressions coincide with the ones predicted by the Poincaré-Melnikov theory, and therefore their size is $O(\mu\varepsilon^{p-r}e^{-\frac{a}{\varepsilon}})$, where ai is the pole of the derivative of the homoclinic solution of the unperturbed equation, and r its order. The main ideas of the proof of these asymptotic formulas are presented, assuming $p \geq r-1$, and that the first Fourier coefficients of the Poincaré-Melnikov function $M(s,\varepsilon)$ are different from zero.

1. Introduction and examples.

The effective transversality of invariant manifolds associated to weak hyperbolic objects, like fixed points of planar maps, or periodic orbits of non-autonomous planar o.d.e., has begun very recently to be established. In spite of being a central point in order to provide the existence and size of the stochastic layer in the low-dimensional systems, and the basis of a mechanism to detect Arnold diffusion in higher dimensional symplectic systems, its exponentially smallness with respect to the parameter of perturbation has become a hard obstacle to be overcome. The first analytic example of an exponentially small angle appears in the works of Lazutkin and co-workers [La84], [LST89], [GLT90], for the case of the standard mapping and the generalized standard mapping

$$SM(x,y) = (x+y', y' = y+\varepsilon f(x)),$$

$f(x)$ being a polynomial or trigonometric polynomial in the variable x ($f(x) = \sin(x)$ for the standard mapping). Concerning o.d.e., Holmes, Marsden and

This work has been partially supported by the DGICYT Grant PB90–0580.

Scheurle [HMS88] considered the rapidly forced pendulum equation

$$\ddot{x} + \sin x = \mu \varepsilon^p \sin \frac{t}{\varepsilon} \ ,$$

and they found lower and upper bounds for the distance between invariant manifolds, for μ, ε small enough, and $p \geq 8$. This result was improved by Gelfreich ($p > 5$) [Ge90], and by Delshams and M. Seara ($p \geq 0$) [DS91a]. In this talk we consider more general o.d.e., and we want to show that the exponentially small splittings that have been found up to now only in very particular cases, can be also detected in a broader setting.

Let us consider the second order equation

$$\ddot{x} + f(x) = \mu \varepsilon^p g\left(\frac{t}{\varepsilon}\right) , \tag{1}$$

where ε, μ are independent and small parameters and $p \geq 0$. We will assume that this system verifies:

H_1. The unperturbed equation

$$\ddot{x} + f(x) = 0 \ ,$$

considered like a hamiltonian system:

$$\dot{x} = y \ , \qquad \dot{y} = -f(x) \ , \tag{2}$$

has a saddle point at the origin ($f'(0) < 0$) and a homoclinic orbit Γ associated to it:

$$\Gamma = \{(x_0(t), y_0(t))\} \ , \qquad \lim_{t \to \pm\infty} (x_0(t), y_0(t)) = (0,0) \ .$$

H_2. f is a real entire function, and $y_0(t) = \dot{x}_0(t)$ is analytic on a strip $|\Im t| < a$, with one pole of order r on each line $\Im t = \pm a$.

H_3. g is a C^1, 2π-periodic function, with zero mean: $\int_0^{2\pi} g(s) ds = 0$.

H_4. The $2\pi\varepsilon$-periodic Poincaré-Melnikov function

$$M(s,\varepsilon) = \int_{-\infty}^{\infty} y_0(\sigma + s) g\left(\frac{\sigma}{\varepsilon}\right) d\sigma = \sum_{k \neq 0} M_k(\varepsilon) e^{i \frac{k}{\varepsilon} \sigma} \ . \tag{3}$$

has non-zero first Fourier coefficients: $M_{\pm 1} \neq 0$.

Some classical examples verifying these hypothesis are:

1) The forced pendulum equation,

$$\ddot{x} + \sin x = \mu \varepsilon^p \sin \frac{t}{\varepsilon} \ , \tag{4}$$

with homoclinic orbits $\Gamma_\pm = \{(x_0(t), \pm y_0(t) = \pm \dot{x}_0(t))\}$, where $x_0(t) = 2\arctan(\sinh t)$, and $\dot{x}_0(t)$ has simple poles at $t = \pm\frac{\pi}{2}i$.

2) The Duffing equation,

$$\ddot{x} - x + x^3 = \mu\varepsilon^p \cos\frac{t+c}{\varepsilon}\,, \quad c \in \mathbb{R}\,, \tag{5}$$

with homoclinic orbits $\Gamma_\pm = \{\pm(x_0(t), y_0(t) = \dot{x}_0(t))\}$, where $x_0(t) = \frac{\sqrt{2}}{\cosh t}$, and $\dot{x}_0(t)$ has double poles at $t = \pm\frac{\pi}{2}i$.

3) The "fish" equation

$$\ddot{x} - x + x^2 = \mu\varepsilon^p \cos\frac{t}{\varepsilon}, \tag{6}$$

with homoclinic orbit $\Gamma = \{(x_0(t), y_0(t) = \dot{x}_0(t))\}$, where $x_0(t) = \frac{3}{2(\cosh\frac{t}{2})^2}$, and $\dot{x}_0(t)$ has triple poles at $t = \pm\pi i$.

2. Main results.

The Poincaré map associated to equation (1) is defined by:

$$P(x_0, y_0) = (x(2\pi\varepsilon), y(2\pi\varepsilon)),$$

where $(x(t), y(t) = \dot{x}(t))$ is the orbit of the system associated to equation (1) with initial condition $(x(0), y(0)) = (x_0, y_0)$. When $\mu = 0$ the phase portrait of this map is filled up by the level curves of the hamiltonian

$$h^0(x,y) = \frac{y^2}{2} + V(x)\,, \qquad V'(x) = f(x)\,,$$

associated to the unperturbed system (2). One of these level curves ($h^0 = 0$ if we assume $V(0) = 0$) contains the homoclinic orbit Γ associated to the origin, a fixed point of P.

Shifting the time if necessary, we can assume that the poles of $\dot{x}_0(t)$ are located at $\pm ai$, and we will focus our attention on the neighborhood of the homoclinic point $(x_0(0), y_0(0))$ of the unperturbed map P.

If we consider now $\mu \neq 0$ but small, P still has a hyperbolic fixed point near $(0,0)$, and in general the associated stable and unstable curves do not coincide (concerning equation (1), there exists a hyperbolic periodic orbit γ with associated stable and unstable manifolds $W^u(\gamma)$, $W^s(\gamma)$ that do not coincide either). However, since equation (1) can be written as a hamiltonian system with hamiltonian

$$h(x,y) = h^0(x,y) + \mu\varepsilon^p x g\left(\frac{t}{\varepsilon}\right)\,,$$

the Poincaré map is area preserving, and thus the invariant curves have to intersect each other. For instance we will denote $z_h = (x_h, y_h)$ (see Figure 1) the closest homoclinic point to the unperturbed one $(x_0(0), y_0(0))$ (this point belongs to the homoclinic orbit of equation (1)). Let us call α the *angle* between these two curves at the point z_h. The aim of this talk is to present the main ideas utilised to obtain an asymptotic expression of this angle and some related quantities, like the *area* S of the loops that remain between the invariant curves of the Poincaré map, and the *maximum distance* d between the invariant curves inside this loop. Notice that only the area S remains invariant if the homoclinic point z_h is changed.

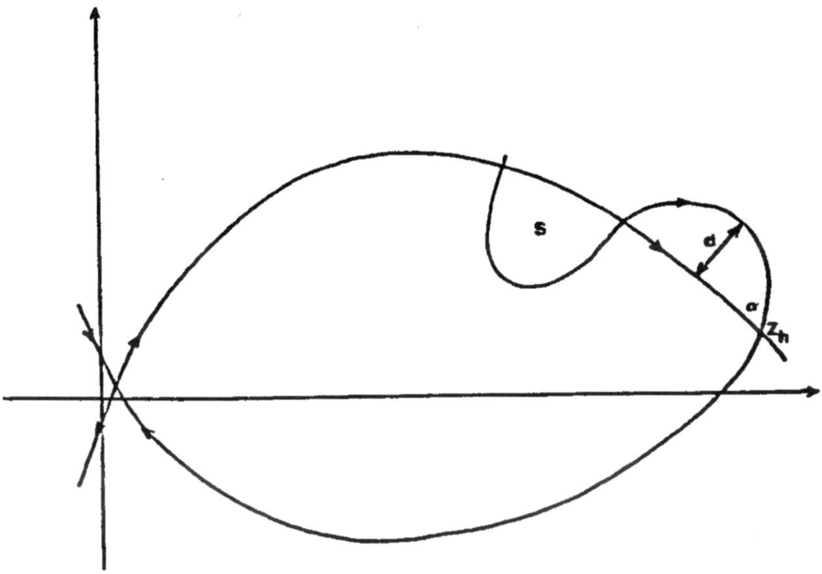

Figure 1. The Poincaré map for $\mu \neq 0$.

Theorem 1. *Assume $p \geq r - 1$. Then for $\varepsilon \to 0^+$, $\mu \to 0$, the following asymptotic expressions hold:*

$$\begin{aligned} \sin\alpha &= \frac{\mu\varepsilon^p}{N^2}\left[M'(s_0,\varepsilon) + O(\mu\varepsilon^\gamma, \varepsilon^2)e^{-\frac{a}{\varepsilon}}\right], \\ d &= \frac{\mu\varepsilon^p}{N}\left[\max_s |M(s,\varepsilon)| + O(\mu\varepsilon^\gamma, \varepsilon^2)e^{-\frac{a}{\varepsilon}}\right], \\ S &= \mu\varepsilon^p\left[\int_0^{\pi\varepsilon} M(s,\varepsilon)ds + O(\mu\varepsilon^\gamma, \varepsilon^2)e^{-\frac{a}{\varepsilon}}\right], \end{aligned} \tag{7}$$

where $M(s,\varepsilon)$ is the Poincaré-Melnikov function given in (3), the constant a is given in the hypothesis H_2, and γ, N are defined by $\gamma = p + 1 - r \geq 0$,

$N^2 = N^2(s_0) = \dot{x}_0(s_0)^2 + f(x_0(s_0))^2$. *The value of* s_0 *is taken as the closest zero of the function* $M(s,\varepsilon)$ *to* 0.

It has to be noticed that, in this kind of singular problems, the function $M(s,\varepsilon)$ depends on the parameter ε. In fact, one can see, using the residues theory, that $M(s,\varepsilon)$ is of order $O(\varepsilon^{1-r}e^{-\frac{a}{\varepsilon}})$. Theorem 1 assures that, even though in this case the Poincaré-Melnikov function is exponentially small in ε, it gives the correct result for these measures like in the regular case. We can apply Theorem 1 to the examples given in section 1, obtaining the following

Corollary.

1 *For the equation (4) we have the following estimates for* $p \geq 0$:

$$\begin{aligned} \sin\alpha &= \frac{\pi\mu\varepsilon^{p-1}}{2\cosh\frac{\pi}{2\varepsilon}}[1+O(\mu\varepsilon^p,\varepsilon^2)]\ , \\ d &\sim 2\varepsilon\sin\alpha\ , \\ S &\sim 4\varepsilon d\ . \end{aligned}$$

2 *For the equation (5) we have the following estimates for* $p \geq 1$:

$$\begin{aligned} \sin\alpha &= \frac{\sqrt{2}\pi\mu\varepsilon^{p-2}}{N^2(\bar{c})\cosh\frac{\pi}{2\varepsilon}}[1+O(\mu\varepsilon^{p-1},\varepsilon^2)]\ , \\ d &\sim N(\bar{c})\varepsilon\sin\alpha\ , \\ S &\sim 2N(\bar{c})\varepsilon d\ , \end{aligned}$$

where $(N(\bar{c}))^2 = (\dot{x}_0(\bar{c}))^2 + (x_0(\bar{c}) - x_0(\bar{c})^3)^2$, *and* $\bar{c} = c + 2k\pi\varepsilon$ *for some* k *such that* $\bar{c} \in [-\frac{\pi\varepsilon}{2}, \frac{\pi\varepsilon}{2}]$.

3 *For the equation (6) we have the following estimates for* $p \geq 2$:

$$\begin{aligned} \sin\alpha &= \frac{8\pi\mu\varepsilon^{p-3}}{3\sinh\frac{\pi}{\varepsilon}}[1+O(\mu\varepsilon^{p-2},\varepsilon^2)]\ , \\ d &\sim \frac{3}{2}\varepsilon\sin\alpha\ , \\ S &\sim 3\varepsilon d\ . \end{aligned}$$

In the next sections we will only sketch the main ideas about the proof of Theorem 1 for the general case, but full details for the case of the pendulum equation (4) can be found in [DS91a]. Let us remark that a direct application of the Poincaré-Melnikov theory does not work, due to the exponentially smallness of formulas (7) with respect to ε. It seems necessary in this context to go to the complex field to parameterize the invariant manifolds and consider $M(s,\varepsilon)$ also defined for complex values of s. The absence of essential singularities of $\dot{x}_0$, as assumed in hypothesis H_2, is crucial for our method, and seems to be necessary, according to an example [SMH91] by Scheurle, Marsden and Holmes . On the contrary, hypothesis H_4 is only assumed for the sake of the simplicity, in order to assure that the relevant part of $M(s,\varepsilon)$ is not zero. In case of reversibility of equation (1), the location of zeros of $M(s,\varepsilon)$ is known in advance, and the formulation of Theorem 1 is easier (see [DS91b]).

3. The Birkhoff normal form.

For $\mu\varepsilon^p$ small enough and a general g, it is well known that equation (1) has a hyperbolic $2\pi\varepsilon$-periodic orbit γ near to the origin. Taking also into account that g has zero mean, it turns out that the existence of γ is already guaranteed for $\mu\varepsilon^{p+2}$ small enough. A translation and standard linear arguments (Floquet theory) bring the hamiltonian h associated to equation (1) into its quadratic normal form. Since γ is a hyperbolic orbit of an analytic, non-automous, one-degree of freedom hamiltonian system, the subsequent transformation to nonlinear (Birkhoff) normal form is *convergent* on a neighborhood of the new origin (see [Mo56]), and consequently endows equation (1) with an analytic first integral on a neighborhood of γ. A very important property, already stressed by Fontich and Simó [FS90] in the case of area preserving maps, is that the size of this neighborhood can be bounded by a constant independent of μ, ε (see [DS91a]). We put these arguments all together in the following theorem.

Theorem 2. The Birkhoff normal form. *For $\mu\varepsilon^{p+2}$ small enough, equation (1) has a $2\pi\varepsilon$-periodic orbit near $(0,0)$:*

$$\gamma = (x_p(t), \dot{x}_p(t)) , \quad \textit{with} \quad x_p(t) = O(\mu\varepsilon^{p+2}) , \tag{8}$$

and there exists an analytic canonical change, $2\pi\varepsilon$-periodic in t:

$$\begin{aligned} X &= \Phi(x, y, \frac{t}{\varepsilon}, \mu, \varepsilon) , \\ Y &= \Psi(x, y, \frac{t}{\varepsilon}, \mu, \varepsilon) , \end{aligned} \tag{9}$$

defined in a neighborhood of size $2r$ of γ, with r independent of μ, ε, such that transforms the system associated to equation (1):

$$\begin{aligned} \dot{x} &= y , \\ \dot{y} &= -f(x) + \mu\varepsilon^p g(\frac{t}{\varepsilon}) , \end{aligned} \tag{10}$$

into its normal form near γ:

$$\begin{aligned} \dot{X} &= F'(XY,\mu,\varepsilon)X \ , \\ \dot{Y} &= -F'(XY,\mu,\varepsilon)Y \ , \end{aligned} \tag{11}$$

that is also a hamiltonian system with hamiltonian

$$\begin{aligned} H(X,Y,\mu,\varepsilon) = F(XY,\mu,\varepsilon) &= \omega XY + O_2(XY) \ , \\ \omega = F'(0) &= \omega_0 + O(\mu\varepsilon^{p+2}) \ . \\ \omega_0 &= \sqrt{-f'(0)} \ . \end{aligned}$$

4. The Extension Theorem.

System (11) can be easily integrated using the fact that XY is a first integral of it. In particular we can get useful parameterizations of the (one-dimensional) invariant manifolds of the origin of (11). For instance, we get the following parameterization for the unstable manifold

$$(X^u(t,s), Y^u(t,s)) = (e^{\omega(t+s)}, 0) \ ,$$

and an analogous one for the stable manifold. Performing the change (9) we transfer now these parameterizations to the (two-dimensional) local invariant manifolds $W^u_{loc}(\gamma)$, $W^s_{loc}(\gamma)$ associated to the periodic orbit γ:

$$x^u(t,s) = \phi(e^{\omega(t+s)}, 0, \frac{t}{\varepsilon}, \mu, \varepsilon) \ , \qquad \text{for} \quad t \in \mathbb{R} \ , \quad s \in \mathbb{C} \ , \quad t + \Re s \le -\frac{T}{2} \ , \tag{12}$$

$$x^s(t,s) = \psi(0, e^{-\omega(t+s)}, \frac{t}{\varepsilon}, \mu, \varepsilon) \ , \qquad \text{for} \quad t \in \mathbb{R} \ , \quad s \in \mathbb{C} \ , \quad t + \Re s \ge \frac{T}{2} \ , \tag{13}$$

where we have denoted (ϕ, ψ) the inverse change of (9), and T is a constant independent of μ, ε. It is straightforward to check that these parameterizations verify

$$\begin{aligned} x^\beta(t + 2\pi\varepsilon, s) &= x^\beta(t, s + 2\pi\varepsilon) \ , \\ x^\beta(t,s) - x_0(t+s) &= O(\mu\varepsilon^{p+2}) \ , \quad \beta = u, s \ . \end{aligned} \tag{14}$$

At this point we have parameterizations for the *local* invariant manifolds, and in particular that means that the above parameterizations are defined only for different sets of values of t, s. As we want to compare both manifolds, it is now necessary to extend one of the above parameterizations. The next theorem, called the *Extension Theorem*, will guarantee that such prolongation for the parameterization of the unstable manifold is possible, thanks to the fact that

$x_0(t+s)$ comes back to the origin when t grows. However, it has to be noticed that $x_0(t+s)$ has a singularity in the complex field for $t+s = \pm ai$. Therefore we will not be able to control the growth of the parameterization for $\Im(t+s) = \pm a$, and consequently the unstable manifold is extended for complex values of s but with the restriction $|\Im s| \leq a - \varepsilon$. As we will see in the last section, this range of values will be sufficient for the proof of Theorem 1.

Theorem 3. Extension Theorem. *Let $x_0(t+s)$ the unperturbed separatrix, defined for $t \in \mathbb{R}$, $|\Im s| < a$. Let $s \in \mathbb{C}$, $|\Im s| \leq a - \varepsilon$, and $x^u(t,s)$ the unstable manifold defined in (12).*

Then $x^u(t,s)$ can be extended for $-T \leq t + \Re s \leq T$, and satisfies:

$$x^u(t,s) - x_0(t+s) = O(\mu\varepsilon^{p+1-r}) \ ,$$
$$\dot{x}^u(t,s) - y_0(t+s) = O(\mu\varepsilon^{p+1-r}) \ .$$

Sketch of the proof.

In order to extend the unstable manifold we will use the fact that it remains near the unperturbed homoclinic orbit, and this one is defined for any real value of t and s. In this way, we introduce the functions

$$\xi(t,s) = x^u(t,s) - x_0(t+s) \ , \quad \eta(t,s) = \dot{\xi}(t,s) \ , \tag{15}$$

and we consider the system of differential equations verified by (ξ, η) as a perturbation of the first variational equations associated to x_0:

$$\dot{\xi} = \eta \ ,$$
$$\dot{\eta} = -f'(x_0(t+s))\xi \ .$$

One solution of this system is given by $(y_0(\tau), \dot{y}_0(\tau))$, with $\tau := t+s$. Another independent solution can be obtained in the form $\xi(\tau) = y_0(\tau)W(\tau)$, where

$$W(\tau) = \int_b^\tau \frac{1}{y_0^2(\sigma)} d\sigma,$$

b being an arbitrary constant. In the region $\Im\tau > 0$, $y_0(\tau)$ has a pole of order r at $\tau = ai$ and thus the solutions of the first variational equations become very big when τ is close to ai. This *bad* behavior for $\tau = ai$ can be avoided in the second solution of the mentioned variational equations, choosing $b = a$ in the expression of W. In this way the associated fundamental matrix

$$\begin{pmatrix} y_0(\tau) & (y_0W)(\tau) \\ y_0'(\tau) & (y_0W)'(\tau) \end{pmatrix}$$

behaves near the pole ai like

$$\begin{pmatrix} O((\tau - ai)^{-r}) & O((\tau - ai)^{r+1}) \\ O((\tau - ai)^{-(r+1)}) & O((\tau - ai)^{r}) \end{pmatrix} ,$$

and is better suited for subsequent bounds.

The proof of the Extension Theorem is performed through three propositions that will assure the extension of $x^u(t,s)$, in principle only defined for $t + \Re s = -T$, to the whole strip described in the hypothesis. First we extend in the next proposition the unstable invariant manifold for the values of (t,s) verifying

$$0 \le \Im s \le a - \varepsilon^{\frac{r+1}{2r+1}} \qquad \text{and} \qquad -T \le t + \Re s \le T \, . \tag{16}$$

Proposition 4.1. *Let $(\xi(t,s), \eta(t,s))$ the functions introduced in (15), defined on the strip (12) where $(x^u(t,s), y^u(t,s))$ satisfy (14). Then, if $p \ge r-1$ there exists $\mu_0 > 0$, such that for $|\mu| < \mu_0$, $(\xi(t,s), \eta(t,s))$ can be extended for (t,s) in the strip (16), satisfying the following bounds:*

$$\left.\begin{aligned} |\xi(t,s)| &\le c_1 \mu \varepsilon^{p+1-r} \\ |\eta(t,s)| &\le c_1 \mu \varepsilon^{p+1-r} \end{aligned}\right\}$$

c_1 being a constant independent of μ and ε.

In order to have the same extension for the values of $\Im s$ that are nearer the pole, we need to break the procedure in two steps. First, we extend this manifold up to a distance of order $\varepsilon^{\frac{r+1}{2r+1}}$ to the singularity of $x_0(t+s)$, or equivalently for

$$-T \le t + \Re s \le \varepsilon^{\frac{r+1}{2r+1}} \, , \qquad a - \varepsilon^{\frac{r+1}{2r+1}} \le \Im s \le a - \varepsilon \, . \tag{17}$$

Next, we introduce the norm $||\xi||_r = \sup |\xi(t,s)(t+s-ai)^r|$, and we prove that

$$||x^u(t,s) - x_0(t+s)||_r \le c_2 \mu \varepsilon^{p+2} \quad \text{for} \ \ (t,s) \text{ in (17)},$$

as is stated in the following proposition.

Proposition 4.2. *If $p \ge r-1$ there exists $\mu_0 > 0$, such that for $|\mu| < \mu_0$, $(\xi(t,s), \eta(t,s))$ can be extended for (t,s) to the strip (17), satisfying the following bounds:*

$$\left.\begin{aligned} |\xi(t,s)| &\le c_2 \frac{\mu \varepsilon^{p+2}}{|t+s-ai|^r} \, , \\ |\eta(t,s) - \mu \varepsilon^{p+1} G\left(\frac{t}{\varepsilon}\right)| &\le c_2 \left(\frac{\mu \varepsilon^{p+2}}{|t+s-ai|^{r+1}} + \mu \varepsilon^{p+1-r} |t+s-ai|^r \right) , \end{aligned}\right\} \tag{18}$$

c_2 being a constant independent of μ and ε, and $G(t) = \int_0^t g(s)ds$.

Finally, we continue the manifold in the remaining strip

$$t_1 + s \leq t + s \leq T\,, \quad a - \varepsilon^{\frac{r+1}{2r+1}} \leq \Im s \leq a - \varepsilon\,, \quad \text{with} \quad t_1 + \Re s = \varepsilon^{\frac{r+1}{2r+1}}, \tag{19}$$

utilising the norm $||\xi||_{-(r+1)} := \sup \dfrac{|\xi(t,s)|}{|t+s-ai|^{r+1}}$, and obtaining

$$||x^u(t,s) - x_0(t+s)||_{-(r+1)} \leq c_3 \mu \varepsilon^{p+1-r}\,.$$

Proposition 4.3. *Let $(\xi(t,s), \eta(t,s))$ satisfying (18) for the initial condition t_1 given by (19). Then, if $p \geq r-1$, there exists $\mu_0 > 0$, such that for $|\mu| < \mu_0$, $(\xi(t,s), \eta(t,s))$ can be extended to (19) and verifies*

$$\begin{aligned} |\xi(t,s)| &\leq c_3 \mu \varepsilon^{p+1-r}\,, \\ |\eta(t,s)| &\leq c_3 \mu \varepsilon^{p+1-r}\,, \end{aligned}$$

c_3 being a constant independent on μ, ε.

These three propositions prove the Extension Theorem for $0 \leq \Im s \leq a-\varepsilon$. In the case $-(a-\varepsilon) \leq \Im s \leq 0$, we only have to choose $b = -a$ in the expression of $W(\tau)$, and Propositions 4.1, 4.2, 4.3 give now exactly the same results, but for $\Im s < 0$, and the Extension Theorem follows directly from them. □

5. Distance between the invariant manifolds.

Due to the Extension Theorem the unstable manifold comes back to the neighborhood where the normal form is convergent and where the local stable manifold was defined. This fact will permit us to use the first integral provided by the Birkhoff normal form to compare them. Namely, we can transport the first integral $H(X,Y) = F(XY, \mu, \varepsilon)$ from the system (11) through the change (Φ, Ψ), given in (9), and thus we obtain a first integral e of system (10) defined in the neighborhood of the periodic orbit γ. This first integral e is $2\pi\varepsilon$-periodic with respect to the variable t and moreover satisfies:

$$\begin{aligned} e(x,y,\frac{t}{\varepsilon},\mu,\varepsilon) &:= F(\Phi(x,y,\frac{t}{\varepsilon},\mu,\varepsilon)\Psi(x,y,\frac{t}{\varepsilon},\mu,\varepsilon),\mu,\varepsilon) \\ &= h^0(x,y) + O(\mu\varepsilon^{p+2})\,, \end{aligned} \tag{20}$$

for the values (x, y) belonging to the neighborhood of the periodic orbit where the Birkhoff normal form is convergent.

It is easy to see that this first integral vanishes on the local invariant manifolds $W^u_{loc}(\gamma)$, $W^s_{loc}(\gamma)$ of the periodic orbit γ. Moreover, by the Extension Theorem, e is also defined over the global unstable manifold when it comes back to this neighborhood. This allows us to define the function ψ that will give us all the information about the splitting:

$$\begin{aligned}\psi(s) &= e(x^u(t,s), y^u(t,s), \frac{t}{\varepsilon}, \mu, \varepsilon) - e(x^s(t,s), y^s(t,s), \frac{t}{\varepsilon}, \mu, \varepsilon) \\ &= e(x^u(t,s), y^u(t,s), \frac{t}{\varepsilon}, \mu, \varepsilon)\end{aligned}$$

for

$$t \in \mathbb{R}\ , \quad \frac{T}{2} < t + \Re s < T\ , \quad |\Im s| \leq a - \varepsilon\ .$$

Using the fact that function e is a first integral of system (10), and the properties (14) of the parameterizations of the manifolds, ψ does not depend on t and is $2\pi\varepsilon$-periodic in its variable s. Next proposition relates the function ψ with the well known Poincaré-Melnikov integral:

Proposition 5.1. *For $|\Im s| \leq r_\varepsilon = a - \varepsilon$, we have*

$$\psi(s) = \mu\varepsilon^p[M(s) + O(\mu\varepsilon^{p+1-r}) + O(\varepsilon^2)]\ , \tag{21}$$

where $M(s)$ is the Poincaré-Melnikov integral, given at (3).

Sketch of the proof. From (20) and the definition of ψ, it follows that

$$\psi(s) = h^0(x^u(t,s), y^u(t,s)) - h^0(x^s(t,s), y^s(t,s)) + O(\mu\varepsilon^{p+2})$$

for $|\Im s| \leq r_\varepsilon$, $\frac{T}{2} \leq t + \Re s \leq T$. Next, proceeding like in the Melnikov method but using the estimates given by the Extension Theorem for complex values of the parameter s, we get formula (21). □

We can finally proceed to the proof of Theorem 1. For this purpose, we consider the Fourier expansion of ψ,

$$\psi(s) = \sum_k \psi_k e^{i\frac{k}{\varepsilon}s}\ ,$$

where s will denote a real number for the rest of this talk. The Fourier coefficients ψ_k can be computed using proposition 5.1, and shifting along complex lines $\Im\sigma = \pm r_\varepsilon$:

$$\begin{aligned}\psi_k &= \frac{e^{-|k|\frac{r_\varepsilon}{\varepsilon}}}{2\pi\varepsilon}\int_0^{2\pi\varepsilon}\psi(s \pm ir_\varepsilon)e^{i\frac{k}{\varepsilon}s}ds \\ &= \mu\varepsilon^p M_k(\varepsilon) + O\left(e^{-\frac{|k|}{\varepsilon}a}(\mu^2\varepsilon^{2p+1-r} + \mu\varepsilon^{p+2})\right) .\end{aligned}$$

By hypothesis H_4, $M_{\pm 1}$ is non zero, and thus we can write

$$\psi(s) = \psi_0 + \mu\varepsilon^p M(s) + O\left(e^{-\frac{a}{\varepsilon}}(\mu^2\varepsilon^{2p+1-r} + \mu^2\varepsilon^{p+2})\right). \tag{22}$$

Now, we only need to compute ψ_0, and relate function ψ with the quantities d, $\sin\alpha$, and S. This is done in the next proposition:

Proposition 5.2. *The function ψ satisfies the following properties.*

a) *There exist s_1 and s_2 such that $\vec{x}^u(t, s_1) = \vec{x}^s(t, s_2)$ (giving an homoclinic connexion), and consequently $\psi(s_1) = 0$. Moreover,*

$$\psi'(s_1) = \frac{\partial\vec{x}^s}{\partial s}(t, s_2) \wedge \frac{\partial\vec{x}^u}{\partial s}(t, s_1) = \|\frac{\partial\vec{x}^u}{\partial s}(t, s_1)\|\|\frac{\partial\vec{x}^s}{\partial s}(t, s_2)\| \sin\Theta(t, s_1, s_2),$$

where $\vec{x}^\beta(t, s) := (x^\beta(t, s), y^\beta(t, s))$, $\beta = s, u$, $\wedge$ denotes the exterior product on $\mathbb{R}^2$, and $\Theta(t, s_1, s_2)$ is the angle between $\vec{x}^u(t, s_1)$ and $\vec{x}^s(t, s_2)$.

b) $\psi_0 = \int_{s_1}^{s_1+2\pi\varepsilon}\psi(s)ds = 0.$

c) *$s_1 = s_0 + O(\mu\varepsilon^{p+1-r})$, where s_0 is the smallest zero of $M(s, \varepsilon)$, and $\psi'(s_1) = [N^2(s_0) + O(\mu\varepsilon^{p-r+1})]\sin\alpha$, with $N(s) = (y_0(s))^2 + (f(x_0(s)))^2$*

d) *$S = \int_{s_1}^{\bar{s}_1}\psi(s)ds$, s_1 and $\bar{s}_1$ being the two zeros of $\psi(s)$ in $[0, 2\pi\varepsilon)$*

e) $d = \frac{1}{N(s_0)}\max|\psi(s)|[1 + O(\mu\varepsilon^{p+1-r})].$

All these properties are proven in [DS91a], and they are a consequence of the following facts:

- system (10) is hamiltonian,
- the Poincaré map P is area preserving,
- the change of variables (obtained through the normal form): $(x, y) \to (s, e)$ is symplectic,
- e is close to h_0 (property (20)).

Now, Theorem 1 follows from the previous proposition and formula (22). □

References.

[DS91a] A. Delshams and T. M. Seara. An asymptotic expression for the splitting of separatrices of the rapidly forced pendulum. To appear in *Comm. Math. Phys.*

[DS91b] A. Delshams and T. M. Seara. Splitting of separatrices in rapidly forced systems. To appear in *Proceedings of EQUADIFF 91.*

[FS90] E. Fontich and C. Simó. The splitting of separatrices for analytic diffeomorphisms. *Ergod. Th. & Dynam. Sys.*, 10:295–318, 1990.

[Ge90] V. G. Gelfreich. Splitting of separatrices for the rapidly forced pendulum. *Preprint*, 1990.

[GLT90] V. G. Gelfreich, V. F. Lazutkin and M. B. Tabanov. Exponentially small splitting in hamiltonian systems. *Chaos* 1, no.2 (1991), 137–142.

[HMS88] P. Holmes, J. Marsden and J. Scheurle. Exponentially small splittings of separatrices with applications to KAM theory and degenerate bifurcations. *Contemporary Mathematics*, 81:213–244, 1988.

[La84] V. F. Lazutkin. Splitting of separatrices for the Chirikov's standard mapping. Manuscript No. 6372–84, deposited at *VINITI* , 24 September 1984. (In Russian.)

[LST89] V. F. Lazutkin, I. G. Schachmannski and M. B. Tabanov. Splitting of separatrices for standard and semistandard mappings. *Physica D*, 40:235–248, 1989.

[Mo56] J. Moser. The analytic invariants of an area-preserving mapping near a hyperbolic fixed point. *Comm. Pure Appl. Math.*, 9:673–692, 1956.

[SMH91] J. Scheurle, J. Marsden, and P. Holmes. Exponentially small estimates for separatrix splittings. *Preprint*, June 1991.

A. Delshams: Departament de Matemàtica Aplicada i Anàlisi, U. de Barcelona. Gran via 585, 08071 Barcelona, Spain. Permanent address: Departament de Matemàtica Aplicada I, E.T.S.E.I.B., U. Politècnica de Catalunya. Diagonal 647, 08028 Barcelona, Spain.

T. M. Seara: Departament de Matemàtica Aplicada I, E.T.S.E.I.B., U. Politècnica de Catalunya. Diagonal 647, 08028 Barcelona, Spain.

AN UNUSUAL VARIATIONAL PROBLEM CONNECTED WITH MATHER'S THEORY FOR MONOTONE TWIST MAPPINGS

Jürgen Moser

1. The variational principle by Percival

An important progress in the theory of area-preserving mappings was provided by the work of S. Aubry and J. Mather some 10 years ago (for a review article see [1]). It gave rise to the construction of closed invariant sets of monotone twist mappings for every rotation number. These sets can be either invariant curves or Cantor sets, the so-called Mather sets, if the rotation number is irrational. The approaches by Aubry and by Mather were independent and had quite a different starting point. Here we will restrict ourselves to the original proof of Mather [2] of 1982 which is based on the variational principle, suggested originally by I. C. Percival [3] in 1980. He considered the functional

$$I_\alpha(u) = \int_0^1 h\big(u(\theta), u(\theta+\alpha)\big)d\theta \tag{1}$$

where h is a given function in $C^1(\mathbb{R}^2)$, such that $h(x_0+t, x_1+t)$ has period 1 in t and that the maps $x_1 \to -\partial_{x_0}h(x_0,x_1) = -h_1(x_0,x_1)$ and $x_0 \to -\partial_{x_1}h(x_0,x_1) = -h_2(x_0,x_1)$ * are sense-preserving homeomorphisms of $\mathbb{R}$; in particular, $-\partial_{x_1}h$ and $-\partial_{x_0}h$ are strictly monotonically increasing in the first and second argument, respectively. The problem is to minimize this functional in the class of (not necessarily strictly) monotonically increasing functions $u = u(\theta)$ for which $u(\theta) - \theta$ has the period 1, when α is any given real number. On account of the compactness properties of bounded monotone functions the existence of such a minimizing function, say $u = u^*$, is easily established. The more difficult and the essential part, however, is to prove that $u = u^*$ satisfies the formal Euler equation

$$h_1\big(u(\theta), u(\theta+\alpha)\big) + h_2\big(u(\theta-\alpha), u(\theta)\big) = 0 \tag{2}$$

at all points of continuity of u, i.e. at all but at most denumerably many points. A continuous minimizer gives rise to an invariant curve, and a discontinuous

---

* We employ Mather's notation and write for the derivatives with respect to the first and second argument h_1, h_2, respectively.

one defines a Cantor set for the relevant monotone twist mapping φ, which can be defined implicitly by

$$\begin{cases} \varphi : (x_0, y_0) \longrightarrow (x_1, y_1)\,, \text{where} \\ y_0 = -h_1(x_0, x_1), \quad y_1 = h_2(x_0, x_1)\,. \end{cases} \tag{3}$$

Here h plays the role of the generating function.

2. An unusual variational problem

In this note we present a method to approximate the discontinuous minimizers by smooth ones. This can be achieved by adding to $I_\alpha(u)$ an "artificial viscosity" term in the integrand. Such an approach was suggested in [5] and carried out in [4], 1987 by adding $\nu(\partial_\theta u)^2$ to the integrand, with a small positive parameter ν. The resulting minimizers were smooth indeed and gave rise to smooth curves approximating the Mather sets. However, the approximating curves for different α could intersect, and the question arose whether one can arrange it so that the approximating curves for varying α give rise to a foliation of the cylinder. This is indeed possible and leads to the essentially unique viscosity term $-\nu \log u_\theta$. This way we are led to the unusual variational problem: Minimize, for given $\nu > 0$ and $\alpha \in \mathbb{R}$

$$I_\alpha^\nu = \int_0^1 \{-\nu \log u_\theta + h(u, u^+)\}\, d\theta \tag{4}$$

over the class

$$X = \{u = u(\theta)\,,\ \text{monotone in } \mathbb{R}\,, u(\theta+1) = u(\theta) + 1\}\,. \tag{5}$$

Here we define $u^+(\theta) = u(\theta + \alpha)$ and $u^- = u(\theta - \alpha)$. We point out that discontinuous functions u are admitted in X, and the derivative u_θ in (4) is understood in the classical sense and is defined almost everywhere. Since the logarithm takes all real values it seems that (4) is not bounded from below. In order to see that it *is* we observe that on account of the boundary condition we have

$$\int_0^1 u_\theta\, d\theta \le \int_0^1 du = u(1) - u(0) = 1\,, \tag{6}$$

and we see that

$$I_\alpha^\nu(u) + \nu \ge \int_0^1 \nu(-\log u_\theta + u_\theta) + h(u, u^+)\, d\theta\,.$$

Since the function $-\log x + x$ is ≥ 1 for $x > 0$ it is clear that I_α^ν is bounded from below; moreover this function is convex. More precisely, we can prove

Theorem 1: *For $\nu \geq 0$ the functional I_α^ν attains its minimum for a function $u \in X$. If, moreover, $\nu > 0$ than any such minimal of I_α^ν in X belongs to $X \cap C^2$, satisfies $u_\theta > 0$ as well as the Euler equation*

$$\nu \partial_\theta (u_\theta^{-1}) + h_1(u, u^+) + h_2(u^-, u) = 0 \,. \tag{7}$$

In order to discuss the uniqueness question we note that the functional is invariant under the translation $u(\theta) \to u(\theta + \lambda)$, $\lambda \in \mathbb{R}$. We can show that the minimal is unique up to such translation:

Theorem 2: *Assume that h satisfies the previous assumptions and, in addition,*

$$h \in C^2 \,, \quad h_{12} = \partial_{x_0} \partial_{x_1} h < 0 \,. \tag{8}$$

If $\nu > 0$ and $u, v \in X \cap C^2$ are two solutions of the Euler equation (7) then there exists a constant $\lambda \in \mathbb{R}$ such that

$$v(\theta) = u(\theta + \lambda) \,.$$

Thus we conclude that, for $\nu > 0$, our functional possesses — up to translation — only one extreme point which is a minimum. In the following we will retain the assumption (8).

The proof of theorem 1 can be given by the direct method of calculus of variations. For this purpose one shows that I_α^ν is lower semicontinuous, if X is equipped with the weak*-topology for the measures defined by du. Since du are probability measures on the circle — on account of (6) — X is compact, and we conclude that the solution $u = u^\nu$ of (7) have weak-convergent subsequences u^{ν_i}, $\nu_i \to 0$. This is equivalent to convergence of $u^{\nu_i} \to u$ at all points of continuity of u. One shows:

Theorem 3: *If u^ν is a solution of (7) for $\nu > 0$ than the limit u of any a.e. convergent subsequence u^{ν_i}, $\nu_i \to 0$ satisfies the equation (2) at all its points of continuity. For irrational values of α one has for u^ν, normalized by*

$$\int_0^1 u^\nu d\theta = \frac{1}{2} \,, \tag{9}$$

that $u^\nu \to u$ for $\nu \to 0$ at all points of continuity. Moreover, we have

$$\min_X I_\alpha^\nu(u) \longrightarrow \min I_\alpha(u) \,.$$

In this sense we can view the u^ν as the smooth approximation of the generally discontinuous solution u of (9).

3. Smooth approximation of the Mather sets

We return to the area-preserving monotone twist mapping φ of the cylinder $A = S^1 \times \mathbb{R}$ onto itself given by the formula (3). Any orbit $(x_i, y_i) = \varphi^i(x_0, y_0)$, $i \in \mathbb{Z}$, projects into a sequence $x_i \in \mathbb{R}$ satisfying

$$h_1(x_i, x_{i+1}) + h_2(x_{i-1}, x_i) = 0\,. \tag{10}$$

Conversely, any such sequence gives rise to an orbit, if one sets $y_i = -h_1(x_i, x_{i+1})$.

The invariant sets of φ defined by a solution u of the difference equation are given by the embedding

$$\begin{cases} \beta : \theta \longrightarrow (x = u(\theta), y = v(\theta)) \\ v := -h_1(u, u^+)\,. \end{cases}$$

Then on account of (2) and the periodicity conditions we have

$$\begin{cases} \varphi \circ \beta(\theta) = \beta(\theta + \alpha) \\ \beta(\theta) + e_1 = \beta(\theta + 1)\,; \quad e_1 = \begin{pmatrix} 1 \\ 0 \end{pmatrix}, \end{cases} \tag{11}$$

showing that the image of β is invariant under φ; the parametrization is chosen so that the induced map on this set is a translation by α, the rotation number of the orbits on this set. It is known [2] that u is strictly increasing if α is irrational.

If u is a continuous function then this invariant set defines a closed invariant curve if x is identified mod 1. In this case M_α is defined to be this invariant curve. If, however, u is discontinuous we consider the set $C(u)$ of θ-values at which u is continuous; hence $\mathbb{R}\backslash C(u)$ is countable. Thus, setting $\Gamma(u)=$ image of $C(u)$ under u we can define the inverse

$$u^{-1} : \Gamma \longrightarrow C$$

of u. Eliminating θ from $y = v(\theta) = -h_1(u, u^+)$ we can represent the image of β in the form of a graph

$$\begin{cases} (x, y = w(x)) \quad \text{for} \quad x \in \Gamma(u)\,, \\ w(x) = -h_1\big(x, u^+ \circ u^{-1}(x)\big)\,, \quad w(x+1) = w(x)\,. \end{cases} \tag{12}$$

It is known that w is Lipschitz continuous and therefore it can be continued to $\bar{\Gamma}(u)$, the closure of $\Gamma(u)$. Then we set

$$M_\alpha = \big\{(x, y = w(x)) \;\big|\; x \in \bar{\Gamma}(u)/\mathbb{Z}\big\}\,. \tag{13}$$

This defines the Mather set for continuous as well as the discontinuous case, if α is irrational. In the first case it is a closed invariant curve, in the second case it is a Cantor set.

To approximate these sets M_α by smooth curves we make use of the smooth solution u^ν of (7) — which we may make unique by the normalization (9). We recall that $\partial_\theta u^\nu > 0$ by theorem 1. Therefore $(u^\nu)^{-1}$ is defined and continuous and we can approximate (13) by defining

$$w^\nu(x) = -h_1\big(x, (u^\nu)^+ \circ (u^\nu)^{-1}(x)\big) \tag{14}$$

and the closed curve

$$M_\alpha^\nu = \big\{(x, y = w^\nu(x))\,|x \in \mathbb{R}/\mathbb{Z}\big\}\,. \tag{15}$$

Theorem 4: *For α irrational we have*

$$w^\nu(x) \longrightarrow w(x) \quad \textit{for} \quad x \in \Gamma$$

in the sense of pointwise convergence.

Thus the closed curves M_α^ν converge pointwise (not uniformly) to M_α if we restrict x to the set $\Gamma = \Gamma(u)$.

Remark: It remains open what happens to the curves M_α^ν for $\nu \to 0$ in the gaps $(\mathbb{R}\backslash\bar{\Gamma})/\mathbb{Z}$. Although the functions w satisfy a Lipschitz estimate we have not been able to establish a uniform Lipschitz estimate for the functions w^ν.

However, for bounded α, one has

Proposition: *If $|\alpha| \le \alpha^*$ there exists a constant $c = c(\alpha^*)$, independent of $\nu \in (0,1)$ such that*

$$\max_x |w^\nu| + \int_0^1 |dw^\nu| \le c\,.$$

Because of the compactness of bounded functions of bounded variations with respect to a.e. convergence we can define upper and lower limits

$$w^+(x) = \overline{\lim_{x' \to x}}\ \overline{\lim_{\nu \to 0}}\ w^\nu(x')$$

$$w^-(x) = \underline{\lim_{x' \to x}}\ \underline{\lim_{\nu \to 0}}\ w^\nu(x')$$

so that w^+ is upper semicontinuous, w^- lower semicontinuous and $w^-(x) \le w^+(x)$.

Theorem 5: *If α is irrational one has*

$$w^-(x) = w^+(x) \quad \text{for} \quad x \in \Gamma\,.$$

For all α we can define the set

$$\left\{\left(x, w^-(x) \le y \le w^+(x)\right); x \in \mathbb{R}/\mathbb{Z}\right\} \tag{16}$$

which — for irrational α — contains the Mather set. But one should not expect this set to be invariant under the mapping φ, as the following example illustrates.

Example: We consider the standard map

$$\varphi : (x, y) \longrightarrow (x_1 = x + y_1, y_1 = y + \lambda \sin 2\pi x)$$

with the generating function

$$h(x_0, x_1) = \frac{1}{2}(x_1 - x_0)^2 - \frac{\lambda}{2\pi}\cos 2\pi x_0$$

and we consider the case $\alpha = 0$. Then $u^+(\theta) = u(\theta + \alpha) = u(\theta)$ hence — by (14) —

$$w^\nu(x) = h_1(x, x) = -\lambda \sin 2\pi x\,.$$

Hence the curve M_α^ν for $\alpha = 0$ is independent of ν. The image of this set $(x, y = -\lambda \sin 2\pi x)$ is $(x_1, y_1 = 0)$, hence it is not invariant, if $\lambda \neq 0$. However, it does contain the fixed points $\left(x = 0(\text{mod} \frac{1}{2})\,, y = 0\right)$.

This situation is reminiscent of the "ghost circles" by Angenent and Golé [6], which, however, are constructed in an entirely different way, and therefore one can not expect them to agree with the sets constructed here.

4. Approximate foliation

The main point of this paper is to study the set of curves M_α^ν for variable α, and fixed positive ν. We claim that the M_α^ν, $-\infty < \alpha < +\infty$ provide a smooth foliation of the cylinder A by closed curves.

We change the notation slightly, and denote the functions u^ν, w^ν by $u^\nu(\theta, \alpha)$, $w^\nu(x, \alpha)$ respectively, to express their dependence on the rotation number α.

Theorem 6: *For fixed positive ν the mapping*

$$\rho^\nu : (x, \alpha) \longrightarrow \left(x, w^\nu(x, \alpha)\right)$$

defines a diffeomorphism of $\mathbb{R}^2$ *onto itself, inducing a diffeomorphism of* $A = S^1 \times \mathbb{R}$ *onto itself, since* $w(x+1,\alpha) = w(x,\alpha)$.

The proof requires to show that

$$\partial_\alpha w^\nu(x,\alpha) > 0 \tag{17}$$

and that $w^\nu(x,\alpha) \to \pm\infty$ on $\alpha \to \pm\infty$. The main difficulty is the proof of (17) which is accomplished by applying the maximum principle to the equation satisfied by $\partial_\alpha w^\nu$. Here it is important that the viscosity term has the right form, and in this connection we were forced to introduce the logarithmic term in (4).

Thus we have the following picture: The diffeomorphism ρ^ν take the curves $\alpha =$ const into curves M_α^ν which for $\nu \to 0$ approximate, in the sense of theorem 4, the Mather sets M_α. Moreover, the curves M_α^ν define a smooth foliation of the cylinder, which then approximates the set of Mather sets $\bigcup_\alpha M_\alpha$.

Similarly, one can verify that for $\nu > 0$ the map

$$\sigma^\nu : (\theta,\alpha) \longrightarrow \big(x = u^\nu(\theta,\alpha), y = v^\nu(\theta,\alpha)\big)$$

defines a diffeomorphism of $A = S^1 \times \mathbb{R}$ onto itself. Indeed, σ^ν can be factored into

$$(\theta,\alpha) \longrightarrow \big(x = u^\nu(\theta,\alpha), \alpha\big)$$

and the diffeomorphism ρ^ν. Since $\theta \to u^\nu(\theta,\cdot)$ is a diffeomorphism of $\mathbb{R}$ onto itself one readily concludes that σ^ν is a diffeomorphism. Defining the standard twist map

$$\tau : (\theta,\alpha) \longrightarrow (\theta+\alpha,\alpha)$$

and using (11) one can view the map

$$\varphi^\nu = \sigma^\nu \circ \tau \circ (\sigma^\nu)^{-1} \tag{18}$$

as a diffeomorphism approximating φ in some sense. Here φ^ν has obviously the integral $\alpha \circ (\sigma^\nu)^{-1} = G^\nu$ with nonvanishing gradient. Here we have to print out, however, that, in general, φ^ν will not preserve the area element $dx \wedge dy$.

Finally, we study the limit $\nu \to +\infty$. One shows that for $\nu \to \infty$

$$\sigma^\nu \longrightarrow \sigma^\infty : (\theta,\alpha) \longrightarrow \big(x = \theta, y = -h_1(\theta,\theta+\alpha)\big) \tag{19}$$

which is closely related to the Legendre transformation

$$\lambda : (x_0,x_1) \longrightarrow \big(x_0, -h_1(x_0,x_1)\big)\,.$$

By our conditions on h this transformation λ defines a diffeomorphism of the plane, taking points equivalent under the translation $(x_0, x_1) \to (x_0 + k, x_1 + k)$ $k \in \mathbb{Z}$ into points (x_0, y_0) equivalent under $(x_0, y_0) \to (x_0 + k, y_0)$.

The Legendre transformation λ connects the representation of φ in the "phase space" A with the representation

$$\psi : (x_0, x_1) \longrightarrow (x_1, f(x_0, x_1)) ,$$

where $x_2 = f(x_0, x_1)$ is the solution of the difference equation (10), for $i = 1$. Thus we have

$$\psi = \lambda^{-1} \circ \varphi \circ \lambda .$$

The approximation ψ^ν of ψ, corresponding to (18) is given by

$$\psi^\nu = \lambda^{-1} \circ \sigma^\nu \circ \tau \circ (\sigma^\nu)^{-1} \circ \lambda = \lambda^{-1} \circ \varphi^\nu \circ \lambda$$

which again is a diffeomorphism for all positive values of ν. For $\nu \to \infty$ we obtain $\psi^\nu \to \psi^\infty = \lambda^{-1} \circ \varphi^\infty \circ \lambda$

$$\psi^\infty : (x_0, x_1) \longrightarrow (x_1, 2x_1 - x_0) = (x_1, x_2)$$

which is a translation along the diagonal by $x_1 - x_0$. Thus ψ^ν interpolates the difference equation

$$x_2 - 2x_1 + x_0 = 0 \quad \text{for} \quad \nu = \infty$$

with $\lim_{\nu \to 0} \psi^\nu$ corresponding to the difference equation (2) through a sequence of difference equation possessing an integral.

5. Concluding remarks

By replacing the variational problem (1) of Percival by the modified variational problem (4) we seem to complicate the situation. The Euler equation (2), a difference equation, is replaced by the difference-differential equation. However, the solution of (7), which up to phase shift is unique, is smooth and approximate the solutions of (1) in the sense of a.e. pointwise convergence. More importantly, these solutions of (7) for fixed positive $\nu > 0$ give rise to a foliation of the cylinder A whose curves converge in the above sense to the Mather sets. Finally, we obtain a family of smooth diffeomorphisms φ^ν which, in a weak sense approximate the given map φ, and for $\nu > 0$ possess a smooth integral. Here one has to keep in mind that the maps φ^ν are not area-preserving, and the convergence is a rather weak one. In the same weak sense the smooth integral G^ν of φ^ν can be viewed as an approximate integral for φ which patently has no smooth integral! The proofs of the results announced in this paper will appear elsewhere.

References

1. *V. Bangert*, Mather Sets for Twist Maps and Geodesics on Tori. Dynamics Reported, 1, 1988, 1–56.

2. *J. Mather*, Existence of quasi-periodic orbits for twist homeomorphisms of the annulus. Topology 21, 1982, 457–467.

3. *I. C. Percival*, Variational Principles for Invariant Tori and Canton. American Inst. of Physics, Conference Proceedings No. 57, ser. editor: M. Month, 1980, 1–15.

4. *J. Moser*, On the construction of invariant curves and Mather sets via a regularized variational principle. Proc. Advanced Research Workshop in Periodic Solutions of Hamiltonian Systems and Related Topics, ed. P. Rabinowitz, et al., NATO ASI series, ser. C, Math. and Physics Sci., vol. 209, Reidal Publ. Comp. 1987, 221–334.

5. *J. Moser*, Recent developments in the theory of Hamiltonian systems. SIAM Reviews 28, 1986, 459–485.

6. *S. Angenent* and *C. Golé*, Laminations by Ghost Circles. Preprint, Forschungsinstitut für Mathematik, ETH Zürich, March 1991.

PERIODIC METRICS

D. BURAGO

§1. INTRODUCTION. LIMIT NORM

The topic which served as the starting point for this investigation is the "global" geometry of periodic metrics. We call *periodic* a Riemannian metric ρ on a complete manifold M possessing an isometry group Γ with a compact quotient M/Γ. The word "global" means here that we study "large" objects and do not care of the measurement error of order $\operatorname{diam}(M/\Gamma)$. We consider here only a special (but rather natural) case when ρ is a perturbation (not necessarily small) of a constant curvature metric ρ_0 with the same group of isometries. We have two main possibilities: the flat case when ρ_0 is Euclidean metric on $M \approx \mathbb{R}^n$ and $\Gamma \approx \mathbb{Z}^n$ acts by integer translations, and the hyperbolic case when Γ is a hyperbolic group. We denote geometric structures attached to ρ_0 by marking with a circle like the followings: $\exp^0$ – the exponential map, $< \cdot, \cdot >^0$– the inner product, U^0TM– the unit tangent bundle *etc.*

This paper is the continuation of [2] , and here we give its abstract.

Definition 1. For $(x, v) \in U^0TM$ we define $K(x, v) = \lim_{t\to\infty} \frac{1}{t}\rho(x, \exp^0_x tv)$ if the limit exists. It is simple to check that K depends on the infinity point (which is a class of asymptotic geodesics) $[\gamma(t) = \exp^0_x tv] \in \partial^0 M$ only, and we denote also $K[\gamma] = K(x, v)$ for $[\gamma] = [\gamma(t) = \exp^0_x tv] \in \partial^0 M$.

Definition 2. We define *maximal distortion* $\lambda(\rho, \rho_0)$ to be

$$\lambda(\rho, \rho_0) = \frac{\sup\{\sqrt{< v, v >} \mid < v, v >^0 = 1, \quad v \in TM\}}{\inf\{\sqrt{< v, v >} \mid < v, v >^0 = 1, \quad v \in TM\}} .$$

The following theorem is the main result of [2] :

Theorem 1. *Let $\rho^0(x, y) = |x - y|$ be Euclidean metric on $M \approx \mathbb{R}^n$ and $\Gamma \approx \mathbb{Z}^n$ act by integer translations (flat case). Then*

(1) *The expression $\|x\|_\rho = |x| \cdot K\left(\frac{x}{|x|}\right)$ correctly determines a norm $\|\cdot\|_\rho$.*
(2) *For all x, y* $\quad \left|\rho(x, y) - \|x - y\|_\rho\right| \le C(n) \cdot \left(\lambda(\rho, \rho_0) + 1\right)$.

Remark. The reasons of "convergence of a periodic metric to a norm at the infinity" have appeared in a number of papers ([4] for instance). The estimate (2), which shows that a periodic metric cannot be distinguished from a Banach one by the measurement with precision less than $C(n) \cdot \big(\lambda(\rho.\rho_0)+1\big)$, is of the author's main interest.

We call $\|\cdot\|_\rho$ the *limit norm* for the metric ρ.

The hyperbolic case differs from the flat one essentially:

Theorem 2. *Let ρ_0 be a metric of constant negative curvature. Then*

(1) *$K(v)$ is correctly defined for almost all $v \in \partial^0 M$.*
(2) *In the generic case the estimate $\big|\rho(x, \exp_x^0 tv) - tK(x,v)\big| \leq o(t)$ <u>does not</u> hold (for little o independent of v).*

Proof. See [2]. □

Remark. One can prove that lim sup and lim inf in Definition 1 are not equal to zero or infinity, but it is not clear whether $K(v)$ is defined for all $v \in \partial^0 M$.

Later on we consider only the flat case. The next section contains some results on behaviour of geodesic lines, and the third section reveals the connection with Finsler geometry. Complete proofs of the theorems below are contained in the author's thesis, but they are not technically difficult and can be easily restored by the sketch–proofs given below.

§2. Geodesics on periodic metrics

There were several papers on this topic (see a brief historical review in [1]), here we prove some more results.

Theorem 1 demonstrates that any periodic metric is close to a Banach one. But it is known that the proximity of metrics does not imply the proximity of shortest arcs and moreover the proximity of geodesic lines. However, Hedlund [5] has proved that in the case of dimension 2 any shortest arc in a periodic metric ρ lies in c–neighbourhood of the straight-line segment between its endpoints where c depends only on ρ.

Theorem 3. *There exists a periodic metric on $\mathbb{R}^3$ for which the above discussed Hedlund theorem does not hold. Moreover, fore some constant c there are straightline segments of arbitrary large length L with the following property: they do not have a shortest arc between their endpoints contained in their cL-neighbourhood.*

Proof of this theorem can be simply obtained by the construction of V. Bungert [1]. The idea is to consider $d\rho^2 = \lambda\rho_0^2$ where $\lambda = 1$ outside of 0.01–neighbourhood of the straight lines $\{x_i = z_1, x_j = z_2 | i,j = 1,2,3;\ z_1, z_2 \in \mathbb{Z}\}$ and $\lambda = 0.01$ on these straight lines. Any shortest arc has to go in the narrow channels around these straight lines and makes only several (say not more than 10) jumps between them. □

Theorem 4. *If a periodic metric ρ on $\mathbb{R}^2$ is sufficiently close (as a tensor field in C^k with some k) to the flat one, then there are no self-intersecting geodesics in ρ.*

Sketch-proof. This theorem is an easy consequence of KAM theory and standard topological considerations. The required number of derivatives is equal to that in KAM theory. □

Theorem 5. *There exist periodic metrics on $\mathbb{R}^n$ arbitrary close to the flat one in C^r, $r < n/2$, which have closed geodesics.*

Sketch-proof. We need the following algebraic lemma.

Lemma. *There exists a plane $p \in G_n^2$ such that for some $c > 0$*

$$\mathit{dist}(z, p) \geq c|z|^{-\frac{2}{n-2.1}} \quad \forall z \in \mathbb{Z}^n \setminus \{0\}.$$

Proof. Standard volume estimates in G_n^2. □

Now let $S_R \subset p$ be the circle of the radius R centered at zero (where p is the plane guaranteed by the lemma), T_R be the ε-neighbourhood of S_R, $\varepsilon = 0.25R^{-\frac{2}{n-2.1}}$, and T_R^z be the translation of T_R by $z \in \mathbb{Z}^n$. We will construct a family of metrics ρ_R such that S_R is a geodesic line in ρ_R. We retain ρ_R to be Euclidean outside of $\bigcup_{z\in\mathbb{Z}^n} T_R^z$. Note that $T_R^{z_1}$ and $T_R^{z_2}$ do not intersect if $z_1 \neq z_2$ because of the estimate of the lemma. This allows us to define ρ_R in T_R and then translate it into other T_R^z's by corresponding translations. Let $\mu\colon \mathbb{R} \to \mathbb{R}$ be a C^∞–function such that $\mu(x) = 0$ if $|x| \geq 1$ and $\mu(x) = 1$ if $|x| \leq 0.5$. We define ρ_R in T_R by the formula $d\rho_R^2 = \lambda_R^2 d\rho_0^2$ where

$$\lambda_R = 1 + \frac{R - |x|}{R} \cdot \mu\left(\frac{\mathrm{dist}(x, S_R)}{\varepsilon}\right).$$

One can check that S_R satisfies the equation for geodesic lines and $\|d^k\lambda_R\| \to 0$ as $R \to \infty$ $(k < n/2)$ using the relation $\varepsilon = 0.25R^{-\frac{2}{n-2.1}}$. □

While Theorems 4 and 5 are dealing with the case of a metric close to the flat one, the following result considers metrics maximally far in some sense far from the flat one.

Theorem 6. *Let a metric ρ be such that the geodesic flow on $UT(Torus) = UT((M \approx \mathbb{R}^n)/(\Gamma \approx \mathbb{Z}^n))$ is ergodic. Then for almost all $(x, v) \in UTM$ the distance $\rho_0(x, \exp_x tv)$ increases slower that linearly. Consequently the measure of geodesic rays starting at almost any point is zero.*

Remark. It is not difficult to construct examples of metrics on 2-torus with ergodic geodesic flow in the following way: take a surface of genus $k > 1$ with a negative curvature metric and cut it along a number of nonintersecting closed geodesics to get a torus with several holes with geodesic boundaries. Then it is sufficient to glue these holes with half-sphere caps.

Sketch-proof. Define $f\colon UT(\mathbb{R}^n/\mathbb{Z}^n) \to \mathbb{R}^n$ by the condition

$$f\big(p(x), dp(v)\big) = \exp_x v - x\,, \quad (x,v) \in UT(\mathbb{R}^n)\,,$$

where p is the projection $p\colon \mathbb{R}^n \to \mathbb{R}^n/\mathbb{Z}^n$. Then for any $(x,v) \in UT(\mathbb{R}^n)$,

$$\rho_0(x, \exp_x kv) = |\exp_x kv - x| = \left|\sum_{i=0}^{k-1} f\big(T^i(p(x), dp(v))\big)\right|\,, \quad k \in \mathbb{N}\,,$$

where T^t is the geodesic flow for ρ/Γ. Since T^t is ergodic, we have to check $\int_{UTM} f = 0$ only. Then the statement follows from the ergodic theorem. But for the measure-preserving involution $i\colon (x,v) \mapsto (\exp_x v, -d_v \exp_x v)$ we have

$$f(i(x,v)) = -f(x,v)\,,$$

hence $\int f = \int -f$ and therefore $\int f = 0$. □

I finish the section with the following nonmathematical remark. Let us think of geodesics on periodic metrics as trajectories of particles in crystal. Then one can simply invent from the above approach a "fiction" theory of opaqueness, transparency, channeling *etc.* The author would like to hope that some "actually physical" consideration can be done.

§3. Approximations for metrics

Theorem 1 allows to construct for any periodic metric ρ the norm $\|\cdot\|_\rho$. The question arises: what kind of norms can be obtained this way? It is not difficult $\|\cdot\|_\rho$ with nonsmooth (*i.e.* having angles) unit ball. The author's conjecture is that there is a connection between (possible) nonsmoothness of the norm unit ball at any direction and the quality of rational approximations of this direction coefficients, and this connection is the only obstacle for the representation of any norm as a limit norm for some periodic metric. The only result in this direction proved by F. Nazarov is that for dim $= 2$ the unit ball of $\|\cdot\|_\rho$ is smooth in irrational directions.

However the set of limit norms is dense in the space of all norms:

Theorem 7. *For any norm $\|\cdot\|$ on $\mathbb{R}^n$ there exists a sequence of $\mathbb{Z}^n$-periodic metrics ρ_k such that $\|\cdot\|_{\rho_k} \to \|\cdot\|$ and $\lambda(\rho_k, \rho_0)$ are bounded.*

Sketch-proof. Let $\{v_i^\varepsilon, i = 1, 2, \ldots, N = N(\varepsilon)\}$ be an ε-net on the unit sphere $|v| = 1$ and $v_i^\varepsilon \in \mathbb{Q}^n$. Let $f\colon \mathbb{R} \to [0,1]$ be a smooth function such that $f(x) = 0$ if $|x| \geq 1$ and $f(0) = 1$. Denote also $M = \sup\big(\|x\|/|x|\big)/\inf\big(\|x\|/|x|\big)$. We define $\rho_{\varepsilon,\delta}$ to be $d\rho^2_{\varepsilon,\delta} = \lambda^2_{\varepsilon,\delta} d\rho_0^2$, where $\lambda^2_{\varepsilon,\delta} \equiv 2M$ outside of the union of channels $= (\delta - neighbourhoods\ of\ lines\{tv_i^\varepsilon + z | t \in \mathbb{R}\}, z \in \mathbb{Z}^n, i = 1, \ldots, N)$, and in each such a channel $\lambda^2_{\varepsilon,\delta} = 2M + (\|v_i^\varepsilon\| - 2M) f(\mathrm{dist}(x, \{v_i^\varepsilon t + \mathbb{Z}^n\}))$. Certainly this definition is incorrect in the intersection of these channels, and we improve it anyhow in $\delta-$neighbourhoods of these intersections, retaining only $\mathbb{Z}^n-$invariance and the condition $\lambda \le 2M$. Like in Theorem 3 (if ε is less than for example 0.1 and δ is sufficiently small) any long shortest arc has to go in our channels mainly, and one can check $\|\cdot\|_{\rho_{\varepsilon,\delta}} \to \|\cdot\|_\varepsilon\ as\ \delta \le 0$, where $\|\cdot\|_\varepsilon$ is a polyhedron norm whose unit ball is $\mathrm{conv}\,(\{\pm\|v_i^\varepsilon\| \cdot v_i^\varepsilon, i = 1, 2, \ldots, M\})$. Hence, for sufficiently small $\delta(\varepsilon)$, we have $\|\cdot\|_{\rho_{\varepsilon,\delta(\varepsilon}} \to \|\cdot\|$ as $\varepsilon \to 0$. □

Theorem 8. *For any Finsler metric ρ on a compact manifold there exists a sequence of Riemannian metrics ρ_k with bounded maximal distortions $\lambda(\rho_i, \rho_k)$, converging to ρ (as distance functions).*

Sketch-proof. It is enough to prove the theorem for a region in $\mathbb{R}^n$ and glue then by a partition of unity. Let us cover our region by $u_i = \mathrm{Ball}_\varepsilon x_i$, $i = 1, 2, \ldots, k = k(\varepsilon)$, and denote the length element of the given Finsler metric ρ at x_i as $\|\cdot\|_i$. Approximate $\|\cdot\|_i$ by $\|\cdot\|_{\rho_i}$ where ρ_i is a $\mathbb{Z}^n-$periodic Riemannian metric. Let $\{\lambda_i\}$ be a partition of unity for $\{u_i\}$.

Finsler metrics $\|\cdot\|_\varepsilon = \sum \lambda_i \|\cdot\|_i$ converge to the given one as $\varepsilon \to 0$. Hence, using the estimate (2) of Theorem 1, we obtain that the Riemannian metrics $d\rho_{\varepsilon,N}(x)^2 = \sum \lambda_i(x) d\rho_i^2(Nx)$ do the same as $\varepsilon \to 0$, $N \to \infty$. □

Definition 3. We call *quasiperiodic* a sequence ρ_k of Riemannian metrics in $\Omega \subset \mathbb{R}^n$ such that:

(1) For any k there exists an action $\mathcal{G}_k$ of a subset of $\mathbb{Z}^n$ conjugated with the action of $\varepsilon_k \mathbb{Z}^n$ by translations,, the derivatives of conjugating diffeomorphisms being uniformly bounded.
(2) $\lambda(\rho_i, \rho_j)$ are bounded; $\varepsilon_k \to 0$.
(3) $\lim_{k\to\infty} \sup_{x,y\in\Omega} \inf_{z\in\mathbb{Z}^n} \rho_k(x, \mathcal{G}_k(z)(y)) = 0$.
(4) $\left\|\overline{\rho_k(g(x))} - d_x g(\overline{\rho_k(x)})\right\| \le C\rho_0(x, g(x))\, \forall k \in \mathbb{N} \forall g \in \mathcal{G}_k(\mathbb{Z}^n)$, where $\overline{\rho_k(x)}$ is the metric tensor of ρ_k at x.

Roughly speaking it means that "for large k ρ_k looks like a periodic metric with a very small period locally, and slightly changing from the period to the next one. In some sense this definition gives a discrete analog of Lipschitz family: we may verify the Lipschitz condition for points joined by the action of $\mathcal{G}_k$ only."

Example. Let $p \in \mathbb{R}^n$ be a linear subspace, and ρ be a $\mathbb{Z}^n-$periodic metric. Denote $d\rho_k(x)^2 = d\rho(kx)^2$. Then the restriction of the sequence ρ_k onto p is a quasiperiodic sequence (the limit of which is not $\|\cdot\|_\rho|_p$). In this context the problem of isometric embeddings of Finsler manifolds naturally arises (see [3]).

Theorem 9.

(1) *The set of limits of quasiperiodic sequences of Riemannian metrics in Ω coincides with the set of all Finsler metrics.*
(2) *Any quasiperiodic sequence of Riemannian metrics contains a converging subsequence.*

Sketch-proof. As it is mentioned above, the fact that any Finsler metric is a limit of a quasiperiodic sequence of Riemannian ones can be proved by means of a slight modification of the proof of Theorem 8. Here we prove that any quasiperiodic sequence contains a subsequence converging to a Finsler metric.

Using estimates from Definition 3, we can construct an $\varepsilon\mathbb{Z}^n$–periodic metric ρ_i^k such that $\|\overline{\rho_k(x)} - \overline{\rho_i^k \varphi^{-1}(x)}\| \leq 2C\rho_0(x_i, x)$. Let $\| \cdot \|_i^k = d\varphi_k|_{x_i}^{-1} \left(\| \cdot \|_{\rho_i^k} \right)$.

The space of bounded norms is compact (Blaschke theorem), therefore for some sequence of indices k_j the norms $\| \cdot \|_i^{k_j}$ converge to a norm $\| \cdot \|_i$, the sequence k_j can be made independent of i by choosing the diagonal sequence. Note that $|\| \cdot \|_i - \| \cdot \|_j| \leq 8C\rho_0(x_i, x_j)$ and hence there exists a continuous field of norms $\| \cdot \|_*$ such that $\| \cdot \|_*(x_i) = \| \cdot \|_i$. Using the estimate of Theorem 1, one can check that $\{\rho_{kI}\}$ converges to the Finsler metric $\| \cdot \|_*(x)$. □

REFERENCES

1. Bungert V., *Minimal geodesics*, Ergod. Th. Dynam. Sys. **10** (1989), 263–286.
2. Burago D., *Periodic metrics*, Advances in Soviet math. **9** (1992), New York, 241–248.
3. Burago D., Ivanov S., *Isometric embedding of Finsler manifolds* , Algebra i Analis (to appear).
4. Gromov M., Lafontaine J., Pansu P., *Structures metriques pour les varietés riemanniennes*, In ser."Textes mathématiques", No.1, Paris, 1981.
5. Hedlund G., *Geodesic lines on two-dimensional Riemannian manifolds with periodic coefficients*, Annals of Math **44** (1932), 719–739.

ON THE INCLUSION OF ANALYTIC SYMPLECTIC MAPS IN ANALYTIC HAMILTONIAN FLOWS AND ITS APPLICATIONS

SERGEI KUKSIN, JÜRGEN PÖSCHEL

0. INTRODUCTION

Everybody knows that the time-1-shift of the flow of a hamiltonian vectorfield is a symplectic diffeomorphism homotopic to the identity. Moreover, if the underlying symplectic structure is exact, then this diffeomorphism is exact symplectic. Thus one may ask what the set of all maps arising this way looks like. That is, which exact symplectic diffeomorphisms homotopic to the identity can be included in the flow of a hamiltonian vector field?

Asked in such a global manner, the answer to this question is unknown, and we will not try to tackle it, either. Instead, we restrict ourselves to a local, perturbative situation. Given a small, exact symplectic perturbation of some integrable map, is this map included in the flow of some hamiltonian vector field? This vector field may be autonomous or non-autonomous. In the latter case, however, we ask the time dependence to be of period 1.

Posing the question this way, the answer is essentially "yes". Within the category of *smooth* maps and flows the argument is actually fairly straightforward, using the technique of generating functions. See the note [5] by Raphaël Douady. Within the category of *real analytic* maps and flows, however, the situation is less clear and more involved. Here, the first affirmative answer was given again by Raphaël Douady in his thesis [6] in a more qualitative manner. A more explicit, quantitative construction was recently given by the first author in [12].

Unfortunately, both these references are not easily available, and the argument in [12] is quite cumbersome. In this note we therefore want to describe one more version of this analytic interpolation theorem, which is more quantitative and explicit than the result in [5], yet whose proof is — we think — more straightforward and comprehensible than the one in [12].

There are at least two reasons for being interested in this interpolation problem. First, the problem is interesting in itself. But second, there is a significant number of results in the analytic perturbation theory of symplectic maps and hamiltonian flows, which are parallel and almost identical, yet are proven independently. But while it is easier to think a problem over in terms of maps, it is usually simpler to give a proof in terms of flows. Using interpolation, one can make use of this advantage and avoid redoing lengthy proofs for maps.

We illustrate this point by deriving an exponential stability estimate — also known as Nekhoroshev estimate — for almost integrable exact symplectic maps from the corresponding estimate for flows. The latter are well established, and we refer to the original paper by Nekhoroshev [18], the recent papers [13,19], and the references therein. For maps the corresponding result was conjectured in [18], and some special cases were recently proven in [3] and elsewhere. The proofs, however, are quite technical. By interpolation, they are greatly shortened.

We conclude this introduction by describing the two kinds of integrable maps whose perturbations we are going to study.

In the first case, let $D \subset \mathbb{R}^n$, $n \geq 1$, be a bounded, convex domain, let $\mathbb{T}^n = \mathbb{R}^n/\mathbb{Z}^n$ be the usual n-torus, and let $D \times \mathbb{T}^n$ be the symplectic manifold endowed with the standard exact symplectic structure $\upsilon = d\alpha$, where $\alpha = \sum_j I_j d\phi_j$. Suppose the map

$$F_0\colon\ D \times \mathbb{T}^n \to D \times \mathbb{T}^n, \quad (I, \phi) \mapsto (I, \phi + \omega(I))$$

is real analytic and symplectic. Then $0 = \sum_j d\omega_j(I) \wedge dI_j = d\left(\sum_j \omega_j dI_j\right)$, so by convexity there exists a real analytic function h on D such that

$$\omega(I) = \frac{\partial h}{\partial I}.$$

The function h defines an integrable hamiltonian system on $D \times \mathbb{T}^n$ with equations of motions $\dot{I} = 0$, $\dot{\phi} = \partial_I h = \omega(I)$. Hence its flow X_h^t interpolates F_0. That is, we have

$$X_h^1 = X_h^t\big|_{t=1} = F_0$$

on $D \times \mathbb{T}^n$.

In the second case, let $\mathbb{R}^{2n} = \mathbb{R}^n \times \mathbb{R}^n$ be the euclidean $2n$-space with coordinates $z = (x, y)$ endowed with the standard exact symplectic structure

$$\upsilon = \sum\nolimits_j dx_j \wedge dy_j = \langle J\,\cdot\,,\,\cdot\rangle, \qquad J = \begin{pmatrix} 0 & I \\ -I & 0 \end{pmatrix},$$

where $\langle\,\cdot\,,\,\cdot\,\rangle$ denotes the usual scalar product and I the n-dimensional identity matrix. Suppose the linear map

$$F_*\colon\ \mathbb{R}^{2n} \to \mathbb{R}^{2n}, \quad z \mapsto \Lambda z$$

is symplectic. It is a standard fact, recalled in Appendix B, that one can write $\Lambda = \exp(JA)$ with a real symmetric matrix A, provided that either the spectrum of Λ contains no zero or negative eigenvalues, or Λ is the square of another symplectic matrix. The hamiltonian $h = \frac{1}{2}\langle Az, z\rangle$ with equations of motions $\dot{z} = JAz$ then gives rise to a flow X_h^t on $\mathbb{R}^{2n}$ such that

$$X_h^t\big|_{t=1} = \exp(JA) = F_*$$

as required.

In both these cases the interpolating hamiltonian is autonomous. This, however, is *not typical*, and in general one has to allow for *time-dependent* hamiltonians. Consider, for example, a real analytic, exact symplectic perturbation F of a one degree of freedom annulus map $F_0\colon (I,\phi) \mapsto (I, \phi + \omega(I))$. If the interpolating hamiltonian were autonomous, then it would be *integrable*, and so F would be integrable, too. But generically, arbitrarily small perturbations of F_0 give rise to transversal homoclinic intersections, thus destroying integrability [10,23]. So generically, the interpolating hamiltonian has to be time-dependent. — It is an open problem how to characterize all those maps which arise from *autonomous* hamiltonian flows.

1. Statement of the Interpolation Theorems

Again, let $D \subset \mathbb{R}^n$ be bounded and convex. We consider a real analytic *family* of real analytic maps

$$F_\epsilon\colon\ D \times \mathbb{T}^n \to \mathbb{R}^n \times \mathbb{T}^n, \qquad -\epsilon_0 < \epsilon < \epsilon_0,$$

perturbing an integrable map $F_0\colon (I,\phi) \mapsto (I, \phi + \omega(I))$, where $\omega(I) = \partial h/\partial I$ with some real analytic function h on D. Moreover, the F_ϵ are assumed to be *exact symplectic*: there exists a family of differentiable functions W_ϵ on $D \times \mathbb{T}^n$ such that, for $\alpha = \sum_j I_j d\phi_j$,

$$F_\epsilon^*\alpha - \alpha = dW_\epsilon, \qquad -\epsilon_0 < \epsilon < \epsilon_0.$$

The domains of analyticity are assumed to be *uniform* and *independent* of ϵ. That is, each F_ϵ is assumed to be real analytic on a fixed complex neighbourhood $V_r D \times V_r \mathbb{T}^n$ of $D \times \mathbb{T}^n$, where

$$V_r D = \bigcup_{I_0 \in D} \{ I \in \mathbb{C}^n : |I - I_0| < r \} \subset \mathbb{C}^n,$$

$|\cdot|$ the euclidean norm, and likewise $V_r\mathbb{T}^n$. The same domain of analyticity is assumed for h. Possibly decreasing r and ϵ_0 we then also have a uniform bound for the sup-norms $|F_\epsilon|_{V_r D \times V_r \mathbb{T}^n}$ for all ϵ. Moreover,

$$|F_\epsilon - F_0|_{V_r D \times V_r \mathbb{T}^n} = O(\epsilon)$$

by Cauchy's estimate.

Theorem 1. *Suppose F_ϵ satisfies the preceding assumptions. Then for all sufficiently small ϵ there exists a real analytic, 1-periodic time dependent hamiltonian H_ϵ on $D \times \mathbb{T}^{n+1}$, such that*

$$X^t_{H_\epsilon}\Big|_{t=1} = F_\epsilon$$

on $D \times \mathbb{T}^n$. Moreover, there exists a $\rho > 0$ such that H_ϵ is real analytic in $V_\rho D \times V_\rho \mathbb{T}^{n+1}$ for all small ϵ and satisfies

$$|H_\epsilon - h|_{V_\rho D \times V_\rho \mathbb{T}^{n+1}} = O(\epsilon).$$

as $\epsilon \to 0$.

In general, the flow $X^t_{H_\epsilon}$ of H_ϵ does *not* stay in $D \times \mathbb{T}^n$. But its time-1-map is still well defined for all small ϵ, since H_ϵ extends to a uniform neighbourhood of $D \times \mathbb{T}^n$ (that is, a δ-neighbourhood with respect to some norm).

For symplectic maps near fixed points the corresponding result is simpler to state. Let

$$F\colon\ U \to \mathbb{R}^{2n}, \quad z \mapsto \Lambda z + \hat{F}(z), \qquad \hat{F}(z) = O(z^2)$$

be a real analytic, symplectic map in some neighbourhood U of the origin in $\mathbb{R}^{2n}$.

Theorem 2. *Suppose that $\Lambda = \exp(JA)$ with some real symmetric matrix A. Then there exists a 1-periodic time-dependent hamiltonian*

$$H = \frac{1}{2}\langle Az, z\rangle + \hat{H}(z,t), \qquad \hat{H}(z,t) = O(z^3),$$

which is jointly real analytic in some neighbourhood of the origin in $\mathbb{R}^{2n}$ and in t, such that

$$X^t_H\Big|_{t=1} = F$$

on that neighbourhood.

The proof of Theorem 2 is a variation of the proof of Theorem 1. In the following we therefore focus attention on the latter and add a few remarks on the former.

It would be natural to construct the interpolating time-dependent hamiltonian H_ϵ directly on the phase space $P = D \times \mathbb{T}^{n+1}$, for example by some kind of implicit function theorem. However, we are *not* able to do this. Instead, we first construct another family of real analytic hamiltonians $\bar{H}_\epsilon$ on the *extended phase space*

$$\bar{P} = \bar{D} \times \mathbb{T}^{n+1}, \quad \bar{D} = D \times \mathbb{R},$$

together with a family of symplectic section surfaces Σ_ϵ in the energy levels $\bar{H}_\epsilon = 0$ such that the induced Poincaré map Φ_ϵ of the hamiltonian flow is well defined and conjugate to F_ϵ, for all small ϵ. Then H_ϵ is found by the standard procedure of reducing $\bar{H}_\epsilon$ to its zero energy level [1,§45.B].

To set the stage let us first consider the unperturbed, integrable case. If the coordinates in $\bar{P}$ are denoted by I, E, ϕ, θ, then one naturally chooses the hamiltonian $\bar{H}_0 = h(I) + E$ with flow

$$X^t_{\bar{H}_0}\colon\ \bar{P} \to \bar{P}, \quad (I, E, \phi, \theta) \mapsto (I, E, \phi + t\omega(I), \theta + t).$$

Its Poincaré map Φ_0 with respect to the surface $\{\theta = 0\}$ is well defined and coincides with its time-1-shift: $\Phi_0 = X^1_{\bar{H}_0}$. Its further restriction to the symplectic, isoenergetic surface

$$\Sigma_0 = \left\{ \bar{H}_0 = 0,\ \theta = 0 \right\} \subset \bar{P}$$

is conjugate to F_0 in the sense that $\Phi_0 \circ j_0 = j_0 \circ F_0$, where j_0 is the canonical real analytic, symplectic embedding of P into $\bar{P}$, which is the identity in I and ϕ:

$$j_0\colon\ P \hookrightarrow \Sigma_0, \quad (I, \phi) \mapsto (I, -h(I), \phi, 0).$$

The isoenergetic reduction of $\bar{H}_0$ to $\{\bar{H}_0 = 0\}$ then yields $H_0 = h$.

To state the corresponding result for the family F_ϵ the following notation turns out to be convenient. We write

$$T_\epsilon\colon\ X \underset{\epsilon}{\longrightarrow} Y$$

for a family of real analytic maps T_ϵ from a bounded domain X in some euclidean space into another euclidean space containing Y, if first the T_ϵ have a — necessarily unique — analytic extension to a uniform neighbourhood of X for all small ϵ, and second, if for every $a > 0$ there exists a $b > 0$ such that

$$T_\epsilon\colon\ U_{a\epsilon} X \to U_{b\epsilon} Y \quad \text{and} \quad T_\epsilon\colon\ U_{-b\epsilon} X \to U_{-a\epsilon} Y$$

for all sufficiently small ϵ, depending on a. Here, $U_\rho X = V_\rho X \cap \mathbb{R}^m$ and $U_{-\rho} X = \mathbb{R}^m \backslash U_\rho(\mathbb{R}^m \backslash X)$ for $X \subset \mathbb{R}^m$.

For example,

$$F_\epsilon\colon P \underset{\epsilon}{\longrightarrow} P, \qquad F_\epsilon^{-1}\colon P \underset{\epsilon}{\longrightarrow} P,$$

since $F_\epsilon - F_0 = O(\epsilon)$. The composition of two families of such "ϵ-maps" is again a family of "ϵ-maps".

Theorem 3. *Suppose the assumptions of Theorem 1 hold. Then for all sufficiently small ϵ there exists a real analytic hamiltonian $\bar{H}_\epsilon$ on the extended phase space $\bar{P} = \bar{D} \times \mathbb{T}^{n+1}$ and a real analytic, symplectic embedding*

$$j_\epsilon\colon\ P \underset{\epsilon}{\longrightarrow} \Sigma_\epsilon = \left\{ \bar{H}_\epsilon = 0,\ \theta = 0 \right\} \subset \bar{P},$$

such that the Poincaré map Φ_ϵ of $\bar{H}_\epsilon$ is well defined for the embedded manifold Σ_ϵ and satisfies

$$\Phi_\epsilon \circ j_\epsilon = j_\epsilon \circ F_\epsilon.$$

Moreover, there exists a $\rho > 0$ such that $\bar{H}_\epsilon$ and j_ϵ extend analytically to $V_\rho \bar{P}$ and $V_\rho P$, respectively, for all sufficiently small ϵ, and satisfy

$$\left|\bar{H}_\epsilon - \bar{H}_0\right|_{V_\rho \bar{P}}, \ |j_\epsilon - j_0|_{V_\rho P} = O(\epsilon)$$

as $\epsilon \to 0$.

Theorem 1 follows from Theorem 3 by isoenergetic reduction [1]. By the estimates we have

$$\frac{\partial \bar{H}_\epsilon}{\partial E} = 1 + O(\epsilon)$$

uniformly on $V_{\rho/2}\bar{P}$. Hence the equation $\bar{H}_\epsilon = 0$ can be solved for E everywhere by

$$E = -H_\epsilon(I, \phi, \theta), \qquad \text{or} \qquad H_\epsilon(I, \phi, \theta) + E = 0,$$

where H_ϵ is real analytic in some smaller fixed neighbourhood of $D \times \mathbb{T}^{n+1}$ for all small ϵ, with $|H_\epsilon - h| = O(\epsilon)$. Moreover, we may introduce the angle θ as time instead of t, since $d\theta/dt = \partial \bar{H}_\epsilon/\partial E = 1 + O(\epsilon)$. On the hypersurface $\bar{H}_\epsilon = 0$ one then finds

$$\frac{\partial I}{\partial \theta} = -\frac{\partial H_\epsilon}{\partial \phi}, \quad \frac{\partial \phi}{\partial \theta} = \frac{\partial H_\epsilon}{\partial I}.$$

This proves Theorem 1.

Conversely, Theorem 3 obviously follows from Theorem 1, so the two are equivalent.

Theorem 3 is a slimmed down version of another, more quantitative interpolation theorem mentioned in the introduction. To state this result, assume that

$$|h|, |Dh|, \left|D^2 h\right| \le K$$

uniformly on $V_r D$ with respect to some fixed norms for vectors and matrices.

Theorem 4. *Suppose the map $F\colon P \to \mathbb{R}^n \times \mathbb{T}^n$ is real analytic in $V_r P$ and exact symplectic. If*

$$|F - F_0|_{V_r P} = \epsilon < \epsilon_0(K, n, r),$$

then there exists a real analytic hamiltonian $\bar{H}$ on $\bar{P}$ with a regular energy surface $\{\bar{H} = 0\}$ and a real analytic, symplectic embedding

$$j\colon\ P \hookrightarrow \Sigma = \left\{ \bar{H} = 0,\ \theta = 0 \right\},$$

such that the Poincaré map Φ of $\bar{H}$ is well defined on the embedded surface and satisfies $\Phi \circ j = j \circ F$. Moreover, $\bar{H}$ and j are real analytic on $V_\rho \bar{P}$ and $V_\rho P$, respectively, and satisfy

$$\left|\bar{H} - \bar{H}_0\right|_{V_\rho \bar{P}}, \quad |j - j_0|_{V_\rho P} \leq c\epsilon,$$

where ρ and c only depend on K, n, r. In particular, $\rho = \dfrac{r}{(1+3K)^2}$.

Theorem 4 is proven in [12]. It sharpens the original result by Douady [6] in two important respects. First, the "smoothness of the interpolating hamiltonian is under control" — that is, there is an explicit control of the radius of analyticity ρ in terms of r and K. Second, $H - H_0$ and $j - j_0$ are shown to be of the order of $F - F_0$, and not just to converge to zero as $F - F_0$ converges to zero. These improvements are essential for more quantitative applications such as Nekhoroshev estimates.

Theorem 3 is simpler to prove than Theorem 4 as the map F is included in a real analytic family F_ϵ of maps. Thus we are able to state the result "for all sufficiently small ϵ" without making the smallness condition explicit. The proof itself is based on the Grauert embedding theorem and mostly follows the rather natural scheme proposed by Douady [6].

2. Applications

1. Nekhoroshev Estimates. As a first application of the preceding results we derive an exponential stability estimate for symplectic maps from corresponding estimates for hamiltonian flows, which are also known as Nekhoroshev estimates.

Again, let $D \subset \mathbb{R}^n$ be bounded and convex, and consider a family

$$F_\epsilon \colon\ D \times \mathbb{T}^n \to \mathbb{R}^n \times \mathbb{T}^n, \qquad -\epsilon_0 < \epsilon < \epsilon_0,$$

of real analytic, exact symplectic maps as in Theorem 1. In particular, F_ϵ is a perturbation of an integrable map

$$F_0 \colon\ D \times \mathbb{T}^n \to D \times \mathbb{T}^n, \quad (I, \phi) \mapsto (I, \phi + \omega(I)),$$

where $\omega(I) = \partial h / \partial I$ with some real analytic function h on D.

We call F_0 *m-steep on D*, if its extended hamiltonian

$$\bar{h} = h(I) + E$$

is steep on $\bar{D} = D \times \mathbb{R}$ as defined in [18] or [14]. We do not repeat this definition here, however, as it is quite technical and not very illuminating. Moreover, an elegant, sufficient characterization of steepness may be found in [11].

We just observe the following. The map F_0 is in particular m-steep on D, if h is strictly *convex* on D, because then $\bar{h}$ is quasi-convex on $\bar{D}$. Moreover, steepness is a generic property in the following sense. The set of all non-steep functions h is given by infinitely many polynomial relations in the Taylor coefficients of H at any given point in D. The set of non-steep functions thus has infinite codimension [18].

With every initial position (I_0, ϕ_0) in $D \times \mathbb{T}^n$ we associate its — possibly finite — orbit

$$(I_n, \phi_n) = F_\epsilon^n(I_0, \phi_0),$$

which is defined as long as its iterates (I_n, ϕ_n) are again in $D \times \mathbb{T}^n$ for positive or negative n. For simplicity, we do not indicate its dependence on ϵ. For $\epsilon = 0$, we have $I_n = I_0$ for all integers n on every orbit. For $\epsilon \neq 0$ the result is the following.

Theorem 5. *Suppose F_ϵ satisfies the assumptions of Theorem 1. If F_0 is m-steep on D, then for all sufficiently small ϵ one has*

$$|I_n - I_0| \leq c_1 \epsilon^b \quad \text{for} \quad |n| \leq c_2 \exp\left(c_3 \epsilon^{-a}\right)$$

for every initial position (I_0, ϕ_0) in $D \times \mathbb{T}^n$, where the positive constants a and b depend on h and n, while the constants c_1, c_2, c_3 depend on h, n and the analyticity properties of F_ϵ. In particular, one has

$$a = \frac{1}{2n+2} = b,$$

if h is strictly convex.

Proof. Interpolating F_ϵ with the help of Theorem 3 we obtain a family $\bar{H}_\epsilon$ of real analytic perturbations of $\bar{H}_0 = h + E$. The latter is steep by assumption, and in particular quasi-convex, if h is strictly convex. So the estimates of [18, 13,19] apply, giving the exponential stability of the flow of $\bar{H}_\epsilon$:

$$|I(t) - I(0)| \leq c_1 \epsilon^b \quad \text{for} \quad |t| \leq c_2 \exp\left(c_3 \epsilon^{-a}\right)$$

for every initial position in $\bar{D} \times \mathbb{T}^{n+1}$. This implies the corresponding estimate for F_ϵ with a different c_1, since the embedding j_ϵ is ϵ-close to j_0. □

Instead of considering a family F_ϵ we may also consider a single real analytic, exact symplectic map F, requiring that $|F - F_0|_{V_r P}$ is sufficiently small for some $r > 0$. In this case we have to appeal to Theorem 4 instead of Theorem 3 in the proof below.

Theorem 5*. *Suppose F_0 is m-steep on D, and F satisfies the conditions of Theorem 4. If $|F - F_0|_{V_r P} = \epsilon \leq \epsilon_0(h, n, r)$, then one has*

$$|I_n - I_0| \leq c_1 \epsilon^b \quad \text{for} \quad |n| \leq c_2 \exp\left(c_3 \epsilon^{-a}\right)$$

for every initial position (I_0, ϕ_0) in $D \times \mathbb{T}^n$, where the positive constants a and b depend on h and n, while c_1, c_2, c_3 depend on h, n, r. In particular, $a = 1/(2n+2) = b$, if h is strictly convex.

This result was conjectured by Nekhoroshev, and stated as a theorem in [18], but no proof was given yet.

2. KAM-Theorems. For the same family F_ϵ of symplectic maps we may also derive, by interpolation, the well known classical KAM theorem about the persistence of invariant tori from the corresponding result for flows. In the analytic category this was first done by Douady [5] – indeed, this was the very motivation for his interpolation theorem. To this end we assume that the unperturbed integrable map F_0 is *nondegenerate on* D in the sense that

$$\det \frac{\partial^2 h}{\partial I^2} = \det \frac{\partial \omega}{\partial I} \neq 0$$

on D. This condition is also known as the twist condition.

Theorem 6. *Suppose F_ϵ satisfies the assumptions of Theorem 1. If F_0 is nondegenerate on D, then for all sufficiently small ϵ the map F_ϵ possesses a Cantor family of real analytic invariant n-tori on which the mapping is conjugate to a rigid translation $\varphi \mapsto \varphi + \omega$. Moreover, the measure of its complement in $D \times \mathbb{T}^n$ is of the order of $\sqrt{\epsilon}$, provided the boundary of D is piecewise smooth.*

Sketch of Proof. Again we interpolate F_ϵ by Theorem 3 with a family $\bar{H}_\epsilon$ of real analytic hamiltonians perturbing $\bar{H}_0 = h + E$. The latter is *isoenergetically nondegenerate* on $\bar{D}$, since

$$\det \begin{pmatrix} \partial^2 \bar{H}_0 & \partial \bar{H}_0 \\ \partial \bar{H}_0^T & 0 \end{pmatrix} = \det \begin{pmatrix} \partial^2 h & 0 & \partial h \\ 0 & 0 & 1 \\ \partial h^T & 1 & 0 \end{pmatrix} = -\det \partial^2 h \neq 0$$

on $\bar{D}$. Hence the isoenergetic KAM theorem [1,2] applies, and for sufficiently small ϵ the level set $\{\bar{H}_\epsilon = 0\}$ is filled, up to a set of measure $O(\sqrt{\epsilon})$, by an n-dimensional Cantor family of real analytic invariant $n+1$-tori, which is a $O(\sqrt{\epsilon})$-deformation of some trivial Cantor subfamily of invariant $n+1$-tori for $\bar{H}_0$. Moreover, on this family of tori there are real analytic coordinates $\bar{\varphi}$, depending smoothly on the torus, so that the flow is given by $\bar{\varphi} \mapsto \bar{\varphi} + \bar{\omega} t$ for some $\bar{\omega}$ parametrizing the tori.

In these coordinates, $\bar{\varphi}_{n+1} = 0$ defines a transversal family of n-tori, which fills a $2n$-dimensional section up to measure $O(\sqrt{\epsilon})$, and on which the induced flow map is a rigid translation. In the coordinates of the phase space of $\bar{H}_\epsilon$, this in turn defines a section S_ϵ which is $O(\sqrt{\epsilon})$-close to the section $\Sigma_\epsilon = \{\bar{H}_\epsilon = 0, \theta = 0\}$ considered in Theorem 3. Arguing as in section 4.3 below the map F_ϵ is also conjugated to the flow map on S_ϵ as well, and the conclusion of Theorem 6 follows. □

Along the same lines we may also obtain another type of KAM theorem for maps concerned with the preservation of *lower dimensional* tori. For hamiltonian flows such a theory was established recently — see [9,20] and the references therein — but for symplectic maps it seems to be new. For a reversible analogue see [21]

We briefly indicate the result. We consider a real analytic family F_ϵ of exactly symplectic maps perturbing the integrable map

$$F_0\colon\ D \times \mathbb{T}^n \times \mathbb{R}^{2m} \to D \times \mathbb{T}^n \times \mathbb{R}^{2m}$$
$$(I, \phi, z) \mapsto \big(I, \phi + \omega(I), \Lambda(I) z\big),$$

where $n, m \geq 1$, $\omega(I) = \partial h / \partial I$ with some real analytic function h, and $\Lambda(I)$ is diagonal with eigenvalues

$$\lambda_1(I), \ldots, \lambda_m(I), \lambda_1(I)^{-1}, \ldots, \lambda_m(I)^{-1}.$$

This map admits an n-parameter family $\mathbb{T}^n \times \{I\} \times \{0\}$ of invariant n-tori filling completely a $2n$-dimensional submanifold of the $2n + 2m$-dimensional phase space. The objective is to prove the persistence of a large subfamily of it for small $\epsilon \neq 0$.

To this end the following *nondegeneracy conditions* are imposed. First, $\det \partial^2 h / \partial I^2$ does not vanish identically on D. Second, also none of the functions

$$e^{ik\cdot\omega} - \lambda_j, \quad e^{ik\cdot\omega} - \frac{\lambda_j}{\lambda_l}, \quad e^{ik\cdot\omega} - \lambda_j \lambda_l$$

vanishes identically on D for all $k \in \mathbb{Z}^n$ and $1 \leq j, l \leq m$. — So in particular, no eigenvalue is identically equal to 1 or -1, and no two eigenvalues are identically equal. Note that the second condition is automatically satisfied for all large k, so it is in fact a *finite* condition.

Theorem 7. *Suppose F_0 satisfies the preceding assumptions, and F_ϵ is jointly real analytic in a uniform complex neighbourhood of $\mathbb{T}^n \times D \times \{0\}$ and $-\epsilon_0 < \epsilon < \epsilon_0$. Then for all sufficiently small ϵ there exists an n-parameter Cantor family of real analytic invariant n-tori filling some $2n$-dimensional submanifold in phase space up to a subset whose measure tends to zero with ϵ. Moreover, on each torus the map is conjugate to a rigid translation, and around it the variational equations (with discrete time) can be put into constant coefficient form.*

The proof consists in interpolating the map F_ϵ by combining the ideas of Theorems 1 and 2 and applying a slightly modified version of the KAM theorem on lower dimensional tori in [20]. We forego the technical details. We just point out that the measure of the complementary set can not be made more explicit because of the non-quantitative nature of the nondegeneracy conditions.

3. Another Application. As another possible application of the interpolation theorems we mention the problem of establishing the exponentially small splitting of separatrices in nearly integrable maps. For the standard map, for instance, one rather laborious approach was proposed by Lazutkin in 1984 – see [15]. However, the recent work of Gelfreich in St. Petersburg and Delshams and Seara in Barcelona made it clear that this approach is much simpler in the framework of vector fields. It is conceivable that by interpolation the splitting problem for the standard map is more easily solved to hamiltonian flows, although more work is still required.

3. Proof of Theorem 3

The proof proceeds in four steps. First, an abstract real analytic manifold is constructed, on which the interpolation problem is trivially solved. Second, this manifold is embedded into a manifold with action angle coordinates, but with a nonstandard symplectic structure. In the third step, this structure is put back into constant standard form by the Moser-Weinstein Theorem. Finally, the surface of section defining the Poincaré map is straightened out.

Step 1. Abstract Suspension Manifold. We introduce the space

$$A = D \times \mathbb{T}^n \times \mathbb{R} \times \Theta,$$

where $\Theta = (\theta_0, \theta_1)$ is some interval of length $\theta_1 - \theta_0 < 2$ containing $[0,1]$. The A-coordinates are denoted by $\tilde{I}, \tilde{\phi}, \tilde{E}, \tilde{\theta}$ to distinguish them from the usual action angle coordinates later on. We identify points in A through the map

$$T_\epsilon\colon\ (\tilde{I}, \tilde{\phi}, \tilde{E}, \tilde{\theta}) \mapsto (F_\epsilon(\tilde{I}, \tilde{\phi}), \tilde{E}, \tilde{\theta} - 1).$$

In particular, $T_0\colon (\tilde{I}, \tilde{\phi}, \tilde{E}, \tilde{\theta}) \mapsto (\tilde{I}, \tilde{\phi} + \omega(\tilde{I}), \tilde{E}, \tilde{\theta} - 1)$. We then have

$$T_\epsilon\colon\ A_+ \underset{\epsilon}{\longrightarrow} A_- \quad \text{and} \quad T_\epsilon^{-1}\colon\ A_- \underset{\epsilon}{\longrightarrow} A_+$$

for the subdomains $A_- = \{\tilde{\theta}_0 < \tilde{\theta} < \theta_1 - 1\}$ and $A_+ = \{\tilde{\theta}_0 + 1 < \tilde{\theta} < \tilde{\theta}_1\}$ of A by the analogous properties of the map F_ϵ. Note that A_- and A_+ are *disjoint*, since $\theta_1 - \theta_0 < 2$.

The map T_ϵ is real analytic and preserves the symplectic structure

$$\tilde{\upsilon} = \sum\nolimits_j d\tilde{I}_j \wedge d\tilde{\phi}_j + d\tilde{E} \wedge d\tilde{\theta},$$

since F_ϵ is symplectic. Hence, the quotient space

$$B_\epsilon = A / T_\epsilon$$

is a real analytic manifold with a real analytic symplectic structure $\tilde{\upsilon}_\epsilon$. The hamiltonian $\tilde{H} = \tilde{E}$ is real analytic and well defined on B_ϵ, since it is T_ϵ-invariant, too. Its flow $X^t_{\tilde{H}}$ is simply a shift of the $\tilde{\theta}$-variable, and starting at $\tilde{\theta} = 0$ we find that

$$X^1_{\tilde{H}}(\tilde{I}, \tilde{\phi}, \tilde{E}, 0) = (\tilde{I}, \tilde{\phi}, \tilde{E}, 1) \cong (F_\epsilon(\tilde{I}, \tilde{\phi}), \tilde{E}, 0).$$

Thus, $X^1_{\tilde{H}} \circ \tilde{\imath} = \tilde{\imath} \circ F_\epsilon$ on P, where $\tilde{\imath}$ denotes the canonical symplectic embedding of P into the isoenergetic surface of section

$$\tilde{S} = \{\, \tilde{H} = 0,\ \tilde{\theta} = 0 \,\} \subset \bar{P}.$$

That is, $\tilde{\imath}$ is the identity on corresponding I- and ϕ-coordinates. Obviously, $\tilde{H}$ and $\tilde{\imath}$ extend to uniform complex neighbourhoods of B_ϵ and P, respectively, for all sufficiently small ϵ. — This is the "abstract solution" of the interpolation problem.

Step 2. Embedding of B_ϵ. We now seek a real analytic embedding of B_ϵ into the symplectic space $\bar{P} = \bar{D} \times \mathbb{T}^{n+1}$, where $\bar{D} = D \times \mathbb{R}$. The $\bar{P}$-coordinates are the usual action angle coordinates I, E, ϕ, θ.

For $\epsilon = 0$ this embedding is given as the inverse of the map

$$\Gamma_0\colon \begin{cases} \tilde{I} = I \\ \tilde{E} = h(I) + E \\ \tilde{\phi} = \phi - \theta\omega(I) \\ \tilde{\theta} = \theta \end{cases} .$$

One checks that $T_0 \circ \Gamma_0 = \Gamma_0 \circ \sigma_\theta$, where $\sigma_\theta\colon \theta \mapsto \theta - 1$. So equivalent points are mapped into equivalent points, whence $\Gamma_0\colon\ \bar{P} \to B_0$. Obviously,

$$\begin{aligned} \bar{H}_0 &= \tilde{H} \circ \Gamma_0 = h(I) + E, \\ S_0 &= \Gamma_0^{-1}(\tilde{S}) = \{\, h(I) + E = 0,\ \theta = 0 \,\}, \end{aligned}$$

and one easily calculates that

$$\upsilon_0 = \Gamma_0^* \tilde{\upsilon}_0 = \sum\nolimits_j dI_j \wedge d\phi_j + dE \wedge d\theta,$$

as it ought to be. — For $\epsilon \neq 0$ the key is the following result.

Proposition 1. *For all sufficiently small ϵ there exists a map*

$$G_\epsilon\colon\ B_\epsilon \underset{\epsilon}{\longrightarrow} B_0,$$

which is jointly real analytic in the A-coordinates and ϵ in a fixed complex neighbourhood of $A \times \{0\}$ and reduces to the identity for $\epsilon = 0$. That is to say, there is a lift

$$\tilde{G}_\epsilon\colon\ A \underset{\epsilon}{\longrightarrow} A,$$

satisfying $\tilde{G}_\epsilon \circ T_\epsilon = T_0 \circ \tilde{G}_\epsilon$, having these analyticity properties and reducing to the identity for $\epsilon = 0$. Moreover, G_ϵ is the identity on the E-coordinate, and also $G_\epsilon^{-1}\colon B_0 \underset{\epsilon}{\longrightarrow} B_\epsilon$.

We then define

$$\Gamma_\epsilon = G_\epsilon^{-1} \circ \Gamma_0\colon\ \bar{P} \underset{\epsilon}{\longrightarrow} B_\epsilon.$$

We have $|\Gamma_\epsilon - \Gamma_0| = O(\epsilon)$, and similarly for their derivatives, which is again an abbreviation of the analogous statements for the lifted maps. Hence, for the transformed symplectic structure we find

$$\upsilon_\epsilon = \Gamma_\epsilon^* \tilde{\upsilon}_\epsilon = \Gamma_0^* \tilde{\upsilon}_0 + O(\epsilon) = \upsilon_0 + O(\epsilon)\,.$$

All these estimates hold on some fixed complex neighbourhood of the real domains considered, uniformly for all small ϵ.

Proof of Proposition 1. In the following construction we may ignore the coordinate E, since it does not interfere with any other coordinate through T_ϵ and may thus be mapped identically.

Consider the real analytic manifold $\mathcal{A} = A \times \Delta$ with coordinates (X, δ), where $\Delta = (-\delta_0, \delta_0)$ denotes some small interval, and identify points via the map

$$\mathcal{T}\colon \begin{pmatrix} X \\ \delta \end{pmatrix} \mapsto \begin{pmatrix} T_\delta(X) \\ \delta \end{pmatrix}.$$

For Δ sufficiently small, $\mathcal{T}$ and $\mathcal{T}^{-1}$ are well defined and real analytic on the domains $A_+ \times \Delta$ and $A_- \times \Delta$, respectively, with analytic extensions to some uniform neighbourhoods of them. The quotient manifold $\mathcal{B} = \mathcal{A}/\mathcal{T}$ is thus real analytic, too, with a real analytic extension to $\mathcal{B}^o = \mathcal{A}^o/\mathcal{T}$, where $\mathcal{A}^o$ denotes some uniform neighbourhood of $\mathcal{A}$. Hence, by the Grauert embedding theorem [17], there exists a real analytic embedding

$$\mathcal{G}\colon \ \mathcal{B}^o \hookrightarrow \mathbb{R}^N$$

of this extended manifold into euclidean N-space, where N is a sufficiently large integer.

Consider now the submanifolds $\mathcal{B}^o_\epsilon = \{ (X,\delta) \in \mathcal{B}^o : \delta = \epsilon \}$ and their real analytic embeddings

$$\mathcal{G}_\epsilon = \mathcal{G}|_{\mathcal{B}^o_\epsilon}\colon \ \mathcal{B}^o_\epsilon \hookrightarrow \mathcal{M}^o_\epsilon \subset \mathbb{R}^N.$$

Let $\mathcal{B}_\epsilon = \mathcal{B}^o_\epsilon \cap \mathcal{B} \simeq B_\epsilon$, and let $\mathcal{M}_\epsilon \subset \mathcal{M}^o_\epsilon$ be the image of $\mathcal{B}_\epsilon \subset \mathcal{B}^o_\epsilon$. Around $\mathcal{M}^o_0$ we fix a tubular neighbourhood $\mathcal{U}$ and a real analytic normal projection $\mathcal{P}$ of $\mathcal{U}$ onto $\mathcal{M}^o_0$. Letting $\mathcal{P}_\epsilon = \mathcal{P}|_{\mathcal{M}_\epsilon}$, we have

$$\mathcal{P}_\epsilon\colon \ \mathcal{M}_\epsilon \underset{\epsilon}{\longrightarrow} \mathcal{M}_0, \qquad \mathcal{P}_\epsilon^{-1}\colon \ \mathcal{M}_0 \underset{\epsilon}{\longrightarrow} \mathcal{M}_\epsilon$$

for all sufficiently small ϵ, since $\mathcal{M}_\epsilon$ depends analytically on ϵ and reduces to $\mathcal{M}_0$ for $\epsilon = 0$. Thus we can define a mapping

$$G_\epsilon = \mathcal{G}_0^{-1} \circ \mathcal{P}_\epsilon \circ \mathcal{G}_\epsilon$$

from $\mathcal{B}_\epsilon \simeq B_\epsilon$ into $\mathcal{B}^o_0$ which reduces to the identity for $\epsilon = 0$.

This map can be lifted to a map $\tilde{G}_\epsilon$ of some uniform neighbourhood of A into some neighbourhood of A as follows. The middle portion of A, the domain $\{\theta_1 - 1 < \tilde{\theta} < \theta_0 + 1\}$, is projected *one-to-one* onto B_ϵ, and G_ϵ is close to the identity. So there is a *uniquely* defined lift on this part for all small ϵ, which is ϵ-close to the identity. Extending this lift continuously in the usual manner, it remains uniformly ϵ-close to the identity. Therefore, for all sufficiently small ϵ, it extends to a map $\tilde{G}_\epsilon$ from some small uniform neighbourhood of A into the uniform neighbourhood defining $\mathcal{A}^o$. Moreover, $\tilde{G}_\epsilon\colon \ A \underset{\epsilon}{\longrightarrow} A$.

The relation $\tilde{G}_\epsilon \circ T_\epsilon = T_0 \circ \tilde{G}_\epsilon$ is obvious for a lifting, and the claim about G_ϵ^{-1} also follows immediately. □

Step 3. Standard Symplectic Structure. We now put the symplectic structure υ_ϵ on $\bar{P}$ into standard form, using the Moser-Weinstein theorem [16]. To this end we need to know that υ_ϵ is *exact*.

Proposition 2. *For all sufficiently small ϵ there exists a 1-form α_ϵ on $\bar{P}$ such that $d\alpha_\epsilon = \upsilon_\epsilon$. Moreover, α_ϵ can be chosen to be real analytic jointly in the $\bar{P}$-coordinates and ϵ.*

Proof. We first observe that υ_ϵ is *smoothly* exact, since F_ϵ is exact symplectic. That is, for all small ϵ there exists a 1-form β_ϵ with *smooth* coefficients, such that $\upsilon_\epsilon = d\beta_\epsilon$. The proof is fairly easy and given in Appendix A.

By the abstract de Rham theorem [22] the existence of a smooth solution β_ϵ implies the existence of a real analytic solution α_ϵ, since the real analytic de Rham complex on a real analytic manifold is acyclic [4]. However, this existence result is not constructive, and in particular does not provide the analytic dependence of α_ϵ on the parameter ϵ. Therefore, we are going to construct α_ϵ explicitly, making use of specific properties of the manifold $\bar{P}$.

Fix some $\rho > 0$ so that υ_ϵ extends analytically to $U_\rho \bar{P}$ for all small ϵ. Since D is assumed to be convex, there exists a real analytic retraction

$$\pi_t \colon U_\rho \bar{P} \to U_\rho \bar{P}, \qquad 0 \le t \le 1,$$

such that $\pi_1 = id$, while π_0 retracts $\bar{D}$ to a single point $(I_0, 0)$ and leaves $\mathbb{T}^{n+1}$ untouched. The two 2-forms $\pi_1^* \upsilon_\epsilon = \upsilon_\epsilon$ and $\pi_0^* \upsilon_\epsilon = \upsilon'_\epsilon$ are then analytically cohomological. Indeed, there is an exact formula for a 1-form α'_ϵ such that

$$\upsilon_\epsilon = \upsilon'_\epsilon + d\alpha'_\epsilon,$$

and α'_ϵ is jointly analytic in the $\bar{P}$-coordinates and ϵ in a uniform neighbourhood of $\bar{P}$ [7].

The form υ'_ϵ is real analytic and closed. Its coefficients do not depend on I or E, and it vanishes on the tangent vectors $\partial/\partial I_j$, $1 \le j \le n$, and $\partial/\partial E$. Therefore,

$$\upsilon'_\epsilon = \sum_{i<j} a_{ij}(\bar{\phi})\, d\bar{\phi}_i \wedge d\bar{\phi}_j,$$

where $\bar{\phi} = (\bar{\phi}_1, \ldots, \bar{\phi}_{n+1}) = (\phi, \theta)$. Such a form is cohomological to its averaged form

$$\upsilon''_\epsilon = \sum_{i<j} b_{ij}\, d\bar{\phi}_i \wedge d\bar{\phi}_j, \qquad b_{ij} = \frac{1}{\operatorname{vol} \mathbb{T}^{n+1}} \int_{\mathbb{T}^{n+1}} a_{ij}(\bar{\phi})\, d\bar{\phi}.$$

That is, there exists a 1-form α''_ϵ, such that

$$\upsilon'_\epsilon = \upsilon''_\epsilon + d\alpha''_\epsilon,$$

and α''_ϵ is jointly analytic in the $\bar{P}$-coordinates and ϵ [7].

We thus arrive at a 2-form υ''_ϵ on $\mathbb{T}^{n+1}$ with constant coefficients, which we know is *differentiably* exact: $\upsilon''_\epsilon = d\beta''_\epsilon$ with some differentiable 1-form β''_ϵ. This, however, implies that υ''_ϵ *vanishes*. Consider, for example, the coefficient b_{12}. Averaging over the 2-torus $T = \{\bar\phi_3 = \cdots = \bar\phi_{n+1} = 0\}$ we find

$$b_{12} = \frac{1}{\operatorname{vol} T}\int_T \upsilon''_\epsilon = \frac{1}{\operatorname{vol} T}\int_T d\beta''_\epsilon = 0.$$

Thus $\upsilon''_\epsilon = 0$, whence $\upsilon_\epsilon = \upsilon'_\epsilon + d\alpha'_\epsilon = d\alpha'_\epsilon + d\alpha''_\epsilon$. This proves the proposition. □

We may now put the symplectic structure into standard form.

Proposition 3. *For all sufficiently small ϵ there exists a diffeomorphism*

$$\Delta_\epsilon\colon\ \bar P \underset{\epsilon}{\longrightarrow} \bar P,$$

such that $\Delta^*_\epsilon \upsilon_\epsilon = \upsilon_0$. Moreover, $\Delta_0 = id$, and Δ_ϵ is jointly real analytic in the $\bar P$-coordinates and ϵ in a fixed complex neighbourhood of $\bar P$.

Proof. This follows from the Moser-Weinstein theorem. Just observe that Δ_ϵ is given as the time-1-map of the real analytic, time-dependent vector field X_ϵ on $\bar P$ obtained as the solution of

$$i_{X_\epsilon}\upsilon^t_\epsilon = \alpha_\epsilon - \alpha_0,$$

where $\upsilon^t_\epsilon = (1-t)\upsilon_0 + t\upsilon_\epsilon$. □

Composing with the map Γ_ϵ we obtain, for all sufficiently small ϵ, a diffeomorphism

$$\Lambda_\epsilon = \Gamma_\epsilon \circ \Delta_\epsilon\colon\ \bar P \underset{\epsilon}{\longrightarrow} B_\epsilon, \qquad \Lambda_0 = \Gamma_0,$$

which is symplectic in the sense that

$$\Lambda^*_\epsilon \tilde\upsilon_\epsilon = \upsilon_0$$

for all these ϵ. Moreover, Λ_ϵ is jointly real analytic in the $\bar P$-coordinates and ϵ in a fixed complex neighbourhood of $\bar P$.

In B_ϵ the Poincaré map of the real analytic hamiltonian $\tilde H$ with respect to the isoenergetic section $\tilde S$ is well defined and interpolates the map F_ϵ. Indeed, it is simply the time-1-map of the hamiltonian $\tilde H$. The same is now true for their pull backs to $\bar P$. The time-1-map of the real analytic hamiltonian $\bar H_\epsilon = \tilde H \circ \Lambda_\epsilon$ is well defined on the surface $S_\epsilon = \Lambda^{-1}_\epsilon(\tilde S)$ and interpolates F_ϵ. That is, we have a real analytic, symplectic embedding

$$i_\epsilon = \Lambda^{-1}_\epsilon \circ \tilde\imath\colon\ P \underset{\epsilon}{\longrightarrow} S_\epsilon \subset \bar P$$

such that $X^1_{\bar H_\epsilon} \circ i_\epsilon = i_\epsilon \circ F_\epsilon$ on P for all sufficiently small ϵ.

Step 4. Standard Surface of Section. The section S_ϵ is ϵ-close to the standard isoenergetic section

$$\Sigma_\epsilon = \left\{ \bar{H}_\epsilon = 0,\ \theta = 0 \right\} \subset \bar{P},$$

since they coincide for $\epsilon = 0$ and depend analytically on ϵ. Moreover, the vector field $X_{\bar{H}_\epsilon}$ is transversal to the hypersurface $\{\theta = 0\}$ in $\bar{P}$, since we have $\dot{\theta} = 1$ for $\epsilon = 0$. Hence there exists a well defined Poincaré flow map

$$\Psi_\epsilon \colon S_\epsilon \underset{\epsilon}{\longrightarrow} \Sigma_\epsilon, \qquad \Psi_\epsilon^{-1} \colon \Sigma_\epsilon \underset{\epsilon}{\longrightarrow} S_\epsilon$$

for all sufficiently small ϵ. This map is real analytic and symplectic, and $\Psi_0 = id$.

Thus we also have a real analytic, symplectic embedding

$$j_\epsilon = \Psi_\epsilon \circ i_\epsilon \colon\ P \underset{\epsilon}{\longrightarrow} \Sigma_\epsilon,$$

such that $\Phi_\epsilon \circ j_\epsilon = j_\epsilon \circ F_\epsilon$ on P, where

$$\Phi_\epsilon = \Psi_\epsilon \circ X^1_{\bar{H}_\epsilon} \circ \Psi_\epsilon^{-1} \colon\ \Sigma_\epsilon \underset{\epsilon}{\longrightarrow} \Sigma_\epsilon$$

is the Poincaré map of the hamiltonian vector field $X_{\bar{H}_\epsilon}$ with respect to Σ_ϵ. Finally,

$$\bar{H}_\epsilon\big|_{\epsilon=0} = \bar{H}_0 = h(I) + E, \qquad j_\epsilon|_{\epsilon=0} = j_0 = \Gamma_0^{-1} \circ \tilde{\imath}.$$

Both $\bar{H}_\epsilon$ and j_ϵ have a uniform radius of analyticity for all sufficiently small ϵ. The estimates of the theorem therefore follow from Cauchy's estimate, and the proof is finished.

4. Proof of Theorem 2

Rescaling coordinates by the dilation $z \mapsto \epsilon z$ we obtain a real analytic family of real analytic symplectic maps

$$F_\epsilon \colon\ P \to \mathbb{R}^{2n}, \qquad -\epsilon_0 < \epsilon < \epsilon_0,$$

where $P = \{|z| < r\} \subset \mathbb{R}^{2n}$ with some radius r to be chosen later, and

$$F_\epsilon(z) = \epsilon^{-1} F(\epsilon z) = \Lambda z + \epsilon^{-1} \hat{F}(\epsilon z) = \Lambda z + O(e\,|z|^2).$$

In particular, F_0 is linearly symplectic, and F_ϵ is conjugate to F on an ϵr-neighbourhood of the origin for all small $\epsilon \neq 0$. This family is interpolated in essentially the same way as in the preceding section, with a few modifications, which we indicate now.

Step 1. Abstract Suspension Manifold. We set $A = P \times \mathbb{R} \times \Theta$ and identify points through the map

$$T_\epsilon\colon\ (\tilde z, \tilde E, \tilde\theta) \mapsto (F_\epsilon(\tilde z), \tilde E, \tilde\theta - 1).$$

In particular, $T_0\colon (\tilde z, \tilde E, \tilde\theta) \mapsto (\Lambda\tilde z, \tilde E, \tilde\theta - 1)$. The symplectic form $\tilde\upsilon$ is changed accordingly. Everything else remains the same.

Step 2. Embedding of B_ϵ. We now seek a real analytic embedding of $B_\epsilon = A/T_\epsilon$ into the space $\bar P = P \times \mathbb{R} \times \mathbb{T}$. For $\epsilon = 0$ this embedding is given as the inverse of the map

$$\Gamma_0\colon\ \bar P \to B_0, \qquad \begin{cases} \tilde z = e^{-\theta JA} z \\ \tilde E = \frac12 \langle Az, z\rangle + E \\ \tilde\theta = \theta \end{cases},$$

which takes the symplectic structure on B_0 into the standard structure

$$\upsilon_0 = \sum\nolimits_j dx_j \wedge dy_j + dE \wedge d\theta$$

on $\bar P$. Moreover, we obtain $\bar H_0 = \frac12 \langle Az, z\rangle + E$. — For $\epsilon \neq 0$ we make use of the simple topology of $\bar P$ to normalize the maps G_ϵ in a useful way.

Addendum to Proposition 1. *The map G_ϵ may be defined so that*

$$T_0 \tilde G_\epsilon = id,$$

where $T_0\tilde G_\epsilon$ denotes the tangential map of the lifting $\tilde G_\epsilon$ restricted to the tangent space of A along the submanifold $\{\tilde z = 0\}$.

With this provision we find that $\Gamma_\epsilon = G_\epsilon^{-1} \circ \Gamma_0$ takes the symplectic structure on B_ϵ into $\upsilon_\epsilon = \Gamma_\epsilon^* \tilde\upsilon_\epsilon = \upsilon_0 + O(\epsilon\,|z|)$. Moreover, the hamiltonian $\tilde H = \tilde E$ transforms into

$$\hat H_\epsilon = \frac12 \langle Az, z\rangle + E + O(\epsilon\,|z|^3),$$

since the E-coordinate transforms identically.

Proof of the Addendum. Again, we ignore the coordinate E. Otherwise, the construction of G_ϵ is modified in the following way.

Let $\mathcal{L} = T_0\pi$ be the tangential of the projection

$$\pi\colon\ \mathcal{A} \to \mathcal{A}, \quad (X, \delta) \mapsto (X, 0)$$

restricted to the submanifold $\mathcal{Z} = \{\tilde z = 0\}$. We have $T\mathcal{T} \circ \mathcal{L} = \mathcal{L} \circ T\mathcal{T}$, so $\mathcal{L}$ is also defined on the tangent bundle along $\mathcal{Z}/\mathcal{T} \simeq \mathbb{T}$ in B. Using the Grauert embedding map $\mathcal{G}$, this defines a corresponding map, again denoted by $\mathcal{L}$ for simplicity, on the tangent space to $\mathcal{M}$ along the image $\mathcal{N}$ of the submanifold $\mathcal{Z}$. Moreover, its restriction $\mathcal{L}_\epsilon$ to the tangent space of the slices $\mathcal{M}_\epsilon$ is a linear isomorphism.

As embedded manifolds, $\mathcal{M}$ and each of the $\mathcal{M}_\epsilon$ carry a natural real analytic riemannian metric, so that locally exponential maps are well defined. In particular, we can define an exponential map $\mathcal{E}_\epsilon$ from some neighbourhood of the zero section of the tangent bundle along $\mathcal{N} \cap \mathcal{M}_\epsilon \simeq \mathbb{T}$ orthogonal to the tangent bundle $T\mathcal{N}$, to some neighbourhood $\mathcal{U}_\epsilon$ of $\mathcal{N} \cap \mathcal{M}_\epsilon$ in $\mathcal{M}_\epsilon$. Moreover, those neighbourhoods $\mathcal{U}_\epsilon$ can be chosen as a δ-neighbourhood uniformly for all small ϵ.

This way we obtain a real analytic family of maps

$$\mathcal{E}_0 \circ \mathcal{L}_\epsilon \circ \mathcal{E}_\epsilon^{-1}\colon\ \mathcal{U}_\epsilon \underset{\epsilon}{\longrightarrow} \mathcal{U}_0,$$

whose tangential at $\mathcal{N}$ is equal to $\mathcal{L}_\epsilon$. Pulling them back to the abstract manifolds B_ϵ and choosing the radius r in the definition of P sufficiently small, we obtain a real analytic family of maps $G_\epsilon\colon B_\epsilon \underset{\epsilon}{\longrightarrow} B_0$, whose tangential at the submanifold $\mathcal{Z}$ is equal to $\mathcal{L}$, hence is the identity. □

Step 3. Standard Symplectic Structure. The 2-form υ_ϵ is closed on $\bar{P} = P \times \mathbb{R} \times \mathbb{T}$ and of the form $\upsilon_0 + O(\epsilon\,|z|)$. By the convexity of $P \times \mathbb{R}$ and a retraction argument, υ_ϵ is also exact on $\bar{P}$, with a 1-form

$$\alpha_\epsilon = \alpha_0 + O(\epsilon\,|z|^2),$$

where α_0 is any constant 1-form with $d\alpha_0 = \upsilon_0$. It follows that in the proof of Proposition 3 one obtains $X_\epsilon = O(\epsilon\,|z|^2)$, and consequently

$$\Delta_\epsilon = id + O(\epsilon\,|z|^2)$$

as its time-1-map.

Step 4. Final Transformations. We now proceed as before, observing that the transformed hamiltonian$\bar{H}_\epsilon = \hat{H}_\epsilon \circ \Delta_\epsilon$ is exactly of the same form as $\hat{H}_\epsilon$. Its isoenergetic reduction to $\bar{H}_\epsilon = 0$ is thus given by a hamiltonian

$$H_\epsilon(z,\theta) = \frac{1}{2}\,\langle Az, z\rangle + O(\epsilon\,|z|^3).$$

The time-1-map of H_ϵ interpolates F_ϵ on P for all sufficiently small ϵ. Fixing such an ϵ and scaling coordinates back we find that the time-1-map of

$$H = \epsilon^2 H_\epsilon(z/\epsilon,\theta) = \frac{1}{2}\,\langle Az, z\rangle + O(|z|^3)$$

interpolates F in an ϵr-neighbourhood of the origin. This completes the proof of Theorem 2.

Appendix A. Smooth Exactness of υ_ϵ

We are going to show that the 2-form υ_ϵ is smoothly exact on $\bar{P}$. This is equivalent to showing that upstairs the 2-form $\tilde{\upsilon}$ is smoothly exact in B_ϵ. To simplify the notation we drop the ˜ and make the Ansatz

$$\beta_\epsilon = \alpha_s + E d\theta + dV_\epsilon, \qquad \alpha_s = \sum_j I_j d\phi_j.$$

Then $d\beta_\epsilon = \upsilon$. The point is to choose the function V_ϵ so that $T_\epsilon^*\beta_\epsilon = \beta_\epsilon$ to make β_ϵ a 1-form on B_ϵ.

By hypotheses, F_ϵ is exact, so $F_\epsilon^*\alpha_s = \alpha_s + dW_\epsilon$ with some real analytic function W_ϵ. Hence,

$$\begin{aligned} T_\epsilon^*\beta_\epsilon &= F_\epsilon^*\alpha_s + E d\theta + T_\epsilon^* dV_\epsilon \\ &= \alpha_s + dW_\epsilon + E d\theta + T_\epsilon^* dV_\epsilon \\ &= \beta_\epsilon - dV_\epsilon + dW_\epsilon + d(V_\epsilon \circ T_\epsilon). \end{aligned}$$

So it suffices to find V_ϵ such that

$$V_\epsilon = W_\epsilon + V_\epsilon \circ T_\epsilon.$$

It is easy to solve this equation in terms of *smooth* functions, since A_- and $T_\epsilon^{-1}(A_-)$ are disjoint. If V^o is any smooth function on A_-, then set

$$V_\epsilon = \begin{cases} V^o & \text{on } A_- \\ W_\epsilon + V^o \circ T_\epsilon & \text{on } T_\epsilon^{-1}(A_-) \end{cases},$$

and extend V_ϵ smoothly to the rest of A. □

Appendix B. The Logarithm of an Operator

Lemma B.1. *Let Λ be a nonsingular linear operator on $\mathbb{R}^m$.* (a) *There exists a linear operator B on $\mathbb{C}^m$ such that $\Lambda = \exp(B)$.* (b) *If Λ has no negative eigenvalues, then B can be chosen to be real.* (c) *The same holds, if Λ is the square of another linear operator on $\mathbb{R}^m$.*

Thus, a real logarithm always exists for the square of a nonsingular real operator. The converse is obviously also true: the existence of a real logarithm implies the existence of a real square root.

Proof. (a) Since Λ is nonsingular, there exists a contour Γ in $\mathbb{C}$ enclosing all the eigenvalues of Λ, but not 0. On Γ we may fix a branch of the complex logarithm to define the complex operator

$$B = \log \Lambda \overset{\text{def}}{=} \frac{1}{2\pi i} \oint_\Gamma \frac{\log z}{zI - \Lambda}\, dz.$$

Then $\exp(B) = \Lambda$ by the functional calculus of operators [8].

(b) In the absence of negative eigenvalues we can choose Γ to be symmetric to the real axis, but disjoint from its negative part. On Γ we may then choose the principal branch of the complex logarithm, so that we have $\overline{\log z} = \log \overline{z}$. The reality of B then follows by straightforward computation.

(c) Let $\Lambda = M^2$. Write $M = M_r \oplus M_c$, where M_r has only real and M_c only non-real eigenvalues. By (b) we have $M_r^2 = \exp(B_r)$ and $M_c = \exp(B_c)$ with real operators B_r and B_c. They commute, since M_r and M_c commute. Therefore,

$$\Lambda = \exp(B_r) \oplus \exp(2B_c) = \exp(B_r \oplus 2B_c),$$

and $B = B_r \oplus 2B_c$ is real. □

Let $m = 2n$ and endow $\mathbb{R}^{2n}$ with the standard symplectic structure J.

Lemma B.2. *Let Λ be symplectic. If the assumptions of (b) or (c) above are satisfied, then the real logarithm B of Λ is hamiltonian in the sense that $J^{-1}B$ is symmetric.*

Thus, $\Lambda = \exp(JA)$ with the real symmetric operator $A = J^{-1}B$.

Proof. We have to show equivalently that $JBJ = B^t$. By symplecticity of Λ, we have $J\Lambda J = -\Lambda^{-t}$, and by the definition of $B = \log \Lambda$,

$$JBJ = \frac{-1}{2\pi i} \oint_\Gamma \frac{\log z}{zI + J\Lambda J}\, dz = \frac{-1}{2\pi i} \oint_\Gamma \frac{\log z}{zI - \Lambda^{-t}}\, dz = -\log \Lambda^{-t}$$

Now, under the assumption of (b), we can choose Γ not to intersect the negative real axis, and the complex logarithm to be real on the positive real axis. This implies that $\log z^{-1} = -\log z$ on Γ, and thus $\log \Lambda^{-1} = -\log \Lambda$. It follows that $JBJ = B^t$. — The proof under the assumption of (c) is straightforward. □

References

1. V.I. Arnol'd, *Mathematical Methods of Classical Mechanics*, Springer, New York, 1978.
2. H. W. Broer and G. B. Huitema, *A proof of the isoenergetic KAM-theorem from the Rordinary's one*, J. Diff. Equ. **90** (1991), 52–60.
3. A. Bazzani, S. Marmi, and G. Turchetti, *Nekhoroshev estimates for isochronous non resonant symplectic maps*, Celest. Mech. **47** (1990), 333–359.
4. H. Cartan, *Varietes analitiques reelles et varietes analitiques complexes*, Bull. Soc. Math. France **85** (1957), 77–99.
5. R. Douady, *Une démonstration directe de l'équivalence des théormes de tores invariants pour difféomorphismes et champs de vecteurs*, C. R. Acad. Sc. Paris **295** (1982), 201-204.
6. R. Douady, *Applications du théorme des tores invariantes*, Thesis, Université Paris VII, 1982.
7. B. A. Dubrovin, A. T. Fomenko, and S. P. Novikov, *Modern Geometry Q Methods and Applications Vol.* III, Springer, Berlin, 1990.
8. N. Dunford and J. T. Schwartz, *Linear Operators* I, Interscience, New York, 1958.
9. L. H. Eliasson, *Perturbations of stable invariant tori for Hamiltonian systems*, Ann. Sc. Norm. Sup. Pisa **15** (1988), 115–147.

10. C. Genecand, *Transversal homoclinic points near elliptic fixed points of area-preserving difeomorphisms of the plane*, Preprint, ETH Zürich, 1990.
11. Yu. S. Il'yashenko, *A steepness test for analytic functions*, Russ. Math. Surveys **41** (1986), 229–230.
12. S. B. Kuksin, *On the inclusion of an analytic symplectomorphism close to an integrable one into a hamiltonian flow*, Preprint, ETH Zürich, 1992.
13. P. Lochak, *Canonical perturbation theory via simultaneous approximation*, Russian Math. Surveys (to appear).
14. P. Lochak and C. Meunier, *Multiphase Averaging for Classical Systems*, Appl. Math. Sciences, Springer, 1988.
15. V. F. Lazutkin, I. G. Shachmanski and M. B. Tabanov, *Splitting of separatrices for standard and semistandard mappings*, Physica D **40** (1989), 235–248.
16. J. Moser, *On the volume elements on a manifold*, Trans. Am. Math. Soc. **120** (1965), 286–294.
17. R. Narasimhan, *Analysis on Real and Complex Manifolds*, North-Holland, Amsterdam, 1968.
18. N. N. Nekhoroshev, *An exponential estimate of the time of stability of nearly-integrable Hamiltonian systems* I, Russ. Math. Surveys **32** (1977), no. 6, 1–65.
19. J. Pöschel, *On Nekhoroshev estimates for quasi-convex hamiltonian systems*, Math. Z. (to appear).
20. J. Pöschel, *On elliptic lower dimensional tori in hamiltonian systems*, Math. Z. **202** (1989), 559–608.
21. M. B. Sevryuk, *Invariant m-dimensional tori of reversible systems with a phase space of dimension greater than $2m$*, J. Sov. Math. **51** (1990), no. 3, 2374–2386.
22. R. O. Wells, *Differential Analysis on Complex Manifolds*, Graduate Texts in Mathematics 65, Springer, New York, 1980.
23. E. Zehnder, *Homoclinic points near elliptic fixed points*, Comm. Pure Appl. Math. **26** (1973), 131–182.

POINCARÉ COMPACTIFICATION OF THE KEPLER AND THE COLLINEAR THREE BODY PROBLEMS

J. DELGADO*, E. A. LACOMBA*, J. LLIBRE** AND E. PÉREZ*

INTRODUCTION

The vector field of the n-body problem can always be written as a polynomial vector field. The idea is to regularize binary collisions in such a way that collisions involving more than two bodies become critical points of the new vector field, [Heg]. For three or more bodies, this procedure introduces redundant variables.

In this paper we describe a method to extend analytically the vector field to a compact manifold. For this purpose, we apply Poincaré compactification of Euclidean phase space into a sphere for the polynomial vector field of the n-body problem.

In Section 2 we study the Kepler problem in the line and in the plane. In both cases we obtain the same results as applying blow up, except that we do not have to fix an energy level.

In Section 3 we study the collinear three body problem. We decompose the compact and connected set of all equilibrium points into five pieces in order to identify and interpret them.

1. POINCARÉ COMPACTIFICATION OF A POLYNOMIAL HAMILTONIAN VECTOR FIELD

Let $X = (P^1, P^2, \dots, P^n)$ be a polynomial vector field in $\mathbb{R}^n$ and let $m = \max(\deg(P^1), \dots, \deg(P^n))$ be the degree of X. We denote the time parameter by $\bar{t}$, since more than one time rescaling will be usually involved.

Consider the hyperplane $\Pi = \{y \in \mathbb{R}^{n+1} : y_{n+1} = 1\}$ in $\mathbb{R}^{n+1}$ and let $S^n = \{y \in \mathbb{R}^{n+1} : \|y\| = 1\}$. We take the central projection from the sphere S^n to the hyperplane Π. That is, for each point in Π, we draw the line through this point and the origin in $\mathbb{R}^{n+1}$ and obtain two antipodal points in S^n. Notice that the infinity in the hyperplane corresponds to the equator in the sphere. Of course, if the antipodal points are identified, we obtain the corresponding projective space. For our purposes it is preferable to work with both north and south hemispheres.

If we identify the hyperplane Π and $\mathbb{R}^n$ with coordinates $x_1, \ldots, x_n$, the relation with the coordinates in the sphere is

$$\begin{aligned} y_i &= x_i y_{n+1}, \\ y_{n+1} &= \pm\frac{1}{\sqrt{1+\sum_{i=1}^n x_i^2}}. \end{aligned} \tag{1}$$

This correspondence associates with the vector field X a new vector field defined in the north and south hemispheres. It is known ([CL]) that multiplication by y_{n+1}^{m-1} extends it into the following vector field $\widetilde{X}$ defined on the whole sphere S^n:

$$\begin{pmatrix} y_1' \\ y_2' \\ \vdots \\ y_n' \\ y_{n+1}' \end{pmatrix} = \begin{pmatrix} 1-y_1^2 & -y_1y_2 & \cdots & -y_1y_n \\ -y_2y_1 & 1-y_2^2 & \cdots & -y_2y_n \\ \vdots & & & \\ -y_ny_1 & -y_ny_2 & \cdots & 1-y_n^2 \\ -y_{n+1}y_1 & -y_{n+1}y_2 & \cdots & -y_{n+1}y_n \end{pmatrix} \begin{pmatrix} \widetilde{P^1} \\ \widetilde{P^2} \\ \vdots \\ \widetilde{P^n} \end{pmatrix} \tag{2}$$

where, $\widetilde{P^k} = y_{n+1}^m P^k(y_1/y_{n+1}, y_2/y_{n+1}, \ldots, y_n/y_{n+1})$ are homogeneous polynomials of degree m. The symbol ($'$) here means derivative with respect to the scaled time τ, where $d\bar{t}/d\tau = y_{n+1}^{m-1}$.

In many cases it is preferable to do the computations in local charts; for example, for obtaining the equilibrium points of the flow. There are $2(n+1)$ coordinate charts given by $F_i\colon U_i \to \mathbb{R}^n$, and $G_i\colon V_i \to \mathbb{R}^n$, where

$$U_i = \{y \in S^n \mid y_i > 0\}, \qquad \text{and} \qquad V_i = \{y \in S^n \mid y_i < 0\},$$

for $i = 1, 2, \ldots, n+1$. F_i is defined by

$$(z_1, z_2, \ldots, z_n) = F_i(y) = \left(\frac{y_1}{y_i}, \ldots, \frac{y_{i-1}}{y_i}, \frac{y_{i+1}}{y_i}, \ldots, \frac{y_{n+1}}{y_i}\right)$$

and G_i is defined by the same formula.

Due to the symmetry that the vector field has on the sphere, its expression in the local chart (V_i, G_i) is the same as for (U_i, F_i) multiplied by the factor $(-1)^{m-1}$.

In the case of a *Hamiltonian* vector field, with polynomial Hamiltonian H of degree $m+1$ (so the vector field is polynomial of degree m), with $n = 2d$, the equations (2) become

$$\begin{aligned} y_k' &= \frac{\partial \widetilde{H}}{\partial y_{k+d}} + \lambda\, y_k, \\ y_{k+d}' &= -\frac{\partial \widetilde{H}}{\partial y_k} + \lambda\, y_{k+d}, \\ y_{n+1}' &= \lambda\, y_{n+1}, \end{aligned} \tag{3}$$

for $k = 1, \ldots, d$, where

$$\lambda = \sum_{k=1}^{d} \left(y_{k+d} \frac{\partial \widetilde{H}}{\partial y_k} - y_k \frac{\partial \widetilde{H}}{\partial y_{k+d}} \right),$$

and $\widetilde{H}$ is obtained from the original Hamiltonian by the rule

$$\widetilde{H}(y_1, y_2, \ldots, y_{n+1}) = y_{n+1}^{m+1} H(y_1/y_{n+1}, \ldots, y_n/y_{n+1}).$$

We will call $\widetilde{H}$ the *generating function* of the vector field $\widetilde{X}$.

Let us consider the critical points of the compactified vector field in the Hamiltonian case. We will say that a critical point is in the finite part if $y_{n+1} \neq 0$. A critical point with $y_{n+1} = 0$ will be called a *critical point at infinity.* This infinity in the phase space, corresponds to positions and momenta of the Hamiltonian system.

First notice that any critical point of the original system carries to a critical point of the compactified vector field in the finite part, since the reparametrization $d\bar{t}/d\tau = y_{n+1}^{m-1}$ is by a nonvanishing function. For the critical points at infinity we have the following result.

Proposition 1. *Consider a polynomial Hamiltonian H in the $n = 2d$ variables $x_1, \ldots, x_d, x_{d+1}, \ldots, x_{2d}$ and write it as*

$$H = H_0 + H_1 + \cdots + H_{m+1},$$

where each term H_k is an homogeneous polynomial of degree k. Then the invariant flow at infinity $y_{n+1} = 0$ is given by the system of equations

$$\begin{aligned} y_k' &= \frac{\partial H_{m+1}}{\partial y_{k+d}} + \lambda y_k, \\ y_{k+d}' &= -\frac{\partial H_{m+1}}{\partial y_k} + \lambda y_{k+d}, \end{aligned}$$

for $k = 1, \ldots, d$, with

$$\lambda = \sum_{k=1}^{d} \left(y_{k+d} \frac{\partial H_{m+1}}{\partial y_k} - y_k \frac{\partial H_{m+1}}{\partial y_{k+d}} \right).$$

Proof. From the general equations (2) it follows that $y_{n+1} = 0$ is invariant. By definition

$$\begin{aligned} \widetilde{H} &= y_{n+1}^{m+1} H(y_1/y_{n+1}, \ldots, y_n/y_{n+1}) \\ &= y_{n+1}^{m+1} \left(H_0(y_1/y_{n+1}, \ldots, y_n/y_{n+1}) + \cdots + H_{m+1}(y_1/y_{n+1}, \ldots, y_n/y_{n+1}) \right), \end{aligned}$$

but each term H_k is homogeneous of degree k. Therefore by letting $y_{n+1} = 0$ the corresponding terms with $k \leq m$ vanish, and for $k = m + 1$ we get

$$\widetilde{H}(y_1, \ldots, y_{n+1}) = H_{m+1}(y_1, \ldots, y_n).$$

This completes the proof. □

2. The Kepler problem

In this section we will apply the Poincaré compactification to the Kepler problem in the line and in the plane. Since it is the simplest problem in Celestial Mechanics, it will be helpful to get insight into the advantages (and disadvantages) of this technique.

2.1 The Kepler problem in the line.

The Hamiltonian function in this case is

$$H = \frac{p^2}{2} - \frac{1}{q}$$

with $q > 0$ and $p \in \mathbb{R}$. To obtain a polynomial Hamiltonian, we regularize the singularity by Levi-Civita transformation together with the appropriate scaling of time, on a fixed energy level $H = h$ through the change of variables

$$q = Q^2, \quad p = \frac{P}{2Q}, \quad \frac{dt}{d\bar{t}} = 4Q^2. \tag{4}$$

The new Hamiltonian becomes

$$\overline{H} = \frac{P^2}{2} - 4hQ^2 - 4,$$

in the new energy level $\overline{H} = 0$. Here, the Poincaré sphere will be $S^2 = \{(y_1, y_2, y_3) \mid y_1^2 + y_2^2 + y_3^2 = 1\}$, the degree of the associated polynomial Hamiltonian vector field is $m = 1$, and $d = 1$ is the number of degrees of freedom, $n = 2d = 2$. By making the substitution of variables

$$Q = \frac{y_1}{y_3}, \quad P = \frac{y_2}{y_3},$$

in $\overline{H}$ and multiplying by the factor y_3^2 we get the generating function $\widetilde{H}$ of the vector field $\widetilde{X}$ in the Poincaré sphere S^2:

$$\widetilde{H} = \frac{y_2^2}{2} - 4hy_1^2 - 4y_3^2.$$

The vector field on S^2 is obtained according to (3), as

$$\begin{aligned} y_1' &= y_2(1 - y_1^2(8h + 1)), \\ y_2' &= y_1(8h - y_2^2(8h + 1)), \\ y_3' &= -(8h + 1)y_1y_2y_3. \end{aligned}$$

We remark that in this case the derivatives are with respect to the parameter $\bar{t} = \tau$, since $d\bar{t}/d\tau = 1$.

For $h \geq 0$, the only critical points $y \in S^2$ that satisfy also the energy relation $\widetilde{H} = 0$ are located at infinity $y_3 = 0$ and are given by

$$y_1 = \pm \frac{1}{\sqrt{8h+1}}, \qquad y_2 = \pm \sqrt{\frac{8h}{8h+1}}.$$

If $h > 0$ these are four critical points in the equator, and only two if $h = 0$. The energy levels are then extended to the infinity $y_3 = 0$ as critical points.

We will give a brief discussion of the interpretation of the critical points.

For $h > 0$, if $(y_1(t), y_2(t), y_3(t))$ is a solution with energy h going to a critical point, then

$$Q = \frac{y_1}{y_3} \to \infty \qquad \text{and} \qquad P = \frac{y_2}{y_3} \to \infty.$$

This implies that in the original coordinates

$$q \to \infty \qquad \text{and} \qquad p = \frac{P}{2Q} = \frac{y_2}{2y_1} \to \pm\sqrt{2h}$$

which corresponds to hyperbolic motion.

For $h = 0$, again $Q \to \infty$ but $P \to \pm\sqrt{8h}$ (from the energy relation) and hence $q \to \infty$ and $p \to 0$, corresponding to parabolic motion. On each positive energy level the critical points are nondegenerate.

2.2 The Kepler problem in the plane.

The Hamiltonian in this case is

$$H = \frac{|p|^2}{2} - \frac{1}{|q|}$$

with q, $p \in \mathbb{R}^2$ and $q \neq 0$. As usual, we regularize the singularity by Levi-Civita transformation (4) regarding (q, p) and (Q, P) as complex variables. The regularized Hamiltonian is

$$\bar{H} = \frac{|P|^2}{2} - 4h|Q|^2 - 4$$

on the energy level $\bar{H} = 0$. Here $d = 2$ is the number of degrees of freedom, $n = 2d = 4$ is the number of variables and the Poincaré compactification will give us a vector field on S^4, and the degree of the associated polynomial Hamiltonian vector field is $m = 1$.

By making the substitution of variables

$$Q_1 = y_1/y_5, \qquad P_1 = y_3/y_5,$$
$$Q_2 = y_2/y_5, \qquad P_2 = y_4/y_5,$$

and multiplying by y_5^2 we get the generating function for the vector field on S^4

$$\widetilde{H} = \frac{1}{2}(y_3^2 + y_4^2) - 4h(y_1^2 + y_2^2) - 4y_5^2.$$

The equations of the compactified vector field are

$$\begin{aligned} y_1' &= y_3 + \lambda\, y_1, & y_3' &= 8hy_1 + \lambda\, y_3, \\ y_2' &= y_4 + \lambda\, y_2, & y_4' &= 8hy_2 + \lambda\, y_4, \\ & & y_5' &= \lambda\, y_5, \end{aligned}$$

where $\lambda = -(8h+1)(y_1y_3 + y_2y_4)$.

Since $y_5 = 0$ is invariant, if $h \geq 0$ we can extend the energy relation $\widetilde{H} = 0$ to the sphere at infinity

$$S^3_\infty = \{(y_1, y_2, y_3, y_4, y_5) \mid y_5 = 0, \quad y_1^2 + y_2^2 + y_3^2 + y_4^2 = 1\}.$$

We will consider first the case $h > 0$. In that case we have to glue to the finite part of the level energy E_h the set

$$E_h^\infty = \{(y_1, \ldots, y_5) \in S^3_\infty \mid \quad y_3^2 + y_4^2 - 8h(y_1^2 + y_2^2) = 0\},$$

which in view of the relation $y_1^2 + \cdots + y_4^2 = 1$ reduces to

$$E_h^\infty = \left\{(y_1, \ldots, y_5) \in S^3_\infty \mid y_1^2 + y_2^2 = \frac{1}{8h+1}, \quad y_3^2 + y_4^2 = \frac{8h}{8h+1}\right\}, \tag{5}$$

that is, E_h^∞ is a 2-torus.

The only critical points satisfying the energy relation $\widetilde{H} = 0$ are at infinity and are given by the following equations

$$\begin{aligned} y_3 &= -\lambda\, y_1, & y_1 &= -(\lambda/8h)y_3, \\ y_4 &= -\lambda\, y_2, & y_2 &= -(\lambda/8h)y_4. \end{aligned}$$

Substituting in the expression (5) for E_h^∞, one gets $\lambda^2 = 8h$, and therefore

$$\begin{aligned} y_3 &= \pm\sqrt{8h}y_1, \\ y_4 &= \pm\sqrt{8h}y_2. \end{aligned}$$

From these equations one can easily obtain that the critical points are two circles $C_h^\pm$ in the 2-torus E_h^∞, which can be parametrized by an angle θ

$$(y_1, y_2, y_3, y_4) = \frac{1}{\sqrt{8h+1}}(\cos\theta, \sin\theta, \varepsilon\sqrt{8h}\cos\theta, \varepsilon\sqrt{8h}\sin\theta) \tag{6}$$

where the choice of $\varepsilon = \pm 1$ gives the two circles of equilibria.

Let us take local coordinates to compute the linearization of the vector field at the set of critical points. In terms of the local chart (U_1, F_1) the vector field is expressed as

$$\begin{aligned} z_1' &= -z_1 z_2 + z_3, & z_2' &= -z_2^2 + 8h, \\ z_3' &= -z_2 z_3 + 8h z_1, & z_4' &= -z_2 z_4. \end{aligned}$$

The circles of equilibria C_h^ε are given locally by the equations

$$z_4 = 0, \quad z_2 = a, \quad z_3 = a z_1$$

where $a = \varepsilon\sqrt{8h}$, and the characteristic polynomial of the linearization of the vector field at an equilibrium point is

$$p(\lambda) = \lambda(2a + \lambda)^2(a + \lambda).$$

Since there is one zero eigenvalue, the circles C_h^ε are normally hyperbolic: C_h^+ is an attractor and C_h^- is a repeller.

In fact, the flow on the invariant manifold $E_h^\infty \equiv S^1 \times S^1$ in terms of angular variables (θ, ϕ), where

$$\begin{aligned} y_1 &= r_1 \cos\theta, & y_3 &= r_2 \cos\phi, \\ y_2 &= r_1 \sin\theta, & y_3 &= r_2 \sin\phi, \end{aligned}$$

$r_1 = 1/\sqrt{8h+1}$, and $r_2 = \sqrt{8h/(8h+1)}$, is given by

$$\begin{aligned} \theta' &= \sqrt{8h}\sin(\phi - \theta), \\ \phi' &= -\sqrt{8h}\sin(\phi - \theta). \end{aligned}$$

Therefore, the trayectories are straight lines of slope -1 in the covering plane (θ, ϕ) and the critical points correspond to the lines $\phi = \theta$ and $\phi = \theta + \pi$.

It is interesting to note that in this case the same picture is obtained if one does the blow up of the infinity ([LS]).

The treatment of the case $h = 0$ is similar, except that E_h^∞ is a circle of degenerate critical points.

3. Global regularization of the collinear 3-body problem

In the paper by Heggie ([Heg]), he shows that it is always possible to write the equations of motion for the n–body problem of Celestial Mechanics in polynomial form. To get the equations in this form Heggie makes a global regularization of binary collisions, generalizing Kustanheimo-Stiefel transformation for the Kepler problem. When applying Heggie's tranformation, it is necessary to increase the dimension of the phase space, by adding some redundant variables. In this section we adapt this technique to the collinear 3–body problem. His equations are for the 3–dimensional case and can be restricted to 2 dimensions, but do not work directly for 1 dimension. For the Kepler problem, we used a direct regularization to get polynomial equations, avoiding the redundancy. We give the construction for the collinear 3–body problem in this section. The full details of the collinear 3-body problem and other results are given in [DLLP].

Consider 3 point particles in the line, where m_i are the masses of the particles and q_i' their positions in the following order: $q_3' < q_1' < q_2'$.

The equations of motion are the Hamiltonian equations given by the Hamiltonian function

$$H' = \frac{1}{2}\sum_{i=1}^{3}\frac{(p_i')^2}{m_i} - \frac{m_2 m_3}{q_2' - q_3'} + \frac{m_3 m_1}{q_3' - q_1'} + \frac{m_1 m_2}{q_1' - q_2'}.$$

We introduce now the change of coordinates

$$\begin{aligned} q_1 &= q_2' - q_3' > 0, \\ q_2 &= q_3' - q_1' < 0, \\ q_3 &= q_1' - q_2' < 0, \\ \langle q \rangle &= \frac{m_1}{M}q_1' + \frac{m_2}{M}q_2' + \frac{m_3}{M}q_3', \end{aligned} \tag{7}$$

where $M = m_1 + m_2 + m_3$. We remark that the condition $q_1 + q_2 + q_2 = 0$ holds.

The equations (7) can be writen as

$$q = Aq', \tag{8}$$

where

$$A = \begin{pmatrix} 0 & 1 & -1 \\ -1 & 0 & 1 \\ 1 & -1 & 0 \\ \frac{m_1}{M} & \frac{m_2}{M} & \frac{m_3}{M} \end{pmatrix}, \quad q = \begin{pmatrix} q_1 \\ q_2 \\ q_3 \\ \langle q \rangle \end{pmatrix}, \quad \text{and} \quad q' = \begin{pmatrix} q_1' \\ q_2' \\ q_3' \end{pmatrix},$$

and the Hamiltonian can be expressed in terms of a new function $H''(q, p')$ as

$$H'(q', p') = H''(Aq', p'),$$

with

$$H''(q, p') = \frac{1}{2}\sum_{i=1}^{3}\frac{(p_i')^2}{m_i} - \frac{m_2 m_3}{q_1} + \frac{m_3 m_1}{q_2} + \frac{m_1 m_2}{q_3}.$$

We define new momenta by

$$p' = A^T p, \tag{9}$$

where $(^T)$ means transpose of a matrix, and

$$p' = \begin{pmatrix} p_1' \\ p_2' \\ p_3' \end{pmatrix}, \qquad p = \begin{pmatrix} p_1 \\ p_2 \\ p_3 \\ \langle p \rangle \end{pmatrix}.$$

Next we will consider the new Hamiltonian $H(q,p) = H''(q, A^T p)$, that is

$$H = \frac{1}{2\mu_{23}} p_1^2 + \frac{1}{2\mu_{31}} p_2^2 + \frac{1}{2\mu_{12}} p_3^2 + \frac{1}{2M} \langle p \rangle^2 - \left(\frac{p_2 p_3}{m_1} + \frac{p_3 p_1}{m_2} + \frac{p_1 p_2}{m_3} \right) \\ - \frac{m_2 m_3}{q_1} + \frac{m_3 m_1}{q_2} + \frac{m_1 m_2}{q_3}$$

where $\mu_{ij}^{-1} = m_i^{-1} + m_j^{-1}$.

In order to obtain a polynomial Hamiltonian, we adapt the ideas of Heggie by introducing new coordinates (Q, P). His transformation works for dimensions 2 and 3. In the collinear problem, it is necessary to adjust some signs in a non trivial way. We take

$$q_1 = Q_1^2, \qquad p_1 = \frac{P_1}{2Q_1},$$

$$q_2 = -Q_2^2, \qquad p_2 = -\frac{P_2}{2Q_2},$$

$$q_3 = -Q_3^2, \qquad p_3 = -\frac{P_2}{2Q_3}.$$

Since the Hamiltonian is a first integral, we restrict our attention to the energy level $H = h$. Therefore, if we define

$$\Gamma = Q_1^2 Q_2^2 Q_3^2 (H - h)$$

and a new time scale $\bar{t}$ as

$$\frac{dt}{d\bar{t}} = Q_1^2 Q_2^2 Q_3^2,$$

then the equations of motion of the collinear 3-body problem at $H = h$ correspond to the Hamiltonian equations defined by the Hamiltonian

$$\Gamma = \frac{1}{8} \left(\frac{Q_2^2 Q_3^2 P_1^2}{\mu_{23}} + \frac{Q_3^2 Q_1^2 P_2^2}{\mu_{31}} + \frac{Q_1^2 Q_2^2 P_3^2}{\mu_{12}} \right) \\ - \frac{1}{4} \left(\frac{Q_1^2 Q_2 Q_3 P_2 P_3}{m_1} - \frac{Q_2^2 Q_3 Q_1 P_3 P_1}{m_2} - \frac{Q_3^2 Q_1 Q_2 P_1 P_2}{m_3} \right) \\ - \left(m_2 m_3 Q_2^2 Q_3^2 + m_3 m_1 Q_3^2 Q_1^2 + m_1 m_2 Q_1^2 Q_2^2 + h Q_1^2 Q_2^2 Q_3^2 \right)$$

at the zero level $\Gamma = 0$.

For the purpose of applying Poincaré compactification described in the last section we rename the coordinates as

$$x_1 = Q_1, \quad x_2 = Q_2, \quad x_3 = Q_3,$$
$$x_4 = P_1, \quad x_5 = P_2, \quad x_6 = P_3.$$

In this case the compactification will be defined on the sphere S^6, the degree of the polynomial Hamiltonian vector field will be $m = 5$.

The general procedure is to find the critical points of the vector field in each chart. The ones not depending on the masses are easier to compute. The ones depending on the masses were obtained by straightforward but tedious computations.

The next step is to write the equations describing the critical points in coordinates $y_1, \dots, y_7$ of the sphere S^6. Let us observe that some of these equations are common to several charts.

We divide the set of critical points in S^6 into the subsets given below, and give the physical interpretation of solutions approaching them. Notice first, that from the relation (??), it follows that if $y_7 \neq 0$ then $y_i \to 0$ is equivalent to $x_i \to 0$. In particular for $i = 1, 2, 3$, the last statement means a binary or triple collision, because $x_i \to 0$ is also equivalent to $q_i \to 0$, for $i = 1, 2, 3$.

(1) Triple collision set (TC) is the set of points $y \in S^6$ such that

$$y_1 = y_2 = y_3 = 0,$$
$$y_4^2 + y_5^2 + y_6^2 + y_7^2 = 1,$$

which is homeomorphic to a three sphere S^3. When $y_7 = 0$, we get an equator S^2_∞, is located at the infinity of phase space. For $y_7 \neq 0$, this corresponds to triple collision from the above remark. For $y_7 = 0$, it does not have any physical sense.

(2) Left binary set (LB) is the set of points $y \in S^6$ such that

$$y_1 = \pm y_3 \neq 0,$$
$$y_2 = y_5 = y_7 = 0,$$
$$2y_3^2 + y_4^2 + y_6^2 = 1,$$

which is homeomorphic to two intersecting spheres minus the circle of intersection (C_{LB}). Since $y_7 \to 0$ here, the critical points are at infinity of phase space. From relations (??), and since $y_1 \neq 0$, $y_3 \neq 0$, we have that $x_1 \to \infty$ and $x_3 \to \infty$. On the other hand, we have

$$\frac{y_2}{y_1} = \frac{x_2}{x_1} = \frac{Q_2}{Q_1} \to 0,$$
$$\frac{y_2}{y_3} = \frac{x_2}{x_3} = \frac{Q_2}{Q_3} \to 0,$$
$$\frac{y_5}{y_1} = \frac{x_5}{x_1} = \frac{P_2}{Q_1} \to 0.$$

The first two equations mean that the relative distance between the binary m_3-m_1 remains bounded or goes to infinity at a lower order than any of the distances m_3 to m_2 or m_1 to m_2. Denote by h_{13} the relative limiting energy of the binary m_3-m_1, then if $h_{13} \geq 0$, corresponding to unbounded motion, it has to be zero; otherwise $h_{13} > 0$, $q_2 = \mathcal{O}(t)$ and $q_3 = \mathcal{O}(t)$, then the quotient would not go to zero as t goes to infinity. Hence $h_{13} = 0$, and $q_2 = \mathcal{O}(t^{2/3})$ while $q_3 = \mathcal{O}(t)$.

(3) Right binary set (RB) is the set of point $y \in S^6$ such that

$$\begin{aligned} &y_1 = \pm y_2 \neq 0, \\ &y_3 = y_6 = y_7 = 0, \\ &2y_2^2 + y_4^2 + y_5^2 = 1, \end{aligned}$$

which is symmetrical to the set LB. The physical interpretation is similar to LB, proceeding by symmetry.

(4) Zero energy set (ZE) which exists only for $h = 0$, is the set of points $y \in S^6$ such that

$$\begin{aligned} &y_1y_5 + y_2y_4 = 0, \\ &y_3y_5 - y_2y_6 = 0, \\ &y_1y_6 + y_3y_4 = 0, \\ &y_1^2 = y_2^2 + y_3^2, \\ &y_7 = 0, \\ &2y_2^2 + 2y_3^2 + y_4^2 + y_5^2 + y_6^2 = 1, \\ &y_1y_2y_3 \neq 0. \end{aligned}$$

Recall that $y_i = x_i y_7$. Since $y_1y_2y_3 \neq 0$ and $y_7 = 0$, we have that $x_i \to \infty$ for any $i = 1, 2, 3$. This means that all the particles escape from each other, without any bounded binary, since any relative limiting energy has to be zero.

(5) Positive energy set (PE) which exists only for $h > 0$, is the set of points $y \in S^6$ such that

$$\begin{gathered} y_1^2 = y_2^2 + y_3^2, \\ y_6y_2 - y_3y_5 = \frac{y_3}{y_1}F(y_4y_2 + y_1y_5), \\ \left(\frac{1}{m_1}F^2 + \frac{(F+1)^2}{m_2} + \frac{1}{m_3}\right)(y_4y_2 + y_1y_5)^2 = 8hy_1^2y_2^2, \\ y_1^2 + y_2^2 + y_3^2 + y_4^2 + y_5^2 + y_6^2 = 1, \\ y_7 = 0, \\ y_1y_2y_3 \neq 0, \end{gathered}$$

where $F = (m_1/m_3)(m_2y_3^2 - m_3y_2^2)/(m_2y_1^2 + m_1y_2^2)$.

Note that if all the above equations are rescaled by replacing y_i by $h^{-1/2}y_i$ for $i = 1, 2, 3$, we see that all the equations but the sphere define topologically the same cone, while the sphere is replaced by an ellipsoid. Since the ellipsoid and the sphere have just one point on each ray from the origin, the intersectionss with the cone must be topologically equivalent. Therefore, we have that the topology of PE is independent of h.

By analizing the the closures of each of the subsets, it is possible to show that the whole set of critical points form a compact and connected set.

Acknowledgments. The third author is partially supported by a DGICYT grant number PB90-0695.

References

[CL] A. Cima and A. J. Llibre. *Bounded polynomial vector fields.* Trans.of the A.M.S. **318**, no. 2, (1990), 557–579.

[DLLP] J. Delgado, E.A. Lacomba, J. Llibre and E. Pérez. *Poincaré compactification of the collinear three body problem.* to appear in the proceedings of the International Symposium on Hamiltonian Systems and Celestial Mechanics, Guanajuato, México, 1991.

[Heg] D. C. Heggie. *A global regularization of the gravitational n-body problem.* Cel. Mech. **10**, (1974), 217–241.

[LS] E. A. Lacomba and C. Simó. *Boundary manifolds for energy surfaces in Celestial Mechanics.* Cel. Mech. **28**, (1982), 37–48.

*Departamento de Matemáticas, Universidad Autónoma Metropolitana–Iztapalapa, Apdo. 55534, México, D.F., México.

**Departament de Matemàtiques, Facultat de Ciències, Universitat Autònoma de Barcelona, 08193 Bellaterra, Spain.

A NOTE ON THE EXISTENCE OF HETEROCLINIC ORBITS IN THE PLANAR THREE–BODY PROBLEM

Regina Martínez(1) and Carles Simó(2)

Abstract. The existence and transversality of orbits of the planar three–body problem such that one of the masses escapes to infinity for positive and negative time with zero limit velocity is obtained. An asymptotic expression for the parameters which define the limit periodic orbits for the other two masses at infinity is also given. The problem is considered as a perturbation of two two–body problems, an elliptic one and a parabolic one. The results obtained and the methods used are natural modifications of the corresponding ones for the planar restricted elliptic three–body problem, recently studied in [M–P].

1. Introduction

Let us consider three masses m_1, m_2 and m_3, with $m_1 + m_2 + m_3 = 1$, moving in a plane under the gravitational law. Our purpose is to consider the planar three–body problem as a perturbation of two two–body problems: an elliptic motion for m_1 and m_2, and a parabolic one for the system m_1, m_3. If ε is a small positive quantity, we introduce two finite parameters, μ_2 and μ_3, such that $m_2 = \varepsilon\,\mu_2$, $m_3 = \varepsilon\,\mu_3$.

If $\mathbf{r}_1$, $\mathbf{r}_2$, $\mathbf{r}_3 \in \mathbb{R}^2$ give the position of the masses with respect to the center of masses, we denote by $\mathbf{q} = (q_1, q_2)$ and $\mathbf{Q} = (Q_1, Q_2)$ the Jacobi coordinates, that is, $\mathbf{q} = \mathbf{r}_1 - \mathbf{r}_2$ and $\mathbf{Q} = \dfrac{1}{m_1 + m_2}\,\mathbf{r}_3$.

We scale the angular momentum as well as the energy, by dividing both by ε, and define

$$\begin{aligned} c &= \mu\,\mu_3\,(Q_1\,\dot{Q}_2 - Q_2\,\dot{Q}_1) + \mu_2\,\frac{m_1}{\mu}\,(q_1\,\dot{q}_2 - q_2\,\dot{q}_1)\,, \\ h &= h_1 + h_2 + h_3 \end{aligned} \tag{1}$$

where

$$
\begin{aligned}
h_1 &= \mu_3\,\mu\,\left(\frac{1}{2}\,|\dot{\mathbf{Q}}|^2 - |\mathbf{Q}|^{-1}\right), \quad h_2 = \frac{m_1\,\mu_2}{\mu}\,\left(\frac{1}{2}\,|\dot{\mathbf{q}}|^2 - |\mathbf{q}|^{-1}\right), \\
h_3 &= m_1\,\mu_3\,(\,|\mathbf{Q}|^{-1} - r_{13}^{-1}) + \varepsilon\,\mu_2\,\mu_3\,(\,|\mathbf{Q}|^{-1} - r_{23}^{-1}), \\
m_1 &= 1 - \varepsilon\,(\mu_2 + \mu_3)\,, \quad \mu = 1 - \varepsilon\,\mu_3\,, \\
r_{13} &= \left|\mathbf{Q} - \frac{\varepsilon\,\mu_2}{\mu}\,\mathbf{q}\right|, \quad r_{23} = \left|\mathbf{Q} + \frac{m_1}{\mu}\,\mathbf{q}\right|.
\end{aligned}
\tag{2}
$$

We introduce a new set of real variables $(x, y, \alpha, \rho, \delta_1, \delta_2, \ell, \beta)$ in the following way

$$
\begin{aligned}
&\mathbf{Q} = \frac{2}{x^2}\,s\,, \; s = \exp(i\,\alpha), \quad \dot{\mathbf{Q}} = \left(y + \frac{\rho\,x^2}{2}\,i\right)\,s, \quad \mathbf{q} = r\,\zeta\,, \\
&\zeta = \exp(i\,\ell)\,, \; \dot{\mathbf{q}} = \left(z + \frac{\beta}{r}\,i\right)\,\zeta\,, \; z \in \mathbb{R}\,, \; \delta = \delta_1 + i\,\delta_2 = e\,\Phi, \\
&\text{where} \\
&\Phi = \exp(i\,\Lambda)\,, \; e = \frac{\beta\,z}{\mu\,\sin(\ell - \Lambda)}\,, \; \tan(\ell - \Lambda) = \frac{\beta\,z\,r}{\beta^2 - \mu\,r}\,, \\
&i \text{ being equal to } \sqrt{-1}.
\end{aligned}
\tag{3}
$$

We note that, for $\varepsilon = 0$, e and Λ defined in (3) would be the eccentricity and the argument of the pericenter for the primaries m_1 and m_2, respectively. Classically ℓ is called true anomaly. It is more convenient for the computations to use δ_1 and δ_2 instead of e and Λ, because Λ is not defined when $e = 0$. On the other hand, it is not restrictive to consider that the semiaxis for the elliptic motion of the unperturbed problem ($\varepsilon = 0$) is equal to one. This is equivalent to fix the value of the energy as $h = -\dfrac{\mu_2}{2}$. The mean motion can also be taken equal to one.

The equations of motion in the new variables become

$$
\begin{aligned}
\dot{x} &= -\frac{x^3}{4}\,y, \\
\dot{y} &= -\,\frac{x^4}{4} + \frac{\rho^2\,x^6}{8} - R_1, \\
\dot{\alpha} &= \rho\frac{x^4}{4}, \\
\dot{\rho} &= R_2,
\end{aligned}
\tag{4 a}
$$

$$
\begin{aligned}
\dot{\delta} &= R_3, \\
\dot{\ell} &= \frac{\beta}{r^2}, \\
\dot{\beta} &= -r\,S_2,
\end{aligned}
\tag{4 b}
$$

where

$$
\begin{aligned}
R_1 &= -\frac{x^4}{4} + \frac{x^4}{4\,\mu}\left(\frac{m_1}{\sigma_{13}^3} + \frac{\varepsilon\,\mu_2}{\sigma_{23}^3}\right) + \frac{\varepsilon\, m_1\,\mu_2}{8\,\mu^2}\, r\, x^6\, \cos(\alpha-\ell)\left(-\frac{1}{\sigma_{13}^3}+\frac{1}{\sigma_{23}^3}\right),\\
R_2 &= \frac{\varepsilon\, m_1\,\mu_2}{4\,\mu^2}\, r\, x^4\, \sin(\alpha-\ell)\left(-\frac{1}{\sigma_{13}^3}+\frac{1}{\sigma_{23}^3}\right),\\
R_3 &= \frac{\beta}{\mu}\, S_1\, i\,\overline{\zeta} - \frac{\mu}{\beta}\left(\delta + (2 + e\, \cos(\ell-\Lambda))\,\zeta\right) S_2,\\
S_1 &= \varepsilon\,\mu_3\left\{\frac{x^4}{4}\,\cos(\alpha-\ell)\left(-\frac{1}{\sigma_{13}^3}+\frac{1}{\sigma_{23}^3}\right) + \frac{x^6\, r}{8\,\mu}\left(\frac{\varepsilon\,\mu^2}{\sigma_{13}^3}+\frac{m_1}{\sigma_{23}^3}\right)\right\}, \qquad (5)\\
S_2 &= \varepsilon\,\mu_3\,\frac{x^4}{4}\,\sin(\alpha-\ell)\left(-\frac{1}{\sigma_{13}^3}+\frac{1}{\sigma_{23}^3}\right),\\
\sigma_{13} &= \left\{1-\varepsilon\,\frac{\mu_2}{\mu}\, r\, x^2\,\cos(\alpha-\ell) + \left(\frac{\varepsilon\,\mu_2}{\mu}\,\frac{r\,x^2}{2}\right)^2\right\}^{1/2},\\
\sigma_{23} &= \left\{1+\frac{m_1}{\mu}\, r\, x^2\,\cos(\alpha-\ell) + \left(\frac{m_1}{\mu}\,\frac{r\,x^2}{2}\right)^2\right\}^{1/2},
\end{aligned}
$$

and for the scaled angular momentum and energy we have

$$
\begin{aligned}
c &= \mu_3\,\mu\,\rho + \frac{m_1\,\mu_2}{\mu}\,\beta,\\
h_1 &= \mu\,\mu_3\left[\frac{1}{2}\left(y^2+\frac{\rho^2\,x^4}{2}\right)-\frac{x^2}{2}\right],\quad h_2 = m_1\,\mu_2\,\mu\left(\frac{|\delta|^2-1}{2\,\beta^2}\right), \qquad (6)\\
h_3 &= m_1\,\mu_3\,\frac{x^2}{2}\left(1-\frac{1}{\sigma_{13}}\right)+\varepsilon\,\mu_2\,\mu_3\,\frac{x^2}{2}\left(1-\frac{1}{\sigma_{23}}\right).
\end{aligned}
$$

This is the usual way to extend analytically the flow to infinity, which corresponds to $x=0$ ([E–Mc G], [R]). The angular momentum, c, and the energy, h, are also defined when $x=0$. We call "parabolic infinity", I, the set of points such that $x=y=0$. If we put $x=0$ in the equations (4) we see that I is invariant and the variables α,ρ,δ,β remain constant. On I we have a periodic orbit for each set of values $(\alpha,\rho,\delta)=(\alpha_\infty,\rho_\infty,\delta_\infty)$. We note that from the energy relation on I we have $-\dfrac{\mu_2}{2} = m_1\,\mu_2\,\mu\left(\dfrac{|\delta_\infty|^2-1}{2\,\beta_\infty^2}\right)$. Then $\beta_\infty^2 = m_1\,\mu(1-|\delta_\infty|^2)$. Of course, instead of ρ_∞ one can also specify the value of c.

Robinson [R] proved that each periodic orbit on I has stable and unstable invariant manifolds, which are two–dimensional if we fix the angular momentum and the energy. Our purpose is to get, up to first order in ε, the intersection of these invariant manifolds.

We note that if we take $\mu_3 = 0$ in the equations (4), we get the so called planar, restricted elliptic three–body problem. That problem has been studied in [M–P], where the small parameter was taken equal to m_2, and the pericenter of the primaries was fixed on the positive x axis.

2. The integrable case

If we take $\varepsilon = 0$ in (4) the system decomposes in two integrable problems. The parabolic solutions for the third body have been given in [Ll–S] (see also [M–P]). We have that ρ is constant on these solutions. We put $\rho = \rho_0$ and we introduce a new time $\tau = u/\rho_0$, where u is defined by $t = \dfrac{u^3}{6} + \rho_0^2 \, \dfrac{u}{2}$. Then

$$x(\tau) = \frac{2}{\rho_0(1+\tau^2)^{1/2}}\,, \quad y(\tau) = \frac{2\,\tau}{\rho_0(1+\tau^2)}\,, \quad \alpha(\tau) = \alpha_0 + 2\,\text{arctan}\ \tau. \tag{7}$$

For the elliptic part of the motion we have $\beta = \beta_0 \in \mathbb{R}$, $\delta = \delta_0 = \delta_{1,0} + i\,\delta_{2,0} \in \mathbb{C}$ for some constants β_0, δ_0, and ℓ is obtained by integration of the equation $\dot{\ell} = \dfrac{\beta_0}{r^2}$, where

$$r = \frac{\beta_0^2}{1 + e_0\ \cos(\ell - \Lambda_0)} \tag{8}$$

is the distance between the primaries, and ℓ_0, Λ_0 the corresponding eccentricity and argument of the pericenter. Therefore, if we take initial conditions as

$$\mathbf{Z}_0 = (x_0, y_0, \alpha_0, \rho_0, \delta_0, \ell_0, \beta_0)^\top = \left(\frac{2}{\rho_0}\,, 0, \alpha_0, \rho_0, \delta_0, \ell_0, \beta_0\right)^\top, \tag{9}$$

with $\alpha_0, \ell_0 \in S^1$, $|\delta_0| < 1$ and $\beta_0^2 = 1 - |\delta_0|^2$, then the third mass escapes parabolically to infinity with $\alpha(\tau) \longrightarrow \alpha_0 + \pi$ when $\tau \longrightarrow \infty$. Therefore, for the limit periodic orbit at the infinity, we have $\alpha_\infty = \alpha_0 + \pi$, $\rho_\infty = \rho_0$, $\beta_\infty = \beta_0$ and $\delta_\infty = \delta_0$.

3. The planar three–body problem when $\varepsilon > 0$ is small: biparabolic orbits

For $\varepsilon > 0$ we consider initial conditions

$$\mathbf{Z}_i = (x_i,\, y_i,\, \alpha_i,\, \rho_i,\, \delta_i,\, \ell_i,\, \beta_i)^\top = \mathbf{Z}_0 + \varepsilon\,\Delta\,\mathbf{Z}_0 + O_2, \tag{10}$$

where $\mathbf{Z}_0$ is defined by (9), $\Delta\,\mathbf{Z}_0 = (\Delta\,x_0, 0, 0, 0, 0, 0, 0)^\top$, and O_2 contains terms of order 2 in ε.

We write the system (4) as

$$\dot{\mathbf{Z}} = \mathbf{F}(\mathbf{Z}) + \varepsilon\, \mathcal{T}(\mathbf{Z}) + \mathbf{R}(\mathbf{Z},\, \varepsilon), \tag{11}$$

where $\mathbf{R}(\mathbf{Z},\, \varepsilon)$ is a function of order 2 in ε. We denote by $\mathbf{Z}(t\,,\, \mathbf{Z}_i\,;\, \varepsilon)$ the solution of (11) such that $\mathbf{Z}(0,\, \mathbf{Z}_i\,;\, \varepsilon) = \mathbf{Z}_i$. Then, if $\mathbf{Z}(t,\, \mathbf{Z}_i\,;\, \varepsilon) = \mathbf{Z}(t\,,\, \mathbf{Z}_0\,;\, 0) + \varepsilon\, \mathbf{Z}_b(t,\, \Delta\, x_0) + O_2$, $\mathbf{Z}_b(t,\, \Delta\, x_0)$ is the solution of the variational equations

$$\begin{aligned} \dot{\mathbf{Z}}_b(t,\, \Delta\, x_0) &= D\mathbf{F}\left(\mathbf{Z}(t,\, \mathbf{Z}_0\,;\, 0)\right)\, \mathbf{Z}_b(t,\, \Delta\, x_o) + \mathcal{T}\left(\mathbf{Z}(t,\, \mathbf{Z}_0\,;\, 0)\right)\,, \\ \mathbf{Z}_b(0,\, \Delta\, x_0) &= \Delta\, \mathbf{Z}_0. \end{aligned}$$

It is easy to see that the system above decomposes in two independent systems, corresponding to the variational equations for the parabolic and elliptic motion, respectively. We write the first one

$$\begin{aligned} x_b' &= \left(-\frac{3}{2}\, \rho_0\, y\right)\, x_b + \left(-\, \frac{\rho_0\, x}{2}\right)\, y_b\,, \\ y_b' &= \left(-2\, \rho_0\, x + \frac{3}{2}\, \rho_0^3\, x^3\right)\, x_b + b_1(\tau), \\ \alpha_b' &= (2\, \rho_0^2\, x)\, x_b + \left(\frac{\rho_0\, x^2}{2}\right)\, \rho_b, \\ \rho_b' &= \frac{2\, \rho_0}{x^2}\, \left.\frac{d\, R_2}{d\, \varepsilon}\right|_{\varepsilon=0}, \end{aligned} \tag{12}$$

where $' = \frac{d}{d\,t} = \frac{2\,\rho_0}{x^2}\, \frac{d}{d\,t}$, x, y, α and r are given by (7) and (8), and

$$\begin{aligned} b_1(\tau) &= \left(\frac{\rho_0^2\, x^4}{2}\right)\, \rho_b(\tau) - \frac{2\, \rho_0}{x^2}\, \left.\frac{d\, R_1}{d\, \varepsilon}\right|_{\varepsilon=0} \\ &= \frac{\rho_0^2\, x^4}{2}\, \rho_b(\tau) - \mu_2\, \frac{x^2\, \rho}{2}\, \left(-1 + \frac{1}{\sigma_{23}^3}\right) \\ &\quad - \frac{\mu_2}{4}\, \rho_0\, x^4\, r\, \cos\left(\alpha - \ell\right)\, \left(2 + \frac{1}{\sigma_{23}^3}\right). \end{aligned} \tag{13}$$

We note that if we take $\mu_2 = 1$, the system (12) is the one obtained in [M–P] for the planar elliptic restricted three–body problem, but changing the angle $\alpha - \ell$ in (12) and (13) by $\alpha - f$, where f is the true anomaly of the unperturbed motion of the primaries. Therefore, using the computations made in [M–P] we get that, in order to have a parabolic escape of m_3, a necessary condition is

$$\Delta\, x_0 = -\int_0^{\infty} \frac{\tau}{1 + \tau^2}\, b_1(\tau)\, d\tau\,,$$

where we recall that $b_1(\tau)$ is computed on a solution given by (7) and (8) of the unperturbed problem. So, we can write

$$\alpha - \ell = \alpha_0 + 2 \text{ arctan } \tau - (\ell - \Lambda_0) - \Lambda_0 = \alpha_0 - \Lambda_0 + 2 \text{ arctan } \tau - f, \quad (14)$$

where f is now the true anomaly of the elliptic motion for $\varepsilon = 0$.

Following [M–P] we write the mean anomaly of the primaries as

$$\tilde{\ell} = \frac{\rho_0^3}{2}\left(\frac{\tau^3}{3} + \tau\right) + \omega \,. \quad (15)$$

Then, f can be expressed in terms of $\tilde{\ell}$, using Fourier expansions of the following type

$$r^n \exp(i\, m\, f) = \sum_{k\in\mathbb{Z}} C_k^{n,m} \exp(i\, k\, \tilde{\ell}), \quad (16)$$

for some integer values n, m where $C_k^{n,m}$ are functions which depend only on the eccentricity. Therefore, the computation of $\Delta\, x_0$ can be done as in [M–P] but substituting α_0 by $\alpha_0 - \Lambda_0$, which is the angle between the two pericenters for $\varepsilon = 0$.

Using the symmetry of the system

$$S : (x, y, \alpha, \rho, \delta, \ell, \beta, t) \longrightarrow (x, -y, -\alpha, \rho, \overline{\delta}, -\ell, \beta, -t)$$

and the results of [M–P] we have that a necessary and sufficient condition to have an orbit which tends to I for positive and negative time (a biparabolic orbit), is

$$D(\mathbf{Z}_0) := \Delta\, x_0\,(\mathbf{Z}_0) - \Delta\, x_0\,\big(S\,(\mathbf{Z}_0)\big) = 0,$$

where $S\,(\mathbf{Z}_0)$ stands for the symmetric point of $\mathbf{Z}_0$ with respect to S. It is not difficult to see that, in fact, $D(\mathbf{Z}_0)$ depends on ρ_0, $\alpha_0 - \Lambda_0$, e_0 and ω. We can conclude that, concerning the existence of biparabolic orbits, the result of [M–P] also holds for the planar three-body problem.

Theorem A. *Let be $\varepsilon > 0$ and $e_0 > 0$ sufficiently small, and $\rho_0 > 0$ such that $\gamma = 2\, e\, \rho_0$ is large enough. Then, except for a countable set of values $\{\rho_0^{(j)}\,,\, j > 0\}$, the function $D\,(\rho_0\,,\, \alpha_0 - \Lambda_0\,,\, e_0\,,\, \omega)$ has two continuous curves of zeros, $\omega = \omega\,(a_0)$ and $\omega = \omega\,(a_0) + \pi$, in the torus parametrized by $a_0 := \alpha_0 - \Lambda_0$ and ω. The points of these curves give initial conditions for biparabolic orbits.*

Remarks.

i) For large j, $\rho_0^{(j)}$ behaves like $\dfrac{\pi}{e}\left(j + \dfrac{3}{8}\right)$. At those values the number of solutions, a_0, of $\omega(a_0) = \omega^*$, for a given value of $\omega^* \in [0,\, 2\,\pi)$, increases by 2. When $\rho_0 = \rho_0^{(j)}$ tangential heteroclinic orbits to I exist.

ii) If $e_0 = 0$ and ρ_0 is large enough, then $\omega(a_0) = a_0$.

iii) In fact $D(\rho_0, \alpha_0 - \Lambda_0, e_0, \omega)$ is a function exponentially small in ρ_0. Indeed, it contains terms of the type $\exp\left(-\frac{\rho_0^3}{3}\right)$.

4. The limit orbits

Let us consider a solution of (11) which tends to infinity for positive and negative time. Let be $(\alpha_\infty, \rho_\infty, \delta_\infty)$ and $(\hat{\alpha}_\infty, \hat{\rho}_\infty, \hat{\delta}_\infty)$ the parameters for the corresponding limit periodic orbits in I. If w stands for $\alpha, \rho, \delta_1, \delta_2$ or β, we have

$$w_\infty = w_\infty(0) + \varepsilon\, w_{b\infty}(\mathbf{Z}_0) + O_2,$$

where

$$w_\infty(0) = \begin{cases} w_0 & \text{if } w \neq \alpha, \\ w_0 + \pi & \text{if } w = \alpha, \end{cases} \qquad \text{and} \qquad w_{b\infty}(\mathbf{Z}_0) = \lim_{\tau \to \infty} w_b(\tau_b\,;\, \Delta x_0),$$

and, using the symmetry,

$$\hat{w}_\infty = \hat{w}_\infty(0) + \varepsilon\,(-1)^n\, w_{b\infty}\left(S(\mathbf{Z}_0)\right) + O_2\,,$$

where

$$\hat{w}_\infty(0) = \begin{cases} w_0 & \text{if } \ w \neq \alpha, \\ w_0 - \pi & \text{if } \ w = \alpha, \end{cases} \qquad \text{and} \quad n = \begin{cases} 0 & \text{if } \ w = \rho, \delta_1, \\ 1 & \text{if } \ w = \alpha, \delta_2. \end{cases}$$

For $\alpha_{b\infty}$, $\rho_{b\infty}$ we get the same expressions as the ones obtained for the restricted elliptic three–body problem, but multiplied by μ_2 and with $\alpha_0 - \Lambda_0$ instead of α_0, that is

$$\begin{aligned} \alpha_{b,\infty} = {} & \frac{\mu_2}{\rho_0^4}\left[\frac{3\pi}{4} + e_0^2\left(\frac{9\pi}{8} - \frac{45\pi}{16}\cos 2(\alpha_0 - \Lambda_0) + 80\sin 2(\alpha_0 - \Lambda_0)\right) + O(e_0^3)\right. \\ & \left. + \frac{1}{\rho_0^2}\left(-\frac{15\pi e_0}{2}\cos(\alpha_0 - \Lambda_0) + 50 e_0 \sin(\alpha_0 - \Lambda_0) + O(e_0^3)\right) + O\left(\frac{1}{\rho_0^3}\right)\right], \\ \rho_{b,\infty} = {} & -\frac{c_0\mu_2}{\rho_0^3}\left\{5e_0\cos 2(\alpha_0 - \Lambda_0) + \frac{1}{\rho_0^2}\left[\left(\frac{5}{2} + \frac{15}{8}e_0^2 + O(e_0^4)\right)\cos(\alpha_0 - \Lambda_0)\right.\right. \\ & \left.\left. + \left(\frac{15}{16} + \frac{45}{64}e_0^3 + O(e_0^5)\right)\sin(\alpha_0 - \Lambda_0)\right] + O\left(\frac{1}{\rho_0^3}\right)\right\}. \end{aligned}$$

We remark that β_∞ can be easily obtained from the conservation of the angular momentum. That is, once ρ_∞ is known

$$\mu_2\, m_1\, \beta_\infty = \mu_3\, \mu\,(\rho_0 - \rho_\infty) + \mu_2\, m_1\, \beta_0.$$

As said before $|\delta_\infty|$ can be obtained from β_∞, but we compute directly $\delta_{b\infty} = \int_0^\infty \left.\frac{d}{d\varepsilon}\right|_{\varepsilon=0} R(\tau)\, d\tau$. It is not difficult to see that

$$\begin{aligned}\delta_{b\infty} = \frac{\rho_0\ \mu_3}{2\,\beta_0} \sum_{m\geq 0}\ \sum_{n\geq n_1} \Bigg\{ i\,\frac{\beta_0^2}{2}\ \hat{\zeta}^{(m)}\ \mathcal{C}^{m,-}_{m+2n-1,1} \ - \\ -\ \hat{\gamma}_n^{(m)} \left(\frac{\beta_0^2}{2}\ \mathcal{S}^{m,+}_{m+2n-1,1} + \mathcal{S}^{m,+}_{m+2n,0}\right) - \delta_0\ \hat{\gamma}_n^{(m)}\ \mathcal{S}^{(m)}_{m+2n,0} \Bigg\},\end{aligned} \tag{17}$$

where $n_1 = 1$ if $m \leq 1$, $n_1 = 0$ if $m \geq 2$.

$$\begin{aligned}\hat{\zeta}_n^{(0)} &= -\frac{(2\,n+1)^2}{n+1}\ \Delta_0^{(2n)},\ n\geq 1\ ,\\ \hat{\gamma}_n^{(1)} &= 2\,\frac{(2\,n+1)}{n+1}\ \Delta_0^{(2n)},\ n\geq 1,\\ \hat{\zeta}_n^{(1)} &= 2\frac{(2\,n+1)^2}{n+1}\ \Delta_0^{(2n)},\ n\geq 1\ ,\\ \hat{\gamma}_n^{(m)} &= (-1)^{m-1}\ 4\,m\ \Delta_m^{(2n)},\ m\geq 2,\ n\geq 0,\\ \hat{\zeta}_n^{(m)} &= (-1)^{m-1}\ 4\,(m+2\,n)\ \Delta_n^{(2n)},\ m\geq 2,\ n\geq 0\ ,\\ \Delta_m^{(2n)} &= \frac{(2\,n-1)\,!\,!}{(2\,n)\,!\,!}\ \frac{(2\,m-2\,n-1)\,!\,!}{(2\,m+2\,n)\,!\,!},\ \ \text{using}\ \ (-1)\,!\,!=0,\end{aligned} \tag{18}$$

$$\begin{aligned}\mathcal{C}^{m,-}_{n,k} &:= \int_0^\infty \frac{r^n\ x^{2(n+k)}}{2^n}\ \cos\big(m(\alpha-\ell)\big)\ \exp\left(-i\,\ell\right)\,d\tau,\\ \mathcal{S}^{m,+}_{n,k} &:= \int_0^\infty \frac{r^n\ x^{2(n+k)}}{2^n}\ \sin\big(m(\alpha-\ell)\big)\ \exp\left(i\,\ell\right)\,d\tau\ ,\\ \mathcal{S}^{(m)}_{n,k} &:= \int_0^\infty \frac{r^n\ x^{2(n+k)}}{2^n}\ \sin\big(m(\alpha-\ell)\big)\ d\tau.\end{aligned} \tag{19}$$

Using (14), (15) and (16), the integrals defined in (19) can be expressed in terms of

$$\begin{aligned}\mathcal{J}_k(\nu) = I_k(\nu) + i\,J_k(\nu) &:= \int_0^\infty (1+\tau^2)^{-k}\ \exp\left[i\,\nu\left(\frac{\tau^3}{3}+\tau\right)\right]d\tau\ ,\\ \mathcal{M}_k(\nu) = N_k(\nu) + i\,M_k(\nu) &:= \int_0^\infty \tau\,(1+\tau^2)^{-k}\ \exp\left[i\,\nu\left(\frac{\tau^3}{3}+\tau\right)\right]d\tau,\end{aligned} \tag{20}$$

where $\nu = \frac{\rho_0^3}{2}$ and $k \geq 1$. Asymptotical developments for the integrals of (20) are given in [M–P] (see also [Ll–S] and [B]). Using that we get

$$\delta_{b\infty} = \frac{\mu_3}{2\,\beta_0}\left\{\frac{1}{\rho_0^3}\left[\frac{3}{2}\,\pi\, e_0\; i\;\exp\left(-i\,\Lambda_0\right) + 3\,e_0\;\exp\,\big(-i\,(2\,\alpha_0 - \Lambda_0)\big)\right.\right.$$

$$\left. -\,7\,e_0\;\exp\,\big(i\,(2\,\alpha_0 - \Lambda_0)\big) + 10\,e_0^2\;\delta_0\;\cos 2\,(\alpha_0 - \Lambda_0) + O\left(e_0^3\right)\right]$$

$$+\frac{1}{\rho_0^5}\left[9\left(1+\frac{e_0^2}{2}\right)\left(\frac{1}{3}+\frac{\pi}{8}\,i\right)\exp\left(-i\,\alpha_0\right) + \frac{45}{2}\,e_0^2\left(-\frac{1}{3}+\frac{\pi}{8}\,i\right)\right.$$

$$\exp\,\big(i\,(\alpha_0 - 2\,\Lambda_0)\big) + 3\left(2+\frac{7}{2}\,e_0^2\right)\left(-\frac{1}{3}+\frac{\pi}{8}\,i\right)\exp\left(i\,\alpha_0\right)$$

$$+\frac{75}{4}\,e_0^2\left(\frac{1}{3}-\frac{\pi}{8}\,i\right)\exp\,\big(-i\,(\alpha_0 - 2\,\Lambda_0)\big) + 15\,e_0\;\delta_0$$

$$\left.\left.\left(\frac{1}{3}\;\cos\left(\alpha_0 - \Lambda_0\right) + \frac{\pi}{8}\;\sin\left(\alpha_0 - \Lambda_0\right)\right) + O\left(e_0^3\right)\right] + O\left(\frac{1}{\rho_0^6}\right)\right\},$$

where $O\left(\frac{1}{\rho_0^6}\right)$ contains terms depending on ω.

We recall that if $e_0 = 0$, then Λ_0 and ω are not defined. But in that case we have $r = 1$ and

$$\alpha - \ell = \alpha_0 - \ell_0 + 2\;\arctan\;\tau - \frac{\rho_0^3}{2}\left(\frac{\tau^3}{3} + \tau\right),$$

and so, we can identify ℓ_0 with $\Lambda_0 + \omega$ (see (14)). However, it is easy to check that in the expressions obtained for $D(\mathbf{Z}_0)$, ρ_∞ and α_∞ (see [M–P]) for $e_0 > 0$, the terms which are independent of e_0 have arguments of the type $m\,\big(\alpha_0 - (\Lambda_0 + \omega)\big)$ for $m \geq 0$. In the same way, going back to (17), we see that the corresponding arguments for $\delta_{b\infty}$ are $m\,\alpha_0 - (m-1)\;(\Lambda_0 + \omega)$ and $m\,\alpha_0 - (m+1)\;(\Lambda_0 + \omega)$, $m \geq 0$. Therefore, the final expressions hold for $e_0 = 0$, but replacing $\Lambda_0 + \omega$ by ℓ_0.

Finally we state, as a conclusion, the following result.

Theorem B. *Let $\varepsilon > 0$ be sufficiently small. Except for a countable set of ρ_∞, for any periodic orbit at infinity given by $(\alpha_\infty\,,\ \rho_\infty\,,\ \delta_\infty)$, with $\rho_\infty > 0$ large enough and $|\delta_\infty|$ small enough, there exists an orbit, γ, of the planar three–body problem, such that $\gamma \in W^s\,(\alpha_\infty\,,\ \rho_\infty\,,\ \delta_\infty) \cap W^u\,(\hat{\alpha}_\infty\,,\ \hat{\rho}_\infty\,,\ \hat{\delta}_\infty)$,* *where*

$$\hat{\alpha}_\infty = \alpha_\infty - \varepsilon\mu_2 \left\{ \frac{2}{\rho_\infty^4} \left[\frac{3\pi}{4} + \frac{9\pi}{8} e_\infty^2 - \frac{45\pi}{16} \left(\cos 2\,\alpha_\infty (\delta_{1,\infty}^2 - \delta_{2,\infty}^2) \right. \right. \right.$$

$$\left. \left. \left. + 2\delta_{1,\infty}\delta_{2,\infty} \sin 2\,\alpha_\infty \right) + O(e_\infty^3) + F_1 \right] \right\} + O(\varepsilon^2),$$

$$\hat{\rho}_\infty = \rho_\infty - \varepsilon\mu_2 \left\{ \frac{1}{\rho_\infty^5} \left[\left(\frac{15}{8} + e_\infty^3 \frac{45}{32} \right) (\delta_{1,\infty} \sin \alpha_\infty - \delta_{2,\infty} \cos \alpha_\infty) \right. \right.$$

$$\left. \left. + O\left(\frac{e_\infty}{\rho_\infty^3} \right) \right] + F_2 \right\} + O(\varepsilon^3),$$

$$\hat{\delta}_{1,\infty} = \delta_{1,\infty} - \frac{\varepsilon\mu_3}{(1-e_\infty^2)^{1/2}} \frac{\pi}{\rho_\infty^3} \left\{ \frac{3}{2}\delta_{2,\infty} + \frac{1}{\rho_\infty^2} \left[\frac{3}{8} (1 - 2e_\infty^2) \sin \alpha_\infty \right. \right.$$

$$\left. \left. - \frac{165}{32} e_\infty^2 \sin(\alpha_\infty - 2\Lambda_\infty) + \frac{15}{8} e_\infty \delta_{1,\infty} \sin(\alpha_\infty - \Lambda_\infty) \right] + F_3 \right\} + O(\varepsilon^2),$$

$$\hat{\delta}_{2,\infty} = \delta_{2,\infty} - \frac{\varepsilon\,\mu_3}{(1-e_\infty^2)^{1/2}} \frac{\pi}{\rho_\infty^3} \left\{ \frac{3}{2}\delta_{1,\infty} + \frac{1}{\rho_\infty^2} \left[\frac{15}{8} (1 + e_\infty^2) \cos \alpha_\infty \right. \right.$$

$$\left. \left. - \frac{15}{32} e_\infty^2 \cos(\alpha_\infty - 2\Lambda_\infty) + \frac{15}{8} e_\infty \delta_{2,\infty} \cos(\alpha_\infty - \Lambda_\infty) \right] + F_4 \right\} + O(\varepsilon^2),$$

where F_j, $j = 1, \ldots, 4$ are functions depending on α_∞, ρ_∞, $\delta_{1,\infty}$, $\delta_{2,\infty}$, F_1 is $O(\rho_\infty^{-2})$, F_3 and F_4 are $O(\rho_\infty^{-3})$ and F_2 contains a factor exponentially small $\left(\exp\left(-\frac{\rho_\infty^3}{3} \right) \right)$ but this is the dominant term in $\hat{\rho}_\infty - \rho_\infty$ if $e_\infty = 0$. Moreover the intersection of the stable and unstable manifolds along γ is transversal.

Acknowledgements. This work has been partially supported by a CICYT Grant number ESP91–0403.

References

[B] Benseny, A.: Contribució a l'estudi del problema restringit de 3 cossos per a valors petits del paràmetre de masses, Ph. D. Thesis, Universitat de Barcelona, 1984..

[E–McG] Easton, R., McGehee, R.: Homoclinic phenomena for orbits doubly asymptotic to an invariant three–sphere, Indiana Univ. Math. J. **28** (1979), 211–240.

[Ll–S] Llibre, J., Simó, C.: Oscillatory solutions in the planar restricted three–body problem, Math. Ann. **248** (1980), 153–184.

[M–P] Martínez, R., Pinyol, C.: Parabolic orbits in the elliptic restricted three–body problem, preprint, Univ. Autònoma de Barcelona, 1991.

[R] Robinson, C.: Homoclinic orbits and oscillation for the planar three–body problem, J. Diff. Eq. **52** (1984), 356–377.

(1) Dept. de Matemàtiques, Universitat Autònoma de Barcelona, 08193 Bellaterra, Barcelona.

(2) Dept. de Matemàtica Aplicada i Anàlisi, Universitat de Barcelona, Gran Via 585, 08007 Barcelona.

KAM TORI FOR MODULATED SYMPLECTIC MAPS

ARMANDO BAZZANI

INTRODUCTION

The study of the dynamics of nonautonomous mappings or of parametric dependent dynamical systems has been considered in previous works[1,2,3], where a generalization of some results of autonomous dynamical systems is given under certain conditions. In this paper we present the generalization of Birkhoff normal forms[4,5] and of the KAM theory for the construction of quasi-periodic tori[6,7,8,9,10] to the dynamics of nonautonomous symplectic maps which depend on time in a periodic or quasi-periodic way. In particular we are interested in the stability properties of an elliptic fixed point of an analytic periodically time-dependent diffeomorphism, which is globally symplectic. The interest on this problem arises from accelerator physics: the betatronic motion in a circular particle accelerator (i.e. the motion on a plane perpendicular to the reference orbit) is described by a symplectic map $\mathcal{M}$ in $\mathbb{R}^4$ (the one-turn map) with an elliptic fixed point at the origin corresponding to the reference orbit[11,12]. The multipolar magnetic fields, which are caused by the superconducting magnets[13], introduce nonlinear terms in the one-turn map so that it is necessary to study the stability properties of the origin in order to have previsions on the beam's lifetime. We can write the one-turn map $\mathcal{M}$ in the form

$$\mathbf{X}' = \mathcal{M}(\mathbf{X}) = \mathcal{R}(\omega_1, \omega_2)\left(\mathbf{X} + \sum_{n\geq 2}[\mathcal{M}]_n(\mathbf{X})\right) \qquad \mathbf{X} \in \mathbb{R}^4 \tag{1.1}$$

where $\mathcal{R}(\omega_1, \omega_2)$ is a rotation matrix in phase planes with frequencies ω_1, ω_2, which are called the linear tunes, and $[\mathcal{M}]_n$ are the homogenous terms of order n of the Taylor expansion at the origin.

Recent experiments at CERN[14] have shown that the presence of oscillating currents (ripples) in the power supply of the magnets causes a relevant decreasing of the beam's life time and the accelerator people is now persuaded of the importance of studying this effect for the projects of future accelerators. If we introduce the ripples effect in the model (1.1), we obtain the periodic time-dependent map of period $2\pi/\Omega$

$$\mathbf{X}(t+1) = \mathcal{M}(\mathbf{X}(t),t) = \mathcal{R}(\omega_1+\nu_1(\Omega t),\omega_2+\nu_2(\Omega t))\left(\mathbf{X}+\sum_{n\geq 2}[\mathcal{M}]_n(\mathbf{X};\Omega t)\right) \tag{1.2}$$

where ν_1, ν_2 have zero mean value. We will suppose that the dependence on t is analytic in the strip $|\mathrm{Im}\, t| < \Delta/\Omega$.

In order to study the time dependent dynamics (1.2) in a neighborhood of the origin we enlarge the phase space so that we recover an autonomous dynamical system. In this way we lose the symplectic character, but the extended dynamics still preserves a differential form. Then we develop the Birkhoff Normal forms theory [3,4] for the extended system and we obtain an exponentially small estimate in the distance from the origin for the remainder of a finite order reduction into normal form[15]. This allows to prove the stability of the orbits of the nonautonomous system for exponentially long times in the inverse of the distance from the origin of the initial condition[16,17,18]. Moreover, starting from the results of the perturbation theory, we apply the Newton method of the KAM theory in order to construct quasi-periodic tori for the extended system[19]. In this way we prove the stability for any time of the corresponding orbits of the nonautonomous system (1.2) which are obtained by projecting the invariant tori on a subspace. Moreover the measure of the orbits which do not belong to an invariant tori in the extended phase space is proved to be exponentially small in the distance from the origin[20]; these orbits can diffuse in the phase space according to the mechanism of Arnold's diffusion[21].

Although the estimates we obtain, are not realistic and cannot be directly applied to accelerator physics, the dependence on the relevant parameters like the strength of the nonlinear terms and the modulation frequency Ω, suggests some scaling laws which can be useful to improve the performance of a particle accelerator.

In the paper we use the following conventions in the formulas: the calligraphic letters like $\mathcal{M}$ or $\mathcal{F}$ indicate analytic mappings in $\mathbb{C}^{2d}$ or in $\mathbb{C}^{2d+2}$ and the capital bold letters like $\mathbf{M}$ or $\boldsymbol{\Phi}$ indicate d-dimensional arrays of analytic functions; M_j denotes the j component of the array $\mathbf{M}$. The symbol $[\ \ ]_n$ denotes the homogenous terms of order n of the Taylor expansion of an analytic function; the symbols $[\ \ ]_{<n}$ and $[\ \ ]_{>n}$ have an analogous meaning. The lower-case bold letters like $\mathbf{z}$ and $\boldsymbol{\zeta}$ are d-dimensional arrays, whose components are z_j and ζ_j, $j = 1,..,d$, and we use the conventions

$$\begin{aligned} \boldsymbol{\zeta}\boldsymbol{\chi} &= (\zeta_1\chi_1, ..., \zeta_d\chi_d) \\ e^{i\boldsymbol{\omega}}\mathbf{z} &= (e^{i\omega_1}z_1, ..., e^{i\omega_d}z_d) \\ |\mathbf{z}| &= |z_1| + ... + |z_d| \end{aligned} \tag{1.3}$$

Let f be an analytic function we define the majorant series of f, the series whose coefficients are the absolute value of the coefficients of the Taylor expansion;

the majorant series will be denoted by the symbol $\lceil f \rceil$. Moreover we use the symbol $\prec$ between two real series to say that the coefficients of the series in the l.h.s. are $<$ of the coefficients of the series in the r.h.s. The symbol $B_R(\mathbf{z})$ defines the domain

$$B_R(\mathbf{z}) = \left\{ \mathbf{z} \in \mathbb{C}^d \quad | \quad |\mathbf{z}| \leq R \right\} \tag{1.4}$$

and the same notation is used for all the domains like (1.4).

Acknowledgements. I am in debt with prof. Turchetti for his suggestions and for many fruitful discussions. I would like to thank prof. Lazutkin and Euler International Mathematical Institute of St. Petersbourg for their hospitality.

2. Perturbation Theory

Let $\mathcal{M}(t)$ be a globally symplectic map in $\mathbb{R}^{2d}$ with an elliptic fixed point at the origin depending periodically from a parameter t with period $2\pi/\Omega$; by introducing the complex variables $(\mathbf{z}, \mathbf{w}) \in \mathbb{C}^{2d}$ which reduce the linear part to a diagonal form, $\mathcal{M}$ can be written in the form

$$\mathcal{M}(\mathbf{z}, \mathbf{w}, t) = \begin{cases} e^{i\boldsymbol{\omega} + i\boldsymbol{\nu}(\Omega t)} \left(\mathbf{z} + \sum_{n \geq 2} [\mathbf{F}]_n(\mathbf{z}, \mathbf{w}; \Omega t) \right) \\ e^{-i\boldsymbol{\omega} - i\boldsymbol{\nu}(\Omega t)} \left(\mathbf{w} + \sum_{n \geq 2} [\mathbf{G}]_n(\mathbf{z}, \mathbf{w}; \Omega t) \right) \end{cases} \tag{2.1}$$

where $\boldsymbol{\omega}$ are the linear frequencies of the map at the origin. Since the map (2.1) is a complexification of a real map, the plane $\overline{\mathbf{z}} = \mathbf{w}$ is invariant and it corresponds to the real space. We suppose that the map (2.1) is analytic in the domain

$$\left\{ (\mathbf{z}, \mathbf{w}) \in \mathbb{C}^{2d} \quad | \quad |\mathbf{z}| + |\mathbf{w}| \leq R \right\} \times \left\{ t \in \mathbb{C} \quad | \quad |\mathrm{Im}\, t| \leq \frac{\Delta}{\Omega} \right\}; \tag{2.2}$$

for our convenience we assume $\Delta \geq 2$, but this is not an essential hypothesis. Our aim is to study the stability properties of the origin for the time dependent dynamics associated to the map (2.1). It is convenient to introduce the auxiliary variables

$$\begin{cases} x = e^{i\Omega t} \\ y = e^{-i\Omega t} \end{cases} \tag{2.3}$$

and the extended phase-space $(\mathbf{z}, \mathbf{w}, x, y) \in \mathbb{C}^{2d+2}$. Therefore we consider the map

$$\begin{cases} x' = e^{i\Omega} x \\ y' = e^{-i\Omega} y \\ \mathbf{z}' = e^{i\boldsymbol{\omega}} \left(\mathbf{z} + \sum_{n\geq 2} [\hat{\mathbf{F}}]_n(\mathbf{z}, \mathbf{w}, x, y) \right) \\ \mathbf{w}' = e^{-i\boldsymbol{\omega}} \left(\mathbf{w} + \sum_{n\geq 2} [\hat{\mathbf{G}}]_n(\mathbf{z}, \mathbf{w}, x, y) \right) \end{cases} \tag{2.4}$$

where the Taylor expansion refers to all the variables $(\mathbf{z}, \mathbf{w}, x, y)$; the map (2.4) turns out to be analytic in the domain $B_R(\mathbf{z}, \mathbf{w}) \times B_{e^\Delta}(x) \times B_{e^\Delta}(y)$. Obviously if we project the orbits of the time independent map (2.4) on the space $(\mathbf{w}, \mathbf{z})$ with initial conditions on the unit circle $|x| = |y| = 1$, we recover the time dependent dynamics generated by the map (2.1). The symplectic character of the map (2.1) implies the invariance of the differential form

$$\sum_{j=1}^{d} dz_j \wedge dw_j \wedge dx \wedge dy \tag{2.5}$$

In this section we develop the normal forms theory for the map (2.4) and we obtain the optimal estimate of the remainder for a finite number of steps of perturbation theory in a given neighborhood of the origin. Let us first state the result on formal reduction of the map (2.3) into a normal form when the linear frequencies $(\boldsymbol{\omega}, \Omega)$ do not satisfy any resonance condition

$$\mathbf{k}\omega + k_{d+1}\Omega \neq 2\pi n \qquad (\mathbf{k}, k_{d+1}) \in \mathbb{Z}^{d+1} \backslash \{\mathbf{0}\}, \quad n \subset \mathbb{Z} \tag{2.6}$$

Theorem. [22] *If the condition (2.6) holds, then there exists a formal change of variables (the normalizing transformation) $\mathcal{F}(\boldsymbol{\zeta}, \boldsymbol{\chi}, x, y) \to (\mathbf{z}, \mathbf{w}, x, y)$ tangent to the identity (we omit the x, y components since they are trivial)*

$$\mathcal{F}(\boldsymbol{\zeta}, \boldsymbol{\chi}, x, y) = \begin{cases} \boldsymbol{\zeta} + \boldsymbol{\Phi} = \boldsymbol{\zeta} + \sum_{n\geq 2} [\boldsymbol{\Phi}]_n(\boldsymbol{\zeta}, \boldsymbol{\chi}, x, y) \\ \boldsymbol{\chi} + \boldsymbol{\Psi} = \boldsymbol{\chi} + \sum_{n\geq 2} [\boldsymbol{\Psi}]_n(\boldsymbol{\zeta}, \boldsymbol{\chi}, x, y) \end{cases} \tag{2.7}$$

which reduces the map $\mathcal{M}$ to a normal form $\mathcal{U}$

$$\mathcal{U}(\boldsymbol{\zeta}, \boldsymbol{\chi}, x, y) = \begin{cases} x' = e^{i\Omega} x \\ y' = e^{-i\Omega} y \\ e^{i\boldsymbol{\omega}} \boldsymbol{\zeta} \left(1 + \sum_{n\geq 2} [\mathbf{U}]_n(\boldsymbol{\zeta}\boldsymbol{\chi}, xy) \right) \\ e^{-i\boldsymbol{\omega}} \boldsymbol{\chi} \left(1 + \sum_{n\geq 2} [\mathbf{V}]_n(\boldsymbol{\zeta}\boldsymbol{\chi}, xy) \right) \end{cases} \tag{2.8}$$

according to the conjugation equation

$$\mathcal{M} \circ \mathcal{F} = \mathcal{F} \circ \mathcal{U}. \tag{2.9}$$

Moreover there exist d-functions $\boldsymbol{\Xi}$ which depend only on the products $\boldsymbol{\zeta}\boldsymbol{\chi}, xy$ such that

$$\begin{cases} 1 + \sum_{n\geq 2}[\mathbf{U}]_n(\boldsymbol{\zeta}\boldsymbol{\chi}, xy) = \exp\left(i \sum_{n\geq 2}[\boldsymbol{\Xi}]_n(\boldsymbol{\zeta}\boldsymbol{\chi}, xy)\right) \\ 1 + \sum_{n\geq 2}[\mathbf{V}]_n(\boldsymbol{\zeta}\boldsymbol{\chi}, xy) = \exp\left(-i \sum_{n\geq 2}[\boldsymbol{\Xi}]_n(\boldsymbol{\zeta}\boldsymbol{\chi}, xy)\right) \end{cases} \tag{2.10}$$

as a consequence the products $\boldsymbol{\zeta}\boldsymbol{\chi}$ are first integrals of motion of the normal form $\mathcal{U}$.

Hint of the proof. The construction of the normal form $\mathcal{U}$ can be easily done perturbatively in the order of the Taylor expansion by using the condition (2.6). The formal existence of the function $\boldsymbol{\Xi}$ is proved by calculating the differential form (2.5) in the new variables and by explicitly writing the equations, which $\mathbf{U}, \mathbf{V}$ have to satisfy in order to preserve the differential form itself.♯

We remark that the conjugation equation does not determined univocally the transformation $\mathcal{F}$, but we are left with the freedom of choosing the coefficients of $\mathcal{F}$ corresponding to the monomials which enter in the development of the normal form $\mathcal{U}$. In the sequel we set all these coefficients equal to zero so that the solution $\mathcal{F}$ becomes unique. If we stop the solution of the conjugation equation at a finite order N in the Taylor expansion it is possible to find d polynomials $\boldsymbol{\Xi}_{N-1}$ of order $N-1$ such that

$$\begin{cases} 1 + \sum_{n\geq 2}^{N-1}[\mathbf{U}]_n(\boldsymbol{\zeta}\boldsymbol{\chi}, xy) = \left[\exp\left(i\boldsymbol{\Xi}_{N-1}(\boldsymbol{\zeta}\boldsymbol{\chi}, xy)\right)\right]_{\leq N-1} \\ 1 + \sum_{n\geq 2}[\mathbf{V}]_n(\boldsymbol{\zeta}\boldsymbol{\chi}, xy) = \left[\exp\left(-i\boldsymbol{\Xi}_{N-1}(\boldsymbol{\zeta}\boldsymbol{\chi}, xy)\right)\right]_{\leq N-1} \end{cases} \tag{2.11}$$

In order to estimate the analyticity domain of the normalizing transformation $\mathcal{F}$, when we consider only a finite number of steps of perturbation theory, we use a techniques developed by Siegel-Moser[23] to study the solution of the conjugation equation (2.9). We first observe that if we assume a diophantine condition for the linear frequencies $(\boldsymbol{\omega}, \Omega)$

$$\begin{gathered} |\mathbf{k}\cdot\boldsymbol{\omega} + k_{d+1}\Omega + 2\pi n|^{-1} \leq \Gamma(|\mathbf{k}| + |k_{d+1}|)^{\mu} \\ \forall\, n \in \mathbb{Z}, \quad \forall\, (\mathbf{k}, k_{d+1}) \in \mathbb{Z}^{d+1}\backslash\{\mathbf{0}\}, \end{gathered} \tag{2.12}$$

then according to the previous theorem, it exists an analytic change of variables which reduces the map (2.4) to the form

$$\begin{cases} x' = e^{i\Omega}x \\ y' = e^{-i\Omega}y \\ \mathbf{z}' = e^{i\boldsymbol{\omega}}\left(\mathbf{z} + [\mathbf{M}]_3(\mathbf{z},\mathbf{w}) + \sum_{n\geq 4}[\mathbf{M}]_n(\mathbf{z},\mathbf{w},x,y)\right) \\ \mathbf{w}' = e^{-i\boldsymbol{\omega}}\left(\mathbf{w} + [\mathbf{N}]_3(\mathbf{z},\mathbf{w}) + \sum_{n\geq 4}[\mathbf{N}]_n(\mathbf{z},\mathbf{w},x,y)\right) \end{cases} \tag{2.13}$$

that is analytic in the domain

$$B_{r_0}(\mathbf{z},\mathbf{w}) \times B_{e^{\frac{3}{4}\Delta}}(x) \times B_{e^{\frac{3}{4}\Delta}}(y). \tag{2.14}$$

Then we write the transformation $\mathcal{F}$ which reduces the map (2.13) into the normal form (2.8) according to the following expansion

$$\mathcal{F} = \sum_{(\mathbf{k},k_{d+1})\in \mathbb{Z}^{d+1}} \{\mathcal{F}\}_{(\mathbf{k},k_{d+1})} \tag{2.15}$$

where each component $\{\mathcal{F}\}_{(\mathbf{k},k_{d+1})}$ is defined according to

$$\{\mathcal{F}\}_{(\mathbf{k},k_{d+1})} = \frac{1}{(2\pi)^{d+1}} \int_0^{2\pi} d\mathbf{s} ds_{d+1} \mathcal{F}\left(e^{i\mathbf{s}}\zeta, e^{-i\mathbf{s}}\chi, e^{is_{d+1}}x, e^{-is_{d+1}}y\right) e^{-i(\mathbf{k}\cdot\mathbf{s}+k_{d+1}s_{d+1})} \tag{2.16}$$

We denote $\{\mathcal{F}\}_{(\mathbf{k},k_{d+1})}$ as the $(\mathbf{k},k_{d+1})$ Fourier component. It is straightforward to see that the following property holds $\forall\ (\mathbf{s}, s_{d+1}) \in \mathbb{R}^{d+1}$

$$\{\mathcal{F}\}_{(\mathbf{k},k_{d+1})}\left(e^{i\mathbf{s}}\zeta, e^{-i\mathbf{s}}\chi, e^{is_{d+1}}x, e^{-is_{d+1}}y\right) = e^{i(\mathbf{k}\cdot\mathbf{s}+k_{d+1}s_{d+1})}\{\mathcal{F}\}_{(\mathbf{k},k_{d+1})}(\zeta,\chi,x,y) \tag{2.17}$$

and that the Taylor expansion of the Fourier component $\{\mathcal{F}\}_{(\mathbf{k},k_{d+1})}$ at the origin starts with terms of order $|(\mathbf{k},k_{d+1})| = |k_1| + ... + |k_{d+1}|$. Let $\mathbf{e}_j$, $j = 1,..,d$, the standard basis of $\mathbb{Z}^d$, then the normal form $\mathcal{U}$ is characterized by the property

$$\begin{aligned} \{U_j\}_{(\mathbf{e}_j,0)} &= U_j \\ \{V_j\}_{(-\mathbf{e}_j,0)} &= V_j \end{aligned} \qquad j = 1,..,d \tag{2.18}$$

whereas the condition which guarantees the unicity of the normalizing transformation $\mathcal{F}$ reads

$$\begin{aligned} \{\Phi_j\}_{(\mathbf{e}_j,0)} &= 0 \\ \{\Psi_j\}_{(-\mathbf{e}_j,0)} &= 0 \end{aligned} \qquad j = 1,..,d \tag{2.19}$$

If we project the conjugation equation (2.9) on the Fourier components, we obtain the system

$$\{\mathcal{M}\circ\mathcal{F}\}_{(\mathbf{k},k_{d+1})} = \{\mathcal{F}\circ\mathcal{U}\}_{(\mathbf{k},k_{d+1})} = \exp\left(i(\mathbf{k}\cdot\boldsymbol{\omega} + k_{d+1}\Omega + \mathbf{k}\cdot\boldsymbol{\Xi})\right)\{\mathcal{F}\}_{(\mathbf{k},k_{d+1})} \tag{2.20}$$

By substituting the formal expansions (2.7)and (2.10) in the system (2.20), we obtain

$$\{\Phi_j\}_{(\mathbf{k},k_{d+1})} = \frac{\{M_j(\boldsymbol{\zeta}+\Phi,\boldsymbol{\chi}+\Psi,x,y)\}_{(\mathbf{k},k_{d+1})}}{\exp\left(i(\mathbf{k}-\mathbf{e}_j)\cdot\boldsymbol{\omega}+ik_{d+1}\Omega+i\mathbf{k}\cdot\boldsymbol{\Xi}\right)-1} \qquad \mathbf{k}\neq\mathbf{e}_j$$

$$\{\Psi_j\}_{(\mathbf{k},k_{d+1})} = \frac{\{N_j(\boldsymbol{\zeta}+\Phi,\boldsymbol{\chi}+\Psi,x,y)\}_{(\mathbf{k},k_{d+1})}}{\exp\left(i(\mathbf{k}+\mathbf{e}_j)\cdot\boldsymbol{\omega}+ik_{d+1}\Omega+i\mathbf{k}\cdot\boldsymbol{\Xi}\right)-1} \qquad \mathbf{k}\neq-\mathbf{e}_j \quad (2.21)$$

$$\zeta_j\exp(i\Xi_j) = \zeta_j+\{M_j(\boldsymbol{\zeta}+\Phi,\boldsymbol{\chi}+\Psi,x,y)\}_{\mathbf{e}_j} \qquad j=1,...,d$$

As it is well known no analytic solution $(\boldsymbol{\Phi},\boldsymbol{\Psi},\boldsymbol{\Xi})$ exists for the full system (2.21) in any neighborhood of the origin, then we have to consider a truncated system by introducing a cut off N on the order of the Fourier components of the normalizing transformation $\mathcal{F}$. Therefore we look for an analytic solution $(\boldsymbol{\Phi}_N,\boldsymbol{\Psi}_N,\boldsymbol{\Xi})$ of the system (2.21), where the suffix N indicates that only the Fourier components of order $|\mathbf{k}|+|k_{d+1}|\leq N$ are considered. We assume that the majorant series of the functions $\mathbf{M}$ and $\mathbf{N}$ in eq. (2.13) satisfy to the inequality

$$\lceil M_j\rceil,\ \lceil N_j\rceil \prec \frac{r_0^{-2}(\boldsymbol{\zeta}+\boldsymbol{\chi})^3}{(1-(\boldsymbol{\zeta}+\boldsymbol{\chi})r_0^{-1})(1-e^{-\frac{3}{4}\Delta}x)(1-e^{-\frac{3}{4}\Delta}y)} \qquad j=1,..,d. \quad (2.22)$$

We look to the equations (2.21) as the equation for a fixed point of a certain operator defined by the r.h.s. expressions, so that the existence of the solution follow, according to the Shauder-Tychonov theorem, if we show that the operator is continuous and it maps a convex compact domain of a Banach space into itself. First we introduce the norm on the space of analytic functions with a finite number of Fourier components

$$\|\boldsymbol{\Phi}_N\|_D^* = \sum_{|\mathbf{k}|+|k_{d+1}|\leq N} \|\{\boldsymbol{\Phi}\}_{(\mathbf{k},k_{d+1})}\|_D \tag{2.23}$$

where $\|\cdot\|_D$ indicates the maximum of sup-norms of the components on the domain $D\subset\mathbb{C}^{2d+2}$. By using the definition (2.23) it is not difficult to prove the following property

$$\|\mathbf{M}(\boldsymbol{\zeta}+\boldsymbol{\Phi}_N,\boldsymbol{\chi}+\boldsymbol{\Psi}_N,x,y)\|_D^* \leq \lceil\mathbf{M}\rceil(\|\boldsymbol{\zeta}\|_D+\|\boldsymbol{\Phi}_N\|_D,\|\boldsymbol{\chi}\|_D+\|\boldsymbol{\Psi}_N\|_D,|x\|_D,\|y\|_D) \tag{2.24}$$

We have the following

Lemma. [22]: *Let the linear frequencies* $(\boldsymbol{\omega}, \Omega)$ *satisfy the diophantine condition (2.12) and let* r_N *defined by the equation*

$$4\Gamma(N+1)^{\mu} N \left(1+\frac{2}{N}\right)^3 \frac{r_0^{-2} r_N^2}{\left(1-(1+\frac{2}{N})r_0^{-1} r_N\right)\left(1-e^{-\frac{3}{8}\Delta}\right)^2} = 1 \qquad (2.25)$$

then the truncated system (2.21) has a solution $(\boldsymbol{\Phi}_N, \boldsymbol{\Psi}_N, \boldsymbol{\Xi})$ *which is analytic in the domain* $D = B_{r_N}(\boldsymbol{\zeta}, \boldsymbol{\chi}) \times B_{e^{\frac{3}{8}\Delta}}(x) \times B_{e^{\frac{3}{8}\Delta}}(y)$ *and satisfies the estimates*

$$\begin{aligned} &\|\boldsymbol{\Phi}\|_D^*, \quad \|\boldsymbol{\Psi}\|_D^* \le \frac{r_N}{N} \\ &\|\boldsymbol{\Xi}\|_D \le \frac{1}{2\Gamma N(N+1)^{\mu}} \end{aligned} \qquad (2.26)$$

Proof. The strategy of the proof is to show that the compact and convex set defined by the inequalities (2.26) is invariant for the operator associated to the r.h.s of eqs. (2.21). Indeed by using the diophantine condition, we obtain the estimates on the small divisors $\forall\ (\mathbf{k}, k_{d+1}) \in \mathbb{Z}^{d+1}\backslash\{\mathbf{0}\}$ and $|\mathbf{k}| + |k_{d+1}| \le N$

$$\begin{aligned} &\|\exp\left(i(\mathbf{k}-\mathbf{e}_j)\cdot\boldsymbol{\omega} + ik_{d+1}\Omega + i\mathbf{k}\cdot\boldsymbol{\Xi}\right) - 1\|_D \\ &\ge \frac{\Gamma^{-1}(|\mathbf{k}-\mathbf{e}_j| + |k_{d+1}|)^{-\mu} - \|\boldsymbol{\Xi}\|_D|\mathbf{k}|}{2} \ge \frac{\Gamma^{-1}(N+1)^{-\mu}}{4} \end{aligned} \qquad (2.27)$$

Therefore by applying the property (2.24) to the r.h.s. of eqs. (2.21), we have the estimates

$$\begin{aligned} &\sum_{(\mathbf{k},k_{d+1})\in\mathbb{Z}^{d+1}\backslash\mathbf{e}_j} \left\| \frac{\{M_j(\boldsymbol{\zeta}+\Phi, \boldsymbol{\chi}+\Psi, x, y)\}_{(\mathbf{k},k_{d+1})}}{\exp\left(i(\mathbf{k}-\mathbf{e}_j)\cdot\boldsymbol{\omega} + ik_{d+1}\Omega + i\mathbf{k}\cdot\boldsymbol{\Xi}\right) - 1} \right\|_D^* \\ &\le 4\Gamma(N+1)^{\mu} \sum_{(\mathbf{k},k_{d+1})\in\mathbb{Z}^{d+1}\backslash\mathbf{e}_j} \left\| \{M_j(\boldsymbol{\zeta}+\Phi, \boldsymbol{\chi}+\Psi, x, y)\}_{(\mathbf{k},k_{d+1})} \right\|_D \\ &\le 4\Gamma(N+1)^{\mu} \lceil M_j \rceil (\|\boldsymbol{\zeta}\|_D + \|\Phi\|_D, \|\boldsymbol{\chi}\|_D + \|\Psi\|_D, \|x\|_D, \|y\|_D) \end{aligned} \qquad (2.28)$$

and similar relations for the components N_j. As a consequence by taking into account the definition of the domain D and of the radius r_N, and the inequality (2.22), we obtain

$$\begin{aligned} \|\Phi_j\|_D^* &= \sum_{(\mathbf{k},k_{d+1})\in\mathbb{Z}^{d+1}\backslash\mathbf{e}_j} \left\| \frac{\{M_j(\boldsymbol{\zeta}+\Phi, \boldsymbol{\chi}+\Psi, x, y)\}_{(\mathbf{k},k_{d+1})}}{\exp\left(i(\mathbf{k}-\mathbf{e}_j)\boldsymbol{\omega} + ik_{d+1}\Omega + i\mathbf{k}\boldsymbol{\Xi}\right) - 1} \right\|_D^* \\ &\le \frac{r_0^{-2} r_N^3 4\Gamma(N+1)^{\mu}\left(1+\frac{2}{N}\right)^3}{\left(1-(1+\frac{2}{N})r_0^{-1} r_N\right)\left(1-e^{-\frac{3}{8}\Delta}\right)^2} = \frac{r_N}{N} \end{aligned} \qquad (2.29)$$

and the same for $\|\Psi_j\|^*_D$. On the other hand from the last equation in (2.21) we have

$$\|\zeta_j\|_D \frac{\|\Xi_j\|_D}{2} \leq \|\zeta_j(e^{i\Xi_j} - 1)\|_D \leq \left\| \{M_j(\boldsymbol{\zeta} + \Phi, \boldsymbol{\chi} + \Psi, x, y)\}_{\mathbf{e}_j} \right\|_D$$
$$\leq \lceil M_j \rceil (\|\boldsymbol{\zeta}\|_D + \|\Phi\|_D, \|\boldsymbol{\chi}\|_D + \|\Psi\|_D, \|x\|_D, \|y\|_D) \tag{2.30}$$

so that from the inequality (2.22) and the definition (2.25) we obtain the estimate

$$\|\Xi_j\|_D \leq \frac{2r_0^{-2} r_N^2 \left(1 + \frac{2}{N}\right)^3}{\left(1 - (1 + \frac{2}{N}) r_0^{-1} r_N\right) \left(1 - e^{-\frac{3}{8}\Delta}\right)^2} = \frac{1}{2\Gamma N (N+1)^\mu} \tag{2.31}$$

The equations (2.29) and (2.31) imply the invariance of the domain (2.26) for the operator associated to the r.h.s. of eqs. (2.21). As a consequence to conclude the proof it remains to check the continuity of the operator with respect to the norm $\| \quad \|^*$, which easily follows from the definition.♯

Remark: by solving the equation (2.25) we have

$$r_N \geq \frac{c_1 r_0 (1 - e^{-\frac{3}{8}\Delta})}{2\left(\Gamma (N+1)^{\mu+1}\right)^{\frac{1}{2}}} \tag{2.32}$$

for a suitable constant c_1 which gives the explicit dependence of the analyticity radius from the the cut-off N of the Fourier components. From the previous Lemma we can prove the following

Theorem. *Let us consider a domain* $D_r = B_r(\boldsymbol{\zeta}, \boldsymbol{\chi}) \times B_{e^{-\frac{3}{8}\Delta}}(x) \times B_{e^{-\frac{3}{8}\Delta}}(y)$ *where* $r < r_3/2$ *and let*

$$N = \left(\frac{r_*}{r} \Gamma^{\frac{1}{2}}\right)^{\frac{2}{\mu+1}} \tag{2.33}$$

obtained by inverting the relation (2.32) with $r_N = 2r$ *and* r_* *a suitable constant (it is understood the integer part in the r.h.s.), then it is possible to find a solution to the approximate conjugation equation*

$$\mathcal{M} \circ \mathcal{F}_N = \mathcal{F}_N \circ \mathcal{U}_N + \mathcal{E}_N \tag{2.34}$$

such that

i) *the normal form* $\mathcal{U}_N$ *is the map* $(\boldsymbol{\zeta} \exp(i\boldsymbol{\Omega} + i\boldsymbol{\Xi}_{N-1}, \boldsymbol{\chi} \exp(-i\boldsymbol{\Omega} - i\boldsymbol{\Xi}_{N-1}))$ *where* $\boldsymbol{\Xi}_{N-1}$ *is a real polynomial of order* $N-1$ *depending on the products* $(\boldsymbol{\zeta\chi}, xy)$

ii) *the transformation* $\mathcal{F}_N$ *is analytic and invertible in the domain* D_r *and satisfies the estimate*

$$\|\boldsymbol{\Phi}\|_{D_r}, \quad \|\boldsymbol{\Psi}\|_{D_r} \leq \frac{r}{N} \tag{2.35}$$

iii) *the remainder* $\mathcal{E}_N$ *contains only terms of order* $> N$, *is analytic in the domain* D_r *and satisfies the estimate*

$$\|\mathcal{E}\|_{D_r} \leq c_2 r \left(\frac{r_*}{r}\Gamma^{\frac{1}{2}}\right)^{\frac{4d}{\mu+1}} 2^{-\left(\frac{r_*}{r}\Gamma^{\frac{1}{2}}\right)^{\frac{2}{\mu+1}}} \tag{2.36}$$

where c_2 *is a suitable constant.*

Corollary. *It is possible to conjugate analytically the extended map (2.13) with the map* $\mathcal{U}_N \circ (\mathcal{I} + \hat{\mathcal{E}}_N)$ *in the domain* D_r *where* $\mathcal{I}$ *is the identity map and the perturbation* $\hat{\mathcal{E}}_N$ *satisfies an estimate like (2.36) with another constant* c_3.

Hint of the Proof. Let us consider the solution $(\boldsymbol{\Phi}_N, \boldsymbol{\Psi}_N, \boldsymbol{\Xi})$ of the system (2.21) provided by the Lemma and let us defined $\boldsymbol{\Xi}_{N-1} = [\boldsymbol{\Xi}]_{\leq N-1}$ the truncation at order $N-1$ of the Taylor expansion of $\boldsymbol{\Xi}$, it follows that $(\boldsymbol{\Phi}_N, \boldsymbol{\Psi}_N, \boldsymbol{\Xi}_{N-1})$ is the solution of the approximated conjugation equation (2.34) because $\boldsymbol{\Xi}_{N-1}$ coincides with the perturbative solution (2.10) up to the order $N-1$ and the estimates (2.26) allow to prove the estimate (2.35) and the invertibility of the transformation $\mathcal{F}_N$ in the domain D_r. The estimate of the remainders $\mathcal{E}_n$ and $\hat{\mathcal{E}}_N$ follows from the Cauchy theorem. The factor 2 in the estimate (2.36) is due to our choice $r_N = 2r$.♯

Remark: the result of the previous theorem is a Nekhoroshev like estimate[24] for the remainder of a finite order perturbation theory; indeed by using the estimate (2.36) is possible to obtain an exponentially long stability time in the inverse of radius r for an orbit with initial condition in the domain $D_{\frac{r}{2}}$[17,18]. The exponent $2/(\mu+1)$ is optimal if the second order terms of $\boldsymbol{\Xi}_{N-1}$ are different from zero, otherwise an exponent $q/(\mu+1)$ is expected, where q is the degree of the first non-zero term in the expansion of $\boldsymbol{\Xi}_{N-1}$

3. Invariant tori for the extended map

The construction of the invariant tori for the extended map (2.4) starting from the result (2.36) of perturbation theory, is based on the Newton method of the KAM theory[6,7,8,9,10]. We recall that the real dynamics takes place in the subspace $\overline{\boldsymbol{\zeta}} = \boldsymbol{\chi}$ and $|x| = |y| = 1$ and in the sequel we fix $xy = 1$. Let us introduce the usual polar coordinates

$$
\begin{aligned}
\boldsymbol{\rho} &= \sqrt{\boldsymbol{\zeta}\boldsymbol{\chi}} \\
\boldsymbol{\theta} &= \frac{1}{2i}\log\frac{\boldsymbol{\zeta}}{\boldsymbol{\chi}} \\
\phi &= \frac{1}{2i}\log\frac{x}{y}
\end{aligned}
\tag{3.1}
$$

then the map $\mathcal{U}_N \circ (\mathcal{I} + \mathcal{E}_N)$ provided by the perturbation theory reads

$$
\begin{cases}
\boldsymbol{\theta}' = \boldsymbol{\theta} + \boldsymbol{\omega} + \boldsymbol{\Xi}(\boldsymbol{\rho}) + \mathbf{u}(\boldsymbol{\rho}, \boldsymbol{\theta}, \phi) \\
\boldsymbol{\rho}' = \boldsymbol{\rho} + \mathbf{v}(\boldsymbol{\rho}, \boldsymbol{\theta}, \phi) \\
\phi' = \phi + \Omega
\end{cases}
\tag{3.2}
$$

where we have neglected the index N for simplicity and it is analytic in the domain

$$
D_r = \left\{ (\boldsymbol{\rho}, \boldsymbol{\theta}) \mid (e^{\Sigma} + e^{-\Sigma})|\boldsymbol{\rho}| < r \quad \text{where} \quad \max_{0 \le j \le d} |\mathrm{Im}\, \theta_j| = \Sigma \le \Sigma_{max} \right\}
\times \left\{ \phi \mid |\mathrm{Im}\, \phi| < \frac{3}{8}\Delta \right\}. \tag{3.3}
$$

Moreover the following estimate holds

$$
\|\mathbf{u}\|_{D_r}, \quad \|\mathbf{v}\|_{D_r} \le c_4 r (e^{2\Sigma} + 1) \left(\frac{r_*}{r}\right)^{\frac{4d}{\mu+1}} 2^{-\left(\frac{r_*}{r}\Gamma^{\frac{1}{2}}\right)^{\frac{2}{\mu+1}}} \tag{3.4}
$$

where c_4 is a constant.

In order to construct the invariant tori of the map (3.2), we have to explicit the symplectic character of the mapping. Indeed the following **Lemma** holds[19]:

Lemma. *The map (3.2) has an integral invariant of the form*

$$
\sum_{j=1}^{d} (a_j(\boldsymbol{\rho}) + \hat{a}_j(\boldsymbol{\rho}, \boldsymbol{\theta}))\, d\rho_j \wedge d\phi + \left(b_j(\boldsymbol{\rho}) + \hat{b}_j(\boldsymbol{\rho}, \boldsymbol{\theta})\right) d\theta_j \wedge d\phi \tag{3.5}
$$

which is analytic in the same domain D_r and satisfies the estimates

$$
\begin{gathered}
\|\hat{\mathbf{a}}\|_{D_r}, \quad \|\hat{\mathbf{b}}\|_{D_r} \le c_5 r (e^{2\Sigma} + 1) \left(\frac{r_*}{r}\right)^{\frac{4d}{\mu+1}} \left(\frac{3}{2}\right)^{-\left(\frac{r_*}{r}\Gamma^{\frac{1}{2}}\right)^{\frac{2}{\mu+1}}} \\
\frac{1}{2}|\boldsymbol{\rho}| \le det \left|\frac{\partial \mathbf{b}}{\partial \boldsymbol{\rho}}\right| \le \frac{3}{2}|\boldsymbol{\rho}|.
\end{gathered}
\tag{3.6}
$$

Hint of the Proof. The integral invariant (3.5) is obtained by transforming the differential form

$$\sum_{j=1}^{d} z_j dw_j \wedge d\phi - w_j dz_j \wedge d\phi \tag{3.7}$$

which is an integral invariant for the map (2.4) with $|x| = |y| = 1$. The estimates (3.6) are obtained by using the perturbation theory.♯

Then the existence of the KAM tori is given by the following Theorem.

Theorem. *Let the functions $\boldsymbol{\Xi}(\boldsymbol{\rho})$ satisfy a nondegeneracy condition of the form*

$$\frac{3}{2}|\boldsymbol{\rho}| \le \det \left|\frac{\partial \boldsymbol{\Xi}}{\partial \boldsymbol{\rho}}\right| \le \frac{5}{2}|\boldsymbol{\rho}| \tag{3.8}$$

and let $\omega_* = \boldsymbol{\omega} + \boldsymbol{\Xi}(\boldsymbol{\rho}_*)$ the vector of frequencies associated to the point $\boldsymbol{\rho}_*$ such that

i) *the following inclusion holds*

$$\left\{(\boldsymbol{\rho},\boldsymbol{\theta}) \;/\; |\boldsymbol{\rho} - \boldsymbol{\rho}_*| \le \frac{|\boldsymbol{\rho}_*|}{16}; \quad |Im\ \theta_j| < \Sigma_0, \quad j = 1,..d \quad |Im\ \phi| \le \frac{3}{8}\Delta\right\} \subseteq D_r \tag{3.9}$$

ii) $(\boldsymbol{\omega}_*, \Omega)$ *satisfy a diophantine condition*

$$|\mathbf{k}\cdot\boldsymbol{\omega}_* + k_{d+1}\Omega + 2\pi n|^{-1} \le \Gamma_*(|\mathbf{k}| + |k_{d+1}|)^{\mu_*} \quad \forall\, n \in \mathbb{Z},$$
$$\forall\, (\mathbf{k}, k_{d+1}) \in \mathbb{Z}^{d+1}\backslash\{\mathbf{0}\}, \tag{3.10}$$

then there exists an invariant torus for the map (3.2) in the domain D_r where the dynamics is analytically conjugated with a quasi-periodic motion of frequencies (ω_*, Ω) if the following inequality is satisfied

$$c_6\Gamma_*^2\left(\frac{r_*}{r}\right)^{\frac{4d}{\mu+1}}\left(\frac{\Sigma_0}{48}\right)^{-2\mu_*-2d-4}\left(\frac{4}{3}\right)^{-\left(\frac{r_*}{r}\Gamma^{\frac{1}{2}}\right)^{\frac{4d}{\mu+1}}} < 1 \tag{3.11}$$

Hint of the Proof. The proof is a variant for analytic mappings of Svanidze's[9] proof on the existence of invariant tori for dynamical system with an integral invariant.♯

As a **Corollary** from the condition (3.11), which is a condition on the constant Γ_* which enters in the diophantine estimates (3.10) we have: If the linear frequencies satisfy the diophantine condition (2.12), then the measure of the orbits of the time dependent map (2.1), which do not lie on an invariant tori of the extended map (2.4) is exponentially small in $1/r$ as we approach to the origin[20].

References

[1] L.D. Pustyl'nikhov, *The stability of a semitrajectory under transformation of the plane that preserves area*, Soviet Math. Dokl. **13**, 36-38 (1972)

[2] L.D. Pustyl'nikhov, *The existence of a set of positive measure of oscillating motions in a certain problem of dynamics*, Soviet Math. Dokl. **13**, 94-97 (1972)

[3] H.W. Broer, G.B. Huitema, F. Takens, B.L.J. Braaksma, *Unfoldings and bifurcations of quasi-periodic tori*, Memoirs Am. Math. Soc. **83** n. 421 (1990)

[4] G.D. Birkhoff, *Surface transformations and their dynamical applications*, Acta Math. **43**, 1-119 (1920)

[5] A.D. Brjuno, *The analytical forms of differential equations: part* I, Trans. Mosc. Math. Soc. **25**, 131-288 (1972)

[6] A.N. Kolmogorov, *On conservation of conditionally periodic motion for small change in Hamilton's function*, Dokl. Akad. Nauk SSSR **98**, 527-530 (1954)

[7] V.I. Arnol'd, *Proof of A.N. Kolmogorov theorem on the preservation of quasi-periodic motions under small perturbations of the Hamiltonian* Russian, Math. Surveys **18**, n.6, 9-36 (1963)

[8] J. Moser, *On invariant curves of area-preserving mappings of the annulus*, Nachr. Akad. Wiss. Gott. **1**, 1-20 (1962)

[9] N.V. Svanidze, *Small perturbations of an integrable dynamical system with integral invariant*, Proc. Steklov Inst. Math. **2**, 127-151 (1981)

[10] M.R. Herman, *On the dynamics on lagrangian tori invariant by symplectic diffeomorphisms*, Preprint Ecóle Polytechnique

[11] A. Dragt, J.M. Finn, *Lie Series and Invariant Functions for Analytic Symplectic Maps*, J. Math. Phys. **20**, 2649 (1979)

[12] A. Bazzani, P. Mazzanti, G. Servizi, G. Turchetti, *Normal Forms for Hamiltonian maps and Nonlinear Effects in a Particle Accelerator*, **102 B, N. 1**, 51-80 (1988)

[13] W. Scandale, G. Turchetti (eds.), *Nonlinear Problems in Future Particles Accelerators*, World Scientific (1991)

[14] C. Altuna et al., *The 1991 Dynamic Aperture Experiment at the CERN SPS*, CERN SL **91-43**(AP) (1991)

[15] J. Moser, *Stabiliätsverhalten kanonischer Differentialgleichungssysteme*, Nachr. Akad. Wiss. Göttingen, Math. Phys. K1 IIa, **6**, 87-120 (1955)

[16] J. Glimm, *Formal Stability of Hamiltonian Systems*, Comm. Pure Appl. Math. **17**, 507-526 (1964)

[17] A. Giorgilli, L. Galgani, *Rigorous estimates for the series expansions of hamiltonian perturbation theory*, Cel. Mech. **17** 95-112 (1985)

[18] A. Bazzani, S. Marmi, G. Turchetti, *Nekhoroshev estimates for isochronous nonresonant symplectic maps*, Cel. Mech. **47**, 333 (1990)

[19] A. Bazzani, in preparation (1992)

[20] A.I. Neishtadt, *Estimates in the Kolmogorov theorem on the conservation of conditionally periodic motions*, J. Appl. Math. Mech. **48**, 58-63 (1982)
[21] V.I. Arnol'd, *Instability of dynamical systems with several degrees of freedom*, Sov. Math. Dokl. **5**, 581-585 (1964)
[22] A. Bazzani, *Proprietá di analiticitá delle serie perturbative e stabilitá in dinamica dei fasci*, Ph.d Thesis Univ. of Bologna (1992)
[23] C.L. Siegel, J. Moser, *Lectures on Celestial Mechanics*, Springer-Verlag (1971)
[24] N.N. Nekhoroshev, *An exponential estimate of the time of stability of nearly integrable Hamiltoian systems*, Russ. Math. Surveys **32**, 1-66 (1977)

Dipartimento di Matematica, Università di Bologna INFN, Sezione di Bologna, Italy

ANALYTICTY OF NORMALIZING TRANSFORMATIONS FOR AREA PRESERVING MAPS

A. Bazzani*, G. Turchetti**

It was proved by Poincaré [1] that hamiltonian systems with two degrees of freedom cannot have real analytic integrals of motion beyond the hamiltonian itself. His theorem excludes analyticity in open sets of real phase space, in agreement with KAM theory [2,3,4] on the existence of a Cantor set of invariant manifolds, which admit a $\mathcal{C}^\infty$ interpolation [5,6,7]. The normalizing transformations are given by asymptotic series, whose remainders can be made exponentially small according to Nekhoroshev [8]. We have analyzed a related problem, namely the analyticity properties of an area preserving map in the neighborhood of an elliptic fixed point, by considering its extension to $\mathbf{C}^2$. If the linear frequency is irrational then it is possible to conjugate, by a polynomial diffeomorphism of order N, the map with its normal form up to a remainder, analytic in a polydisc whose radius decreases with N, vanishing as $N \to \infty$ [9,10]. By extending Moser's proof [11] on the existence of invariant curves, we determine a domain of $\mathbf{C}^2$ where the remainder can be set to zero. In polar coordinates the analyticity domain of the normalizing transformation is given by a strip in the angle complex plane and, in the radius complex plane, by the complement of the disc with respect to a Cantor like set of measure exponentially small, which intersects the real and imaginay axis. This is consistent with Neishtadt estimates on the real axis [12] on the measure of KAM tori. We could not prove that the non-analyticity domain is restricted to the real and imaginary axis of the radial plane and we believe that this domain has a finite extension off the coordinate axis, probably subexponentially small. The complex integral of motion is well defined in the analyticity domain whereas in the real phase plane, wherever it exists, is the boundary value of an analytic function. The angle analyticity was not really explored; the singularities in the angle are related to the complex time singularites of the interpolating flow. Rigorous results exist only for algebraically integrable [13] system where the Panlevé conjecture is proved, while for quasi integrable systems only the analyticity structure of hyperbolic manifolds [14] has been explored in the real section.

This investigation was initially motivated by Arnold's work on the circle map [15] and by some numerical explorations of the quadratic Hénon map [16], which suggested the basic mechanisms of divergence and singularity generation [17,18,19].

We consider a mapping $F : \mathbf{C}^2 \to \mathbf{C}^2$ with a fixed point at the origin

$$F := \begin{cases} z' = e^{i\omega_0}\left[z + f(z,w)\right], \\ \\ w' = e^{-i\omega_0}\left[w + g(z,w)\right], \end{cases} \qquad \omega_0 \in \mathbf{C}, \qquad f,g = O\big((|z|+|w|)^2\big) \tag{1}$$

which preserves the 2-form $dz \wedge dw$ and is analytic in a polydisc. A map U in normal form foliates $\mathbf{C}^2$, with leaves specified by the invariant $\rho = zw$

$$U := \begin{cases} z' = e^{i\Omega(\rho)} z \\ \\ w' = e^{-i\Omega(\rho)} w, \end{cases} \qquad \rho = zw \qquad \Omega : \mathbf{C} \to \mathbf{C}, \tag{2}$$

If a map F is conjugated with U by a change of variables Φ, which can be only formal, according to

$$F \circ \Phi = \Phi \circ U, \tag{3}$$

then U is the normal form of F. As it is well known the equation (3) has a solution at the level of formal series if $\omega_0/(2\pi) \notin \mathbf{Q}$. The soluton is not unique; indeed changing Φ into $\Phi \circ T$ where

$$T := \begin{cases} z' = \sqrt{X(\rho)}\, e^{i\Xi(\rho)} z \\ \\ w' = \sqrt{X(\rho)}\, e^{-i\Xi(\rho)} w, \end{cases} \qquad X, \Xi : \mathbf{C} \to \mathbf{C}, \tag{4}$$

which preserves the 2-form $dz \wedge dw$ only when $X = 1$, the normal form is now given by (2) where $\Omega(\rho)$ is changed into $\Omega(\rho X(\rho))$. As a consequence if $\Omega = \rho^m + O(\rho^{m+1})$, it is possible to change $\Omega(\rho)$ into ρ^m by choosing $\rho X(\rho)$ equal to inverse function of $\Omega^{1/m}(\rho)$ which is tangent to the identity. If Ω is a formal series or analytic in a polydisc, the same is true for the gauge transformation T. The integer m is a topological invariant of the map.

In order to construct the analyticity domain of the normalizing transformation Φ, we proceed in two steps. First we conjugate F with a map U_N given by (2) where Ω is replaced with a polynomial of degree $\leq [(N-1)/2]$ and Φ with a polynomial Φ_N of degree N so that the functional equation (3) with

$$F \circ \Phi_N = \Phi_N \circ U_N + R_N \tag{5}$$

where R_N is a remainder. Assuming a diophantine condition for the frequency $\omega_0/(2\pi)$ so that $|e^{i\omega_0} - 1|^{-1} \leq \gamma_0 |k|^{\eta_0}\ \forall\ k \in \mathbf{Z}\backslash\{0\}$, it is found that R_N is analytic in a polydisc of radius r_N and satisfies the estimate

$$||R_N||_r \leq \left(\frac{r}{r_N}\right)^{N+1} \frac{1}{1 - \frac{r}{r_N}}, \qquad r_N = \left[c\gamma_0 (N+1)^{(1+\eta_0)/2}\right]^{-1} \tag{6}$$

for a suitable constant c where $\| \quad \|_r$ denotes the sup-norm in the polydisc of radius r. It is convenient to introduce the polar coordinates r, θ

$$\begin{cases} r = (zw)^{1/2} = \rho^{1/2}, & \theta = \dfrac{1}{2i} \log \dfrac{z}{w} \\ \\ z = re^{i\theta}, & w = re^{-i\theta} \end{cases} \tag{7}$$

and the map $F_N = \Phi_N^{-1} \circ F \circ \Phi_N$ reads

$$F_N : \begin{cases} \theta' = \theta + \Omega_N(r^2) + a_N(r, \theta) \\ \\ r' = r + b_N(r, \theta) \end{cases} \tag{8}$$

The functions a_N, b_N are analytic in the domain $|\operatorname{Im} \theta| \leq \Delta$, $|r| \leq r_N e^{-\Delta}/4$ where Δ is an arbitrary real number and are bounded by 2^{-N}. The map (4) preserves the measure $r + \mu_N(r, \theta)$ where μ_N is analytic in $|\operatorname{Im} \theta| \leq \Delta$, $|r| \leq r_N e^{-\Delta}/4$ and bounded by 2^{-N}. This measure is present since Φ_N is not a symplectic map but rather a symplectic truncation and $1 + d\mu/dr$ is just the jacobian of F_N. The frequency $\Omega_N = \Omega_0 + \Omega_2 r^2 + \ldots$ is a polynomial of order $[(N-1)/2]$ in r^2, is bounded according to $\underline{\Omega}_2 |r|^2 \leq |\Omega_N| \leq \overline{\Omega}_2 |r|^2$ where $\underline{\Omega}_2$ and $\overline{\Omega}_2$ are two constants very close to Ω_2.

Choosing r in the annulus $e^{-\Delta} r_{N+1}/4 \leq |r| \leq e^{-\Delta} r_N/4$ then the functions a, b are bounded by $4 \exp[-(r_*/|r|)^\kappa]$ where

$$\kappa = \frac{2}{1 + \eta_0}, \qquad r_* = e^{-\Delta} \frac{(\log 2)^{1/\kappa}}{4c\gamma_0} \tag{9}$$

which provides an exponentially small estimate of the perturbation in the inverse of the distance from the fixed point[9]. Modifying Moser's proof to take into account the presence of the measure [5], we prove that F_N can be conjugated with the integrable map $\mathcal{F}_N$

$$\mathcal{F}_N : \begin{cases} \theta' = \theta + \Omega_N(r^2) \\ \\ r' = r \end{cases} \tag{10}$$

according to the

Theorem 1. *The map F_N given by (8), analytic with its invariant measure μ in $|\mathrm{Im}\,\theta| < \Delta/2$ and $|r| < r_N e^{-\Delta}/4$, with a_N, b_N, μ_N bounded by 2^{-N} is analytically conjugated with the integrable map $\mathcal{F}_N$ defined by (11) within the strip $|\mathrm{Im}\theta| \leq \Delta/4$ and the disc $|r| \leq r_N e^{-\Delta}/8$ excluding two angular sectors bisected by the real and imaginary axis whose aperture χ is bounded from below by*

$$|\tan\chi| \geq E_1(r_N) \equiv C_1 \exp\left[-\left(\frac{1}{c_1\gamma_0 r_N}\right)^{\kappa}\right] \tag{11}$$

where C, C_1, c_1, are numerical constants. The envelope of the angular sectors with for increasing $N \geq 3$ has an exponential tangency with the real and imaginary axis (see figure 1). The exclusion of the real and imagnary axis in the radius complex plane is due to the appearence at finite perturbative orders of poles in the normalizing transformation Φ due to the nonlinear resonances. However the nature of the singularities of the complete transformation Φ is not yet known.

The invariance with respect to the measure $\mu(r)$ and the presence of a fixed point at the origin play an essential role to replace the intersection condition used by Moser.

Analytic continuation allows to reach the real axis in the radial plane at points which correspond to diophantine frequencies.

Theorem 2. *If the function $\Omega_N(\rho)$ satisfies the nondegeneracy condition*

$$\frac{3}{4}|\Omega_2| \leq \frac{d\Omega_N}{d\rho} \leq \frac{5}{4}|\Omega_2| \tag{12}$$

the map F_N can be analytically conjugated with the map $\mathcal{F}_N$ in $|\mathrm{Im}\theta| \leq \Delta/4$ and in the images by $\rho = r^2$ of the discs in the ρ plane defined by: $|\rho - \rho_c| \leq |\alpha|/2$ with $\rho_c = \tau + i\alpha$ where $\Omega(\tau) = \omega$ is a diophantine number, provided that

$$\gamma^{-1} + \nu|\alpha| \geq E_2(r_N) = C_2 \exp\left[-\left(\frac{1}{c_2\gamma_0 r_N}\right)^{\kappa}\right], \tag{13}$$

where $\Gamma^{-1} = \gamma^{-1} + \nu|\alpha|$ with $\nu = \min\{1,\ |\Omega_2|/2\pi\}$ and γ, η are the diophantine constants of the frequency $\omega = \Omega(\tau)$.

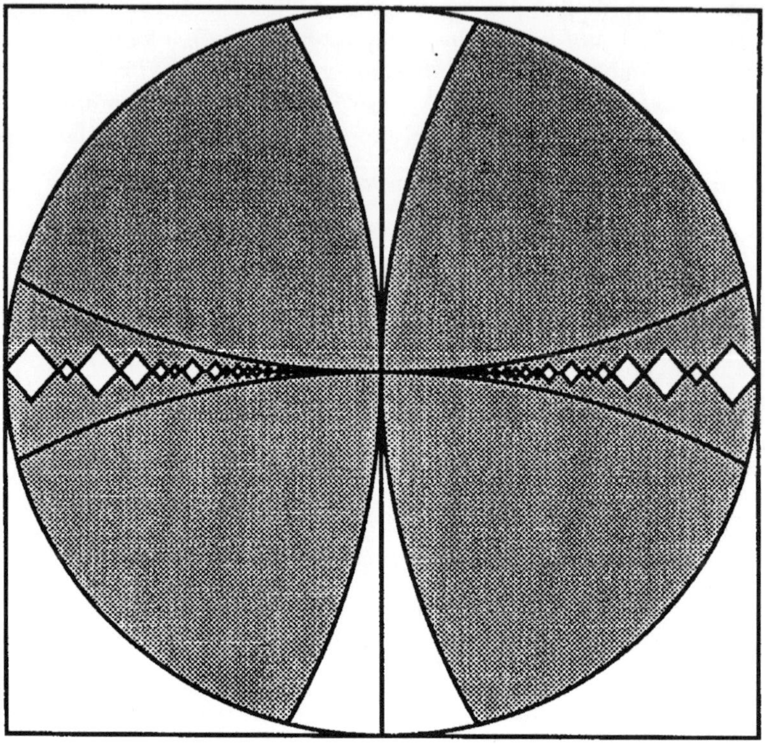

Figure 1
Plot of the analyticity region, dashed, in the complex r plane for the conjugations function Φ

Our estimates still hold when $\gamma^{-1} = 0$: i.e. if ω is resonant. At any point with diophantine frequency, the conjugation is allowed in discs such that $\gamma^{-1} \geq E_2(r_N)$ and their envelope is a cone of aperture $\pi/3$, vertex at $\rho = \tau$ and axis parallel to the imaginary axis.

At any point τ_* with resonant frequency $\Omega(\tau_*) = 2\pi p/q$ the conjugation is allowed for for $\nu|\alpha| > E_2(r_N)$. Moreover if we consider the frequencies defined by the following continued fraction $\omega/(2\pi) = (a_1, \dots, a_\ell, M \dots, M \dots)$ where $p/q = (a_1, \dots, a_\ell)$ with $a_i, M \in \mathbf{Z}$ and observe that for M large $\gamma = M$ and $|\omega - \omega_*| = \gamma^{-1}/q^2$; as a consequence $q^2|\tau - \tau_*| + |\alpha| \geq \nu^{-1} E_2(r_N)$ bounds the analyticity region. Combining this result with the cone estimate at the end points $\tau = \tau_* + \nu^{-1} E_2(r_N)$ the non-analyticity region nearby to a resonant frequency is a rombus with the center at $\rho = \tau_*$ and the ratio of vertical and horizontal diagonals is $\sqrt{3}$. This ratio can be optimized just as other exponents in the proof. In figure 1 a scketch of the non-analyticity domains of the normalizing trasformation is given.

The measure of the non-analticity domain is proportional to $E_2(r_N)$ and the same estimate is obtained for the measure of the the non-analyticity points of the real axis, in agreement with Neishtadt's theorem [12]. When $\Omega_N - \omega_0 = O(\rho^m)$ then in the previous estimates (12) and (13) E_1, E_2 are replaced with E_1^m, E_2^m. In this case we have $2m$ sectors of non analyticity which cover the plane densely when $m \to \infty$; however their measure vanishes at the same time. Heuristically analyticity in the full disc is recovered in the isochronous limit $m \to \infty$, in agreement with Rüssmann theorem [20].

Ackowledgements. We would like to thank prof. J. M. Canille for many fruitful discussions and prof. Lazutkin and Euler International Mathematical Institute for their hospitality.

References

[1] H. Poincaré, *Les Méthodes Nouvelles de la Méchanique Céleste*, vol. 3 Gautier-Villars Paris (1899)
[2] A. N. Kolmogorov, Dokl. Akad. Nauk. SSSR **98**, 527 (1954)
[3] V. I. Arnold, *Russ. Math. Surv.* **18**, 9 (1963)
[4] J. Moser, *Nachr. Akad. Wiss. Göttingen Math. Phys. K1* **1**, 1 (1962)
[5] N.V. Svanidze, Proc. Steklov Inst. Math. **2**, 127 (1981)
[6] J. Poeschel, *Comm. Pure Applied Math.* **35**, 653 (1982)
[7] L. Chierchia, G. Gallavotti, Il Nuovo Cimento **67 B**, 277 (1982)
[8] N. N. Nekhoroshev, *Russ. Math. Surv.* **32**, 1 (1977)
[9] A. Bazzani, S. Marmi, G. Turchetti, *Celestial Mechanics and Dynamical Astronomy* **47**, 333 (1990)
[10] A. Bazzani, *Normal forms for volume preserving maps*, ZAMP in press
[11] C. L. Siegel, J. Moser, *Lectures in Celestial Mechanics*, pag.166 Springer Verlag (1971)
[12] A. I. Neishstadt, *Journal of Applied Math. Mech.* **45**, 58 (1982)
[13] M. Adler, P. Van Moerbee, Adv. in Math. **38**, 267 (1980)
[14] V. F. Lazutkin, *Prépublications mathematiques de l' Université Paris VII* (1991)
[15] V. I. Arnold, *Trans. Am. Math. Soc. ser. II* **46**, 213 (1965)
[16] J. Roels, M. Hénon *Astron. J.* **69**, 73 (1967)
[17] G. Benettin, A. Giorgilli, G. Servizi, G. Turchetti, *Phys. Letters* **A95**, 11 (1983)
[18] G. Servizi, G. Turchetti, *Nuovo Cimento*,**B95**, 121 (1986)
[19] G. Servizi, G. Turchetti, *Phys. Lett* **A151**, 485 (1990)
[20] H. Rüssmann, *Mathematische Annalen* **169**, 55 (1967)

*Dipartimento di Matematica, Università di Bologna INFN, Sezione di Bologna, Italy

** Dipartimento di Fisica, Università di Bologna INFN, Sezione di Bologna, ITALY

ON THE FREQUENCIES OF QUASI PERIODIC SOLUTIONS OF ANALYTIC NEARLY INTEGRABLE HAMILTONIAN SYSTEMS

HELMUT RÜSSMANN

INTRODUCTION

The purpose of this paper is to prove an extension of the local version of Kolmogorov's theorem on the invariance of quasiperiodic motions under small pertubations of the Hamiltonian. However, this proof serves only as an example in order to demonstrate a new calculus of estimates which differs from the one of Arnol'd [2] and Moser [7] in so far as rapid convergence of the iteration process does not take place. In fact, in conjugacy problems without small divisors our approach coincides with the ordinary Lipschitz iteration. On the other hand, the utmost of possible influence of the small divisors is admitted.

In my talk I still used the Newton method. However, since the quantitative conditions for small divisors by means of approximation functions can be formulated much better in the case of slow (linear) convergence I finally wrote down the proof using slow convergence.

In spite of the fact that I had already discovered the principles of this proof many years ago I would not have found enough energy to bring these ideas into a final form unless M.R. Herman had permanently showed his interest in this sort of problems and remembered me that this work had to be done.

Last not least I like to thank V.F. Lazutkin and all the other persons who took care for us participants of the meeting for their overwhelming hospitality which made the stay in St. Petersburg to an unforgettable occurrence.

1. FORMULATION OF THE MAIN THEOREM

1.1 Notations.

1. We supply $\mathbb{C}^n, n \geq 1$, with the scalar product

$$< x, y >= x_1 y_1 + \ldots + x_n y_n, \quad \forall x = (x_1, \ldots, x_n),\ y = (y_1, \ldots, y_n) \in \mathbb{C}^n$$

and the norm

$$|x| = \sqrt{< x, \bar{x} >} = \sqrt{|x_1|^2 + \ldots + |x_n|^2}, \quad \forall x = (x_1, \ldots, x_n) \in \mathbb{C}^n.$$

For all $r > 0$, $s > 0$ we define

$$\mathcal{S}(r) = \{x \in \mathbb{C}^n \big| \, |Imx| < r\}, \quad \mathcal{B}(s) = \{y \in \mathbb{C}^n \big| \, |y| < s\}.$$

2. $\mathcal{P}_c^q(r) = \left\{ F : \mathcal{S}(r) \to \mathbb{C}^q \;\middle|\; \begin{array}{c} F \text{ holomorphic and bounded,} \\ F(x+2\pi k) = F(x), \quad \forall\, k \in \mathbb{Z}^n, x \in \mathcal{S}(r) \end{array} \right\}$,
   $\mathcal{P}^q(r) = \{F \in \mathcal{P}_c^q(r) | F(\mathbb{R}^n) \subseteq \mathbb{R}^q\}, \quad q \geq 1.$
   As a norm we use $|F|_r = \sup\limits_{x \in \mathcal{S}(r)} |F(x)|, \quad \forall\, F \in \mathcal{P}_c^q(r).$
   $\mathcal{P}_c(r) = \mathcal{P}_c^1(r)$, $\mathcal{P}(r) = \mathcal{P}^1(r)$.
3. $\mathcal{P}^q(r,s)$ is the space (over $\mathbb{R}$) of all functions $F : \mathcal{S}(r) \times \mathcal{B}(s) \to \mathbb{C}^q$ which are holomorphic, bounded, and satisfy the relations $F(x+2\pi k, y) = F(x,y), \quad \forall\, k \in \mathbb{Z}^n, \quad \forall\, (x,y) \in \mathcal{S}(r) \times \mathcal{B}(s)$ and $F(\mathbb{R}^n \times \mathbb{R}^n \cap \mathcal{S}(r) \times \mathcal{B}(s)) \subseteq \mathbb{R}^q$.
   $\mathcal{P}(r,s) = \mathcal{P}^1(r,s)$. $\quad |F|_{r,s} = \sup\limits_{(x,y) \in \mathcal{S}(r) \times \mathcal{B}(s)} |F(x,y)|, \quad \forall\, F \in \mathcal{P}^q(r,s).$
4. $\mathcal{P}_*^q(r,s) = \{F \in \mathcal{P}^q(r,s) | F(x,y) = F(x,0) + < F_y(x), y >, \forall\, (x,y) \in \mathcal{S}(r) \times \mathcal{B}(s)\}$.
5. $\mathbb{K}^{n \times n} = \{Q = (Q_{jl}) | Q_{jl} \in \mathbb{K};\, j,l = 1, \ldots, n\}$, $\mathbb{K} = \mathbb{R}$ or $\mathbb{C}$.
   $|Q| = \sup\limits_{|x| \leq 1, x \in \mathbb{K}^n} |xQ| = |Q^T| \; for \; Q^T = (Q_{lj}).$

$$E = \begin{pmatrix} 1 & & 0 \\ & \ddots & \\ 0 & & 1 \end{pmatrix} \in \mathbb{R}^{n \times n} \subseteq \mathbb{C}^{n \times n}.$$

$$\left. \begin{array}{l} \mathcal{P}^{n \times n}(r) \\ \mathcal{P}^{n \times n}(r,s) \end{array} \right\} = \{Q = (Q_{jl}) | Q_{jl} \in \left\{ \begin{array}{l} \mathcal{P}(r) \\ \mathcal{P}(r,s) \end{array} \right. ;\, j,l = 1, \ldots, n\}.$$

$$|Q|_r = \sup_{x \in \mathcal{S}(r)} |Q(x)| \quad , \quad |Q|_{r,s} = \sup_{(x,y) \in \mathcal{S}(r) \times \mathcal{B}(s)} |Q(x,y)|.$$

6. $F \in \mathcal{P}^q(r,s)$, $F_x = \begin{pmatrix} F_{1x_1} & \ldots & F_{1x_n} \\ \vdots & & \vdots \\ F_{qx_1} & \ldots & F_{qx_n} \end{pmatrix}$, $F_y = \begin{pmatrix} F_{1y_1} & \ldots & F_{1y_n} \\ \vdots & & \vdots \\ F_{qy_1} & \ldots & F_{qy_n} \end{pmatrix}$.
   Therefore $S \in \mathcal{P}(r,s)$ implies $S_x = (S_{x_1}, \ldots, S_{x_n})$, $S_{xy} = (S_{x_j y_l}) = S_{yx}^T$, etc.

1.2 Approximation functions.

1. **Definition**: Ω is called an approximation function (AF) iff
   (i) $\Omega : [1, \infty[\to \mathbb{R}$ continuous,
   (ii) $1 = \Omega(1) \leq \Omega(s) \leq \Omega(t)$ for $1 \leq s \leq t < \infty$.
   (iii) $\int\limits_1^\infty \frac{\log \Omega(t)}{t^2} dt < \infty$.
2. **The function associated to an AF**
   If Ω is an AF so is the function $t \mapsto \Omega^*(t) = t\Omega(t)$ which is in addition

strictly monotonically increasing with $\lim_{t\to\infty} \Omega^*(t) = \infty$. Therefore the inverse $\Omega^{*-1} : [1,\infty[\to \mathbb{R}$ exists, and we may define the function $\Phi = \Phi_\Omega$ associated to Ω by

$$\Phi(\varepsilon) = 1/\Omega^{*-1}(\varepsilon^{-1}), \quad \forall\, \varepsilon \in]0,1].$$

It has the properties
(i) $\Phi :]0,1] \to \mathbb{R}$ continuous,
(ii) $1 = \Phi(1) \geq \Phi(t) > \Phi(s)$ for $0 < s < t \leq 1$,
(iii) $\lim_{\varepsilon\to 0} \Phi(\varepsilon) \log \varepsilon^{-1} = 0$,
(iv) $\int_0^\varepsilon \Phi(t) \frac{dt}{t} < \infty$.

The first two properties are obvious, the last two will be proved in Section 3.1.

1.3 The main theorem:.

Under the conditions

1. $n \in \mathbb{N}$, $n \geq 2$,
2. $A \in \mathbb{R}^{n\times n}$, $A^T = A$, $\det A \neq 0$,
3. Ω *is an AF*, $\omega \in \mathbb{R}^n$, $| < k,\omega > |^{-1} \leq \Omega(|k|)$, $\forall\, k \in \mathbb{Z}^n \backslash \{0\}$,
4. $0 < r' < r$, $0 < \varepsilon \leq \frac{7}{8}$, $\Phi = \Phi_\Omega$, $\int_0^{\frac{8}{7}\varepsilon} \Phi(t) \frac{dt}{t} \leq \frac{r-r'}{n(42+8\log n)}$,
5. $P \in \mathcal{P}_*(r,s)$, $s = \frac{\varepsilon}{6|A|}$, $|P|_{r,s} \leq \frac{\varepsilon^2}{10^3|A|^3|A^{-1}|^2}$,
6. $H \in \mathcal{P}(r,s)$, $H(x,y) = < \omega, y > + P(x,y) + \mathcal{O}(|y|^2)$,
7. $|H_{yy} - A|_{r,s} \leq \frac{1}{120|A^{-1}|}$

there exists a canonical transformation

$$(\xi,\eta) \mapsto (x,y) = Z(\xi,\eta) = (\xi + X(\xi), \eta + Y(\xi,\eta)),$$

$$X \in \mathcal{P}^n(r'), \ |X_\xi|_{r'} \leq \frac{2}{21}, \ Y \in \mathcal{P}^n_*(r',s'), \ s' = \frac{s}{18},$$

$$Y(\xi,\eta) = (\eta + f_\xi(\xi))(E + X_\xi(\xi))^{-1} - \eta, \ f \in \mathcal{P}(r')$$

such that $Z(\mathcal{S}(r') \times \mathcal{B}(s')) \subseteq \mathcal{S}(r) \times \mathcal{B}(s)$ *and*

$$H \circ Z(\xi,\eta) = a + < \omega, \eta > + \mathcal{O}(|\eta|^2)$$

with some $a \in \mathbb{R}$.

1.4 Remarks:.

1. The condition $\Omega(1) = 1$ in 1.2.1 (i) is no restriction of generality. It can always be obtained by changing the time scale.
2. The restrictions $n \geq 2$ and $\omega \in \mathbb{R}^n$ are not essential and have only been made for numerical reasons. Namely in the case $n \geq 1$ and $\omega \in \mathbb{C}^n$

the numerical factors in Theorem 2.2 have to be changed a bit, where our extension of Bohr's inequality [8] has to be used. Then the cases without small divisors $n = 1$ and $n = 2, \omega = (\omega_1, \omega_2)$, $\omega_1/\omega_2 \in \mathbb{C}\backslash\mathbb{R}$ are included in which $\Omega(t) = 1$, $\forall\, t \geq 1$ can be chosen.

3. As we have checked, the numerical values for the admitted size of the perturbation P are incredibly much better than those obtained by means of the Newton method. We have not exhausted all numerical possibilities in order not to irritate the reader too much.
4. It is easy to see that condition 1.3.3 for the small divisors is equivalent to the conditions under which Bruno [4] has solved problems with small divisors near a singular point. In his book [5] he also formulates existence theorems for problems with small divisors near an invariant n-torus, $n > 0$. However, for proofs he only refers to his results in the case $n = 0$.
5. According to a counterexample of Perez Marco [6] in the case of the center problem one may conclude that condition 1.3.3 cannot be replaced by a weaker one.

2. Approximative solutions of linear equations with small divisors

2.1 Remark.

It is known that any $F \in \mathcal{P}_c^q(r)$ can be expanded in its Fourier series

$$F(x) = \sum_{k \in \mathbb{Z}^n} F_k e^{i<k,x>}, \quad F_k = \left(\frac{1}{2\pi}\int_{-\pi}^{\pi}\right)^n : F(x) e^{-i<k,x>} dx_1 \dots dx_n$$

which converges uniformly and absolutely in any compact subset of $\mathcal{S}(r)$. The mean value we shall denote by $[F] = F_0$. A trigonometrical polynomial $G(x) = \sum_{|k|\leq T} G_k e^{i<k,x>}$ of order $T \in \mathbb{R}, T > 0$ with coefficients $G_k \in \mathbb{C}^q$ may be considered as an element of $\mathcal{P}_c^q(r)$ for every $r > 0$ we are interested in. A function $F \in \mathcal{P}_c^q(r)$ belongs to $\mathcal{P}^q(r)$ if and only if its Fourier coefficients satisfy the relations $\bar{F}_k = F_{-k}$, $\forall k \in \mathbb{Z}^n$.

2.2 Theorem.

Under the conditions

1. $n \in \mathbb{N}$, $n \geq 2$.
2. $r > 0$, $T > 0$, $\delta = n(5.55 + \log n)T^{-1} < r$.
3. $\omega \in \mathbb{R}^n$, $d > 0$, $d \leq |<k, \omega>|$, $\quad \forall\, k \in \mathbb{Z}^n$ *with* $0 < |k| \leq T$

there are multipliers

$$\lambda_k = \lambda_k(T) = \lambda_{-k} \in \mathbb{R}, \quad \forall\, k \in \mathbb{Z}^n, \, \lambda_k = 0 \, for \, |k| > T$$

such that for any $F \in \mathcal{P}_c(r)$ *with Fourier expansion* $F(x) = \sum_{k\in\mathbb{Z}^n} F_k e^{i<k,x>}$ *the trigonometrical polynomial of order* T

(*) $u(x) = \sum_{0<|k|\leq T} \frac{\lambda_k F_k}{i<k,\omega>} e^{i<k,x>}$

satisfies the inequalities

(i) $|u|_{r-\delta} \le \frac{2}{15}\delta T\, d^{-1}|F-[F]|_r$,
(ii) $|u_x|_{r-\delta} \le \frac{9}{4} T\, d^{-1}|F-c|_r, \quad \forall c \in \mathbb{C}$,
(iii) $|<u_x,\omega> -F+[F]|_{r-\delta} \le \frac{1}{100}|F-[F]|_r$.

Remark. It is easy to extend these inequalities to the general case $\mathcal{P}_c^q(r), q \ge 1$ which, however, is not needed in this paper. Putting $\delta T = n(\alpha + \log n)$ with $\alpha \gg 1$ the numerical factor in (iii) can be made arbitrarily small. In the problem we are going to treat the factor 10^{-2} is a good choice which is obtained for $\alpha = 5.55$.

2.3 Approximation of $F \in \mathcal{P}_c(r)$ by trigonometrical polynomials. *Given $r>0$, $T>0$, $\delta \in]0, n^{-1/2}r[$ there are multipliers*

$$\begin{cases} \lambda_k = \lambda_k(T,\delta) = \lambda_{-k} \in \mathbb{R}, \quad \forall\, k \in \mathbb{Z}^n, \\ \qquad\qquad\qquad \lambda_k = 0 \, for \, |k| > \sqrt{n}T \end{cases} \tag{1}$$

such that for any $F \in \mathcal{P}_c(r)$ with Fourier expansion

$$F(x) = \sum_{k \in \mathbb{Z}^n} F_k e^{i<k,x>}$$

the trigonometric polynomial of order $\sqrt{n}T$

$$F_{T,\delta}(x) = \sum_{|k| \le \sqrt{n}T} \lambda_k\, F_k\, e^{i<k,x>}$$

satisfies the estimate

$$|F - F_{T,\delta}|_{r-\delta\sqrt{n}} \le \left\{ \left(1 + \frac{8}{\pi}e^{-T\delta}\right)^n - 1 \right\} |F|_r. \tag{2}$$

Proof: For every $b \in B(r) = \{b \in \mathbb{R}^n |\, |b| < r\}$ the function $x \mapsto F(x+ib)$ belongs to $\mathcal{P}_c(r-|b|)$ with Fourier coefficients

$$F_k(b) = (2\pi)^{-n} \int_W F(x+ib) e^{-i<k,x>} dx, \quad \forall\, k \in \mathbb{Z}^n,$$

$$W = \{x = (x_1, \ldots, x_n) \in \mathbb{R}^n | -\pi \le x_j \le \pi,\, j = 1, \ldots, n\}.$$

The function $b \mapsto F_k(b)e^{<k,b>}$ is independent of $b \in B(r)$ because $B(r)$ is connected and

$$\frac{\partial}{\partial b_j}\{F_k(b)e^{<k,b>}\} = (2\pi)^{-n}\int_W i\,\frac{\partial}{\partial x_j}\{F(x+ib)\,e^{-i<k,x+ib>}\}dx$$

vanishes as mean value of a periodic derivative, $j = 1,\ldots,n$. Therefore we conclude $F_k(b)e^{<k,b>} = F_k(0) = F_k =$ the k-th Fourier coefficient of F. From this equation we infer

$$(e^{<k,b>} + e^{-<k,b>})F_k = F_k(b) + F_k(-b)$$

such that we obtain the equation

$$F_k = (2\pi)^{-n}\int_W \left\{\frac{F(x+ib)+F(x-ib)}{2\cosh <k,b>}\right\} e^{-i<k,x>}dx$$

which means that F and $x \mapsto (F(x+ib)+F(x-ib))(2\cosh <k,b>)^{-1}$ have the same k-th Fourier coefficient. Repeating this procedure for $b = \delta e_j$, $j = 1,\ldots,n$ where $\{e_1,\ldots,e_n\}$ is the canonical basis of $\mathbb{R}^n$ and putting

$$\delta_\mu = (\pm\delta,\ldots,\pm\delta),\ \mu = 1,\ldots,2^n,\ \delta \in]0,\frac{r}{\sqrt{n}}[,$$

$$\cosh k\delta = \cosh k_1\delta \cdot \cosh k_2\delta \cdot \ldots \cdot \cosh k_n\delta, \quad \forall\, k \in (k_1,\ldots,k_n) \in \mathbb{Z}^n,$$

$$\hat{F}(\delta,x) = 2^{-n}\sum_{\mu=1}^{2^n} F(x+i\delta_\mu),\ \hat{F}(\delta,\cdot) \in \mathcal{P}(r-\sqrt{n}\delta)$$

we conclude that F and $\hat{F}(\delta,\cdot)(\cosh k\delta)^{-1}$ have also the same k-th Fourier coefficient:

$$F_k = (2\pi)^{-n}\int_W \frac{\hat{F}(\delta,x)}{\cosh k\delta}e^{-i<k,x>}dx, \quad \forall\, k \in \mathbb{Z}^n.$$

As a consequence we get the following integral representation of F

$$\begin{cases} F(x) = \displaystyle\sum_{k\in\mathbb{Z}^n} F_k e^{i<k,x>} \\ \qquad = (2\pi)^{-n}\displaystyle\int_W \hat{F}(\delta,x+y)D(\delta,y)dy, \end{cases} \tag{3}$$

where

$$D(\delta,y) = \sum_{k\in\mathbb{Z}^n}\frac{e^{-i<k,y>}}{\cosh k\delta} = \prod_{j=1}^{n} E(\delta,y_i)$$

and

$$E(\delta,t) = 1 + 2\sum_{\nu=1}^{\infty}\frac{\cos\nu t}{\cosh\nu\delta}. \tag{4}$$

This representation is valid for all $x \in \mathcal{S}(r - \sqrt{n}\delta)$.

Now we take for $T > 0$ a trigonometrical polynomial in one variable

$$Q(T,t) = \sum_{|\nu| \le T} Q_\nu e^{i\nu t}$$

with coefficients $Q_\nu = Q_{-\nu} \in \mathbb{R}$. Then the product

$$P(T,x) = \prod_{j=1}^{n} Q(T,x_j) = \sum_{|k|_\infty \le T} P_k e^{i<k,x>}$$

is a trigonometrical polynomial in $x_1, \dots, x_n$ with coefficients $P_k = P_{-k} \in \mathbb{R}$ and

$$\begin{cases} F_{T,\delta}(x) = (2\pi)^{-n} \displaystyle\int_W \hat{F}(\delta, x+y) P(T,y) dy \\ \qquad = \displaystyle\sum_{|k|_\infty \le T} \lambda_k F_k e^{i<k,x>} = \sum_{|k| \le \sqrt{n}T} \lambda_k F_k e^{i<k,x>} \end{cases} \tag{5}$$

is the Fourier polynomial of F of order $\sqrt{n}T$ supplied with mulitpliers

$$\lambda_k = P_k \cosh k\delta = \lambda_{-k} \in \mathbb{R} \text{ for } |k|_\infty \le T \text{ and } \lambda_k = 0 \text{ for } |k|_\infty > T. \tag{6}$$

We like to choose the Q_ν in such a way that the difference $F - F_{T,\delta}$ becomes as small as possible. From (3) and (5) we get

$$\begin{cases} |F - F_{T,\delta}|_{r-\sqrt{n}\delta} \le K |F|_r, \\ \qquad K = (2\pi)^{-n} \displaystyle\int_W |D(\delta,y) - P(T,y)| dy. \end{cases} \tag{7}$$

In order to estimate K we observe the identity

$$\begin{aligned} &D(\delta,y) - P(T,y) \\ &\qquad = \sum_{\nu=1}^{n} \prod_{j=1}^{\nu-1} Q(T,y_j) \prod_{l=\nu+1}^{n} E(\delta,y_l)(E(\delta,y_\nu) - Q(T,y_\nu)). \end{aligned} \tag{8}$$

Since $E(\delta,t)$ is up to a positive factor and stretching of the argument nothing else than the Fourier series of the Jacobian elliptic function dn with a modulus contained in the open unit interval we get $E(\delta,t) > 0, \quad \forall t \in \mathbb{R}$, hence using (4)

$$(2\pi)^{-1} \int_{-\pi}^{\pi} |E(\delta,t)| dt = 1. \tag{9}$$

Writing

$$\varrho(\delta, T, Q) = (2\pi)^{-1} \int_{-\pi}^{\pi} |E(\delta, t) - Q(T, t)| dt$$

the constant K in (7) can be estimated with the aid of the identities (8) and (9) by

$$\begin{cases} K \leq \sum_{\nu=1}^{n} (1 + \varrho(\delta, T, Q))^{\nu-1} \varrho(\delta, T, Q) \\ \quad = (1 + \varrho(\delta, T, Q))^n - 1. \end{cases} \tag{10}$$

Akhiezer [1] has shown that

$$\begin{aligned} \varrho &= \min_{Q_\nu = Q_{-\nu} \in \mathbb{R}, |\nu| \leq T} \varrho(\delta, T, Q) \\ &= \frac{4}{\pi} \sum_{\nu=0}^{\infty} (-1)^\nu ((2\nu + 1) \cosh(2\nu + 1)([T] + 1)\delta)^{-1} \end{aligned}$$

where $[T]$ is the largest integer not greater than T. Since the members of this alternating series decrease monotonically we get the estimate

$$\varrho \leq \frac{4}{\pi} \frac{1}{\cosh([T] + 1)\delta} \leq \frac{8}{\pi} e^{-T\delta}.$$

So inserting the minimizing polynomial $Q^*(T, t) = Q^*(T, \delta, t)$ in (5), (7), and (10) we obtain (2), and (1) is a consequence of (6) because the coefficients P_k depend on T and δ.

Remark. It can be shown that the multipliers λ_k in (1) lie in the unit interval. Even explicite formulae can be obtained. All this and a new proof of Akhiezer's result will appear elsewhere.

2.4 Inequalities of Bernstein and Bohr.

Let

$$F(t) = \sum_{j=1}^{N} F_j e^{i\lambda_j t}$$

be a trigonometrical polynomial with complex coefficients $F_1, \ldots, F_N$ *and real frequencies* $\lambda_1, \ldots, \lambda_N$. *Then the derivative*

$$F'(t) = \sum_{j=1}^{N} i\lambda_j F_j e^{i\lambda_j t}$$

and the indefinite integral

$$\int F(t) = \sum_{j=1}^{N} \frac{F_j}{i\lambda_j} e^{i\lambda_j t}$$

in the case $\lambda_j \neq 0,\ j = 1, \dots, N$ *satisfy the inequalities*

$$|F'|_{\mathbb{R}} \le D|F|_{\mathbb{R}}, \quad D = \max_{1\le j\le N} |\lambda_j| \qquad \textit{(Bernstein)} \tag{11}$$

and

$$\left|\int F\right|_{\mathbb{R}} \le \frac{\pi}{2d}|F|_{\mathbb{R}}, \quad d = \min_{1\le j\le N} |\lambda_j| > 0 \qquad \textit{(Bohr)} \tag{12}$$

where

$$|\cdot|_{\mathbb{R}} = \sup_{t\in\mathbb{R}} |\cdot(t)|.$$

Proof: For a real polynomial $F, F(\mathbb{R}) \subseteq \mathbb{R}$, both inequalities are consequences of the well known inequality of Kolmogorov for real bounded differentiable functions defined in $\mathbb{R}$. Such a deduction can be found in [3] where also Kolmogorov's inequality is proved.

The complex case can be reduced to the real case very easily. We carry out this reduction for (11). For (10) it is done exactly in the same way.

Let $F = G + iH, G(\mathbb{R}) \subseteq \mathbb{R}, H(\mathbb{R}) \subseteq \mathbb{R}$, then $\alpha G + \beta H$ with $\alpha, \beta \in \mathbb{R}, \alpha^2 + \beta^2 = 1$ is a real trigonometric polynomial of the same form as F. By the Cauchy-Schwarz inequality we have $|\alpha G + \beta H| \le \sqrt{\alpha^2+\beta^2}\sqrt{G^2+H^2} = |F|$, hence (11) yields

$$|(\alpha G' + \beta H')(t)| \le D|F|_{\mathbb{R}}, \quad \forall\, t, \alpha, \beta \in \mathbb{R} \text{ with } \alpha^2 + \beta^2 = 1. \tag{13}$$

Given $t \in \mathbb{R}$ with $F'(t) \neq 0$ put $\alpha = G'(t)|F'(t)|^{-1}, \beta = H'(t)|F'(t)|^{-1}$. Then (13) leads to $|F'(t)| \le D|F|_{\mathbb{R}}$. As a result this inequality is true for all $t \in \mathbb{R}$. So (11) follows.

2.5 Estimate for the gradient of a polynomial in $\mathcal{P}_c(r)$.

For any trigonometrical polynomial of order T

$$G(x) = \sum_{|k|\le T} G_k e^{i<k,x>}, \quad G \in \mathcal{P}_c(r) \tag{14}$$

the gradient

$$G_x = (G_{x_1}, \dots, G_{x_n}) \in \mathcal{P}_c^n(r)$$

satisfies the inequality

$$|G_x|_r \le \sqrt{2}T|G|_r. \tag{15}$$

Proof. For any $\omega \in \mathbb{R}^n$ we have

$$| < k, \omega > | \le |k||\omega| \le T|\omega| \quad \text{for } |k| \le T.$$

Hence applying (11) to the function $t \mapsto G(t\omega + x)$ we get

$$| < G_x(x), \omega > | = \left| \frac{d}{dt} G(t\omega + x)|_{t=0} \right| \leq T|\omega||G|_r, \quad \forall x \in \mathcal{S}(r).$$

Putting $\omega = \operatorname{Re} G_x(x)$ and $\omega = \operatorname{Im} G_x(x)$ we infer the inequalities

$$|\operatorname{Re} G_x(x)| \leq T|G|_r, \; |\operatorname{Im} G_x(x)| \leq T|G|_r, \quad \forall x \in \mathcal{S}(r)$$

from which (15) follows immediately.

2.6 The equation $< u_x, \omega >= G(x) - [G]$.

Let a trigonometrical polynomial (14) of order T and a frequency vector $\omega \in \mathbb{R}^n$ be given such that

$$0 < d \leq | < k, \omega > |, \quad \forall k \in \mathbb{Z}^n \quad \text{with } 0 < |k| \leq T \tag{16}$$

for some number d. Then the solution

$$u = \sum_{0<|k|\leq T} \frac{G_n}{i < k, \omega >} e^{i<k,x>}$$

of the equation

$$< u_x, \omega >= G(x) - [G] \tag{17}$$

and its gradient u_x can be estimated by

$$|u|_r \leq \frac{\pi}{2d} |G - [G]|_r, \tag{18}$$

$$|u_x|_r \leq \frac{\pi}{\sqrt{2}} \frac{T}{d} |G - c|_r, \quad \forall c \in \mathbb{C}. \tag{19}$$

Proof. From (17) we infer $\frac{d}{dt} u(t\omega + x) = G(t\omega + x) - [G]$ such that we may apply (12) to the function $t \mapsto G(t\omega + x) - [G]$ because of (16). Thus we obtain for $t = 0$ the inequality

$$|u(x)| \leq \frac{\pi}{2d} |G - [G]|_r, \quad \forall x \in \mathcal{S}(r)$$

from which (18) follows. Differentiating (17) we get

$$<< u_x, b >_x, \omega >=<< u_x, \omega >_x, b >=< G_x, b >\in \mathcal{P}_c(r)$$

with $[< G_x, b >] = 0$ for all $b \in \mathbb{C}^n$. An application of (15) and (18) yields

$$\begin{aligned} | < u_x(x), b > | \leq | < u_x, b > |_r &\leq \frac{\pi}{2d} | < (G - c)_x, b > |_r \\ &\leq \frac{\pi}{2d} |(G - c)_x|_r |b| \leq \frac{\pi}{\sqrt{2}} \frac{T}{d} |G - c|_r |b| \end{aligned}$$

for all $x \in \mathcal{S}(r)$, $b \in \mathbb{C}^n$, and $c \in \mathbb{C}$. Putting $b = \overline{u_x(x)}$ we obtain $|u_x(x)| \leq \pi T(\sqrt{2}d)^{-1} |G - c|_r$ for all $x \in \mathcal{S}(r)$ and $c \in \mathbb{C}$, and (19) follows.

2.7 Proof of Theorem 2.2.

Replacing δ, T in 2.3 by $\delta n^{-1/2}, Tn^{-1/2}$ and observing condition 2 we get for $F - [F] \in \mathcal{P}_c(r)$ a trigonometrical polynomial $(F-[F])_T = (F-[F])_{T,\delta(T)}$ of order T such that the inequalities

$$|F - [F] - (F-[F])_T|_{r-\delta} \leq K|F - [F]|_r \tag{20}$$

and consequently

$$|(F-[F])_T|_{r-\delta} \leq (1+K)|F-[F]|_r \tag{21}$$

are valid where

$$\begin{cases} K = (1 + 8e^{-5.55}(\pi n)^{-1})^n - 1 \\ \qquad < \exp(8\pi^{-1}e^{-5.55}) - 1 < \dfrac{1}{100}. \end{cases} \tag{22}$$

Now we take from 2.6 the solution $u \in \mathcal{P}_c(r-\delta)$ of equation (17) with $G = (F-[F])_T$. We know from 2.3 that $[G] = 0$. Then (iii) follows from (17), (20), and (22). Using conditions 2 and 3 as well as (21) and (22) the estimate (18) gets the form

$$|u|_{r-\delta} \leq \pi \left(\frac{101}{100}\right) (2n(5.55 + \log n))^{-1} \delta T d^{-1} |F - [F]|_r$$

where the numerical factor is less than $2/15$ for $n \geq 2$ as stated in (i). Similarly we get from (19)

$$|u_x|_{r-\delta} \leq \frac{\pi}{\sqrt{2}} \frac{T}{d} |(F-[F])_T - c_1|_r \quad \forall c_1 \in \mathbb{C}. \tag{23}$$

But since the mapping $F \to F_T$ is linear and the image of a constant function is constant according to 2.3 we may write with an arbitrary $c \in \mathbb{C}$

$$\begin{aligned} (F-[F])_T - c_1 &= ((F-c) - [F-c])_T - c_1 \\ &= (F-c)_T - [F-c]_T - c_1 = (F-c)_T \end{aligned}$$

with $c_1 = -[F-c]_T$. So (19), (22), and (23) yield

$$|u_x|_{r-\delta} \leq \frac{\pi}{\sqrt{2}} \left(\frac{101}{100}\right) \frac{T}{d} |F - c|_r, \quad \forall c \in \mathbb{C}$$

where the numerical factor is less than $9/4$ as stated in (ii).

3. Approximation functions

3.1 Existence of integrals.

Let Ω be an AF as described in 1.2 and $\Phi = \Phi_\Omega$ be the associated function. Then the integrals

$$\int^\infty \log \Omega^*(t) \frac{dt}{t^2}, \tag{1a}$$

$$\int^\infty \frac{d \log \Omega^*(t)}{t}, \tag{1b}$$

$$\int_0 \Phi(\zeta) \frac{d\zeta}{\zeta} \tag{1c}$$

exist simultaneously and in case of their existence we have

$$\begin{cases} \int_T^\infty \log \Omega^*(t) \frac{dt}{t^2} & = \frac{\log \Omega^*(T)}{T} + \int_T^\infty \frac{d \log \Omega^*(t)}{t} \\ & = \Phi(\varepsilon) \log \frac{1}{\varepsilon} + \int_0^\varepsilon \Phi(\zeta) \frac{d\zeta}{\zeta}, \\ 0 < \varepsilon \leq 1, & T = \Phi(\varepsilon)^{-1}, \end{cases} \tag{2}$$

$$\frac{\log \Omega^*(T)}{T} \leq \int_T^\infty \log \Omega^*(t) \frac{dt}{t^2} \quad (T \geq 1), \tag{3}$$

and

$$\lim_{T \to \infty} \frac{\log \Omega^*(T)}{T} = 0, \tag{4a}$$

$$\lim_{\varepsilon \to 0} \Phi(\varepsilon) \log \frac{1}{\varepsilon} = 0. \tag{4b}$$

Proof: Since Ω^* is monotonically increasing we have

$$t^{-2} \log \Omega^*(T) \leq t^{-2} \log \Omega^*(t) \quad \text{for} \quad T \leq t < \infty.$$

Integration from T to ∞ gives (3) in the case that (1a) exists. From (3) we infer (4a) and also (4b) putting $T = \Phi(\varepsilon)^{-1}$. Partial integration leads to the formula

$$\frac{\log \Omega^*(N)}{N} + \int_T^N \log \Omega^*(t) \frac{dt}{t^2} = \frac{\log \Omega^*(T)}{T} + \int_T^N \frac{d \log \Omega^*(t)}{t} \tag{5}$$

for $1 \leq T < N$ which shows together with (4a) that the existence of (1a) implies the existence of (1b). Conversly, the existence of (1b) implies that the left integral in (5) remains bounded for $N \to \infty$, hence (1a) exists. In case of the existence of (1a) and (1b) the limit $N \to \infty$ in (5) gives, using (4a), the first equation in (2).

Since Ω^* is continuous and strictly monotonically increasing a change of variables in Stieltjes integrals yields

$$\int_T^N \frac{d\log\Omega^*(t)}{t} = \int_{\Omega^*(T)}^{\Omega^*(N)} \frac{d\log v}{\Omega^{*-1}(v)} = \int_{\Omega^*(N)^{-1}}^{\Omega^*(T)^{-1}} \frac{du}{u\Omega^{*-1}(u^{-1})} = \int_{\varepsilon'}^{\varepsilon} \Phi(\zeta)\frac{d\zeta}{\zeta},$$

$$T = \Phi(\varepsilon)^{-1},\ N = \Phi(\varepsilon')^{-1},: 0 < \varepsilon' < \varepsilon.$$

Now $\varepsilon' \to \infty$ implies $N \to \infty$, and we see that the integrals (1b) and (1c) exist simultaneously. In case of their existence the limit $\varepsilon' \to 0$ gives the second equation in (2).

3.2 Lemma.

Let $\Phi = \Phi_\Omega$ be the function associated to an AF Ω. Then

$$\sum_{\nu=0}^{\infty} \Phi(\varepsilon_\nu) \leq \frac{1}{\log\sigma^{-1}} \int_0^{\sigma^{-1}\varepsilon} \Phi(t)\frac{dt}{t}$$

for $\varepsilon_\nu = \varepsilon\sigma^\nu$, $\nu = 0, 1, \ldots, 0 < \varepsilon \leq \sigma$, $0 < \sigma < 1$.

Proof: Since Φ is monotonically increasing we have

$$\Phi(\varepsilon_\nu) \leq \Phi(\varepsilon_\tau) \quad \text{for} \quad \nu - 1 \leq \tau \leq \nu$$

hence

$$\Phi(\varepsilon_\nu) \leq \int_{\nu-1}^{\nu} \Phi(\varepsilon_\tau)d\tau = \frac{1}{\log\sigma^{-1}} \int_{\varepsilon_\nu}^{\varepsilon_{\nu-1}} \Phi(\zeta)\frac{d\zeta}{\zeta}.$$

Summing up we obtain

$$\sum_{\nu=0}^{\infty} \Phi(\varepsilon_\nu) \leq \frac{1}{\log\sigma^{-1}} \int_0^{\sigma^{-1}\varepsilon} \Phi(\zeta)\frac{d\zeta}{\zeta},$$

because this integral exists by definition of Ω and by 3.1.

4. The general step of the iteration

4.1 The conditions under which the general step is performed.

1. $n \in \mathbb{N}$, $\quad n \geq 2$,
2. $A \in \mathbb{R}^{n\times n}$, $A^T = A$, $\det A \neq 0$, $|A^{-1}| = 1$,
3. Ω is an AF, $\omega \in \mathbb{R}^n$, $|<k,\omega>|^{-1} \leq \Omega(|k|)$, $\quad \forall\, k \in \mathbb{Z}^n\backslash\{0\}$,
4. $0 < r$, $0 < \varepsilon \leq 1$, $\Phi = \Phi_\Omega$, $\delta = n(5.55 + \log n)\Phi(\varepsilon) < r/1.002$,
5. $s = (6|A|)^{-1}\varepsilon$, $0 < M \leq \varepsilon^2(10|A|)^{-3}$,
6. $P \in \mathcal{P}_*(r,s)$, $|P|_{r,s} \leq M$,
7. $H \in \mathcal{P}(r,s)$, $a \in \mathbb{R}$, $H(x,y) = a + <\omega, y> + \mathcal{P}(x,y) + \mathcal{O}(|y|^2)$,
8. $|H_{yy} - A|_{r,s} \leq 1/5$,
9. $r_+ = r - 1.002\delta$, $s_+ = (7/8)s$.

4.2 The inductive lemma.

Under the conditions 4.1 there exists a canonical transformation $(\xi,\eta) \mapsto (x,y) = Z(\xi,\eta)$ defined by

$$\begin{cases} x = \xi + X(\xi), & X \in \mathcal{P}^n(r_+), \\ y = \eta + Y(\xi,\eta), & Y \in \mathcal{P}^n_*(r_+, s_+), \\ \quad = (\eta + f_\xi(\xi))(E + X_\xi(\xi))^{-1}, & f \in \mathcal{P}(r_+) \end{cases}$$

with the following properties:

1. (a) $|X|_{r_+} \le \delta/500,$ (b) $|X_\xi|_{r_+} \le p/(1-p)$, $p = 17|A|M\varepsilon^{-2}$
2. (a) $|Y|_{r_+,s_+} \le (1/16)s,$ (b) $|Y_\eta|_{r_+} \le p,$
3. $H_+ = H \circ Z,\ H_+(\xi,\eta) = a_+ + <\omega,\eta> + P_+(\xi,\eta) + \mathcal{O}(|\eta|^2),$ $a_+ \in \mathbb{R},\ P_+ \in \mathcal{P}_*(r_+,s_+),\ |P_+|_{r_+,s_+} \le M_+ = (8/13)M.$

4.3 Existence of a generating function.

Under the conditions 4.1 we have (see 2.1)

$$\det[B] \neq 0 \; for \; B = H_{yy}(\cdot,0) \in \mathcal{P}^{n\times n}(r),$$

and there exists a function

$$(x,\eta) \mapsto S(x,\eta) - <\lambda, x> \in \mathcal{P}_*(r-\delta, s_+)$$

where

$$\lambda = -[P_y][B]^{-1} \tag{1}$$

such that the relation

$$\eta + tS_x(x,\eta) \subset \mathcal{B}\left(\frac{15}{16}s\right), \quad \forall\, (x,y) \in \mathcal{S}(r-\delta) \times \mathcal{B}(s_+), \quad 0 \le t \le 1 \tag{2}$$

and the following estimates are satisfied:

$$|S_x(\cdot,0) - \lambda|_{r-\delta} \le (9/4)M\varepsilon^{-1}, \tag{3}$$

$$|S_x|_{r-\delta,s_+} \le (41/4)|A|M\varepsilon^{-1}, \tag{4a}$$

$$|S_\eta|_{r-\delta} \le \delta/500, \tag{4b}$$

$$|S_{x\eta}|_{r-\delta} \le 17|A|M\varepsilon^{-2}, \tag{5a}$$

$$|R|_{r-\delta,s_+} \le (1/40)M \tag{5b}$$

where

$$R(x,\eta) =< S_x(x,\eta),\omega > + < \eta B(x) - \omega, \lambda > + P(x,\eta) - [P(\cdot,0)]. \tag{6}$$

Proof: 1. In what follows we often need the estimate

$$|A| \geq 1 \tag{7}$$

which is a consequence of 4.1.2 and of $1 = |AA^{-1}| \leq |A||A^{-1}|$.

Moreover, we get by means of Cauchy's estimate

$$|F_y|_r \leq \bar{M}s^{-1} \text{ for } F \in \mathcal{P}_*^q(r,s) \text{ with } |F|_{r,s} \leq \bar{M} > 0. \tag{8}$$

because $F_y(x,y) = F_y(x,0) = F_y(x)$, $\forall\,(x,y) \in \mathcal{S}(r) \times \mathcal{B}(s)$.

2. From 4.1.8 we infer $|[B]-A| \leq 1/5$ hence, using 4.1.2, we obtain $|[B]A^{-1} - E| \leq |[B]-A||A^{-1}| \leq 1/5$. Thus $C = [B]A^{-1}$ is invertible with $|C^{-1}| \leq 5/4$. Consequently, $[B] = CA$ is invertible with $|[B]^{-1}| \leq |A^{-1}||C^{-1}| \leq 5/4$. From 4.1.6 and (8) we conclude that $|[P_y]| \leq |P_y|_r \leq Ms^{-1}$ and, using (1) as well as the estimate above, that

$$|\lambda| \leq (5/4)Ms^{-1} = (15/2)|A|M\varepsilon^{-1}. \tag{9}$$

3. We define $G \in \mathcal{P}_*(r,s)$ by

$$G(x,\eta) = -P(x,\eta) - < \eta B(x), \lambda > . \tag{10}$$

Then we have $G(x,\eta) + < \eta A, \lambda > = -P(x,\eta) - < \eta(B(x) - A), \lambda >$ and, using (9), 4.2.6, 4.2.8, we obtain

$$|G(\cdot,\eta) + < \eta A, \lambda > |_r \leq M(1 + |\eta|(4s)^{-1}) \quad \forall \eta \in \mathcal{B}(s) \tag{11}$$

and consequently

$$|G(\cdot,\eta) - [G(\cdot,\eta)]|_r \leq M(2 + |\eta|(2s)^{-1}), \quad \forall \eta \in \mathcal{B}(s). \tag{12}$$

4. We apply Theorem 2.2 putting

$$F = G(\cdot,\eta) \in \mathcal{P}_c(r), \quad \forall \eta \in \mathcal{B}(s),\, T = \Phi(\varepsilon)^{-1},\, d = \Omega(T)^{-1}.$$

Then the conditions 2.2.1-2.2.3 follow from 4.1.1-4.1.4. Since $G \in \mathcal{P}_*(r,s)$ we see that for $u = W(\cdot,\eta)$ defined in 2.2(*) the function W belongs to $\mathcal{P}_*(r,s)$. Using (11) with $c = - < \eta A, \lambda >$, (12), and 2.2 (i)-(iii) we obtain

$$|W(\cdot,\eta)|_{r-\delta} \leq (2/15)\delta\varepsilon^{-1}M(2 + |\eta|(2s)^{-1}), \quad \forall \eta \in \mathcal{B}(s), \tag{13}$$

$$|W_x(\cdot,\eta)|_{r-\delta} \leq (9/4)\varepsilon^{-1}M(1 + |\eta|(4s)^{-1}), \quad \forall \eta \in \mathcal{B}(s), \tag{14}$$

$$|< W_x, \omega > -G + [G]|_{r-\delta, s_+} \leq (1/40)M \tag{15}$$

where in the last estimate we have observed 4.1.9.

By means of (8) and 4.1.5 we infer from (13) and (14)

$$|W_\eta|_{r-\delta} \leq (1/3)\delta M\varepsilon^{-1}\delta^{-1} = 2|A|\delta M\varepsilon^{-2}, \tag{16}$$

$$|W_{x\eta}|_{r-\delta} \leq (45/16)M\varepsilon^{-1}\delta^{-1} \leq 17|A|M\varepsilon^{-2}. \tag{17}$$

5. Now we define $S(x,\eta) =< \lambda, x > +W(x,\eta)$. Then (3) follows from (14) for $\eta = 0$. (4a) follows from (14), 4.1.9, (7), and (9). (4b) and (5a) are immediately obtained from (16) and (17), using in the first case 4.1.5 and (7). (5b) and (6) are consequences of (1), (10), and (15) because we have

$$\begin{aligned} R(x,\eta) &=< W_x(x,\eta), \omega > -G(x,\eta) + [G(\cdot,\eta)] \\ &=< W_x(x,\eta), \omega > +P(x,\eta) - [P(\cdot,\eta)]+ < \eta(B(x) - [B]), \lambda > \\ &=< S_x(x,\eta) - \lambda, \omega > +P(x,\eta) - [P(\cdot,0)]+ < \eta B(x), \lambda > . \end{aligned}$$

Finally, (2) follows from (4a), (7), 4.1.5, and 4.1.9.

4.4 Remark:.

The linearization of the problem in each step of the iteration is expressed by the choice of λ and G. The simplest way to define λ and G such that the iteration process works is

$$\lambda = -[P_y]A^{-1}, \quad G = -P.$$

However, the numerical estimates in this case are not as good as in the case (1), (10).

4.5 Canonical transformations.

Under the conditions 4.1 and with the aid of the function S in 4.3 a canonical transformation

$$\begin{cases} x = \xi + X(\xi), & X \in \mathcal{P}^n(r_+), \\ y = \eta + Y(\xi,\eta), & Y \in \mathcal{P}^n_*(r_+, s_+) \end{cases} \tag{18}$$

can be generated having the properties

$$\xi + X(\xi) \in \mathcal{S}(r-\delta), \tag{19}$$

$$\eta + Y(\xi,\eta) \in \mathcal{B}\left(\frac{15}{16}s\right), \quad (\forall(\xi,\eta) \in \mathcal{S}(r_+) \times \mathcal{B}(s_+)) \tag{20}$$

$$X(\xi) + S_\eta(\xi + X(\xi)) = 0, \tag{21}$$

$$\begin{cases} Y(\xi,\eta) = S_x(\xi + X(\xi),\eta) \\ \qquad = (\eta + f_\xi(\xi))(E + X_\xi(\xi))^{-1} - \eta, \; f(\xi) = S(\xi + X(\xi), 0) \end{cases} \tag{22}$$

and satisfying the estimates 4.2.1 and 4.2.2.

Proof: The set $\mathcal{P}^n_\alpha = \{X \in \mathcal{P}^n(r_+) \big| |X|_{r_+} \leq \alpha\}$ with $\alpha = \delta/500$ is a complete metric space with distance function $d(X,\tilde{X}) = |X - \tilde{X}|_{r_+}, \quad \forall X, \tilde{X} \in \mathcal{P}^n_\alpha$. Defining $\mathcal{T}(X)(\xi) = -S_\eta(\xi + X(\xi))$ we have $\mathcal{T} : \mathcal{P}^n_\alpha \to \mathcal{P}^n_\alpha$ because $|Im(\xi + X(\xi))| \leq |Im\xi| + |X(\xi)| < r_+ + \alpha \leq r - \delta$ by 4.1.9. Hence we get (19) and therefore $\mathcal{T}(X) \in \mathcal{P}^n(r_+)$ with $|\mathcal{T}(X)|_{r_+} \leq \alpha$ by (4b). By definition of $\mathcal{T}$ we obtain

$$\begin{aligned}|\mathcal{T}(X) - \mathcal{T}(\tilde{X})|_{r_+} &= \left| \int_0^1 S_\eta(\cdot + X(\cdot) + t(X - \tilde{X}))dt(X - \tilde{X}) \right|_{r_+} \\ &\leq |S_{\eta x}|_{r-\delta}|X - \tilde{X}|_{r_+} \leq p|X - \tilde{X}|_{r_+}, \quad \forall X, \tilde{X} \in \mathcal{P}^n_\alpha,\end{aligned}$$

where we have used 1.1.5, 1.1.6, (19), and (5a) with p defined in (4.2.1). From 4.1.5 and (7) we see that $p \leq .017$ and consequently $\mathcal{T}$ is a contraction and has a fixed point $X \in \mathcal{P}^n_\alpha$ that is to say X satisfies 4.2.1(a) and (21), hence, by differentiation, the equality

$$X_\xi(\xi) + S_{\eta x}(\xi + X(\xi))(E + X_\xi(\xi)) = 0$$

from which the equality in (22) as well as together with (5a) the inequality 4.2.1(b) follow. The function Y defined in (22) belongs to $\mathcal{P}^n_*(r_+, s_+)$, and the estimates in 4.2.2 follow from (4a) and (5a) using 4.1.5 and (7). The relation (20) is a consequence of 4.1.9 and 4.2.2(a). The fact that (18) is canonical follows with (22) from

$$\begin{aligned}< y, dx > - < \eta, d\xi > &=< \eta + Y, d(\xi + X) > - < \eta, d\xi > \\ &=< \eta + f_\xi, d\xi > - < \eta, d\xi >= df.\end{aligned}$$

4.6 Proof of the inductive lemma.

1. First of all we take the generating function from 4.3 and consider the function $(x, \eta) \mapsto H(x, \eta + S_x(x, \eta))$ which belongs to $\mathcal{P}(r - \delta, s_+)$ because of (2). We try to dermine $a_+ \in \mathbb{R}$ in such a way that the function $\hat{P} \in \mathcal{P}_*(r - \delta, s_+)$ defined by the equation

$$H(x, \eta + S_x(x, \eta)) - a_+ - < \omega, \eta >= \hat{P}(x, \eta) + \mathcal{O}(|\eta|^2) \tag{23}$$

satisfies the estimate

$$|\hat{P}|_{r-\delta, s_+} \leq M_+ = (8/13)M. \tag{24}$$

Then we take the canonical transformation (18) which we call Z. Using (19) and (22) we obtain

$$\begin{aligned}H_+(\eta, \xi) &= H \circ Z(\xi, \eta) = H(x, \eta + S_x(x, \eta))|_{x = \xi + X(\xi)} \\ &= a_+ + < \omega, \eta > + P_+(\xi, \eta) + \mathcal{O}(|\eta|^2)\end{aligned}$$

with $P_+(\xi,\eta) = \hat{P}(\xi + X(\xi),\eta)$ such that 4.2.3 is satiesfied by means of (24).

2. The generating function S satisfies equation (6) which can be written in the form

$$< S_x(x,\eta),\omega >= a_+ - a - P(x,\eta) - < \eta H_{yy}(x,0),\lambda > + R(x,\eta)$$

where a_+ is defined by

$$a_+ = a + < \lambda,\omega > + [P(\cdot,0)].$$

With the help of this equation and of 4.1.7 we get (23) where

$$\begin{aligned} \hat{P}(x,\eta) &= Q(x,\eta) + < Q_\eta(x,0),\eta > + R(x,\eta) \\ &\quad + < \eta H_{yy}(x,0), S_x(x,0) - \lambda > + < P_\eta(x), S_x(x,\eta) > \end{aligned} \tag{25}$$

and

$$\begin{aligned} Q(x,\eta) &= H(x,\eta + S_x(x,\eta)) - H(x,\eta) - < H_y(x,\eta), S_x(x,\eta) > \\ &= \int_0^1 (1-t) S_x(x,\eta) H_{yy}(x,\eta + tS_x(x,\eta)) S_x(x,\eta)^T\,dt. \end{aligned}$$

Using (7) we infer from 4.1.8

$$|H_{yy}|_{r,s} \le (6/5)|A|. \tag{26}$$

Therefore, observing (2), 4.1.5, and (4a), Q can be estimated by

$$|Q|_{r-\delta,s_+} \le \frac{1}{2}\left(\frac{6}{5}|A|\right)\left(\frac{41}{4}|A|\frac{M}{\varepsilon}\right)^2 \le \frac{3}{5}\left(\frac{41}{4}\right)^2\left(\frac{1}{10}\right)^3 M \le \frac{2}{31}M$$

such that we obtain by means of Cauchy's estimate

$$|Q(x,0) + < Q_\eta(x,0),\eta > | \le \frac{4}{31}M, \quad \forall\,(x,\eta) \in \mathcal{S}(r-\delta) \times \mathcal{B}(s_+). \tag{27}$$

Similarly, using (26), 4.1.5, (3), and 4.1.9, we find

$$\begin{cases} | < \eta H_{yy}(x,0), S_x(x,0) - \lambda > | \le s_+ (\frac{6}{5}|A|)(\frac{9}{4}\frac{M}{\varepsilon}) = \frac{7}{8}\frac{1}{5}\frac{9}{4}M \le \frac{13}{33}M, \\ \qquad \forall\,(x,\eta) \in \mathcal{S}(r-\delta) \times \mathcal{B}(s_+), \end{cases} \tag{28}$$

and, using (4a), (7), (8), 4.1.5, we find

$$\begin{cases} | < P_\eta, S_x > |_{r-\delta,s_+} & \le |P_\eta|_{r-\delta}|S_x|_{r-\delta,s_+} \le \frac{41}{4}|A|\frac{M^2}{s\varepsilon} \\ & = \frac{123}{2}|A|^2(\frac{M}{\varepsilon})^2 \le \frac{123}{2000}M \le \frac{1}{16}M. \end{cases} \tag{29}$$

Finally, observing (5b), (25), (27), (28), and (29), we obtain the estimate

$$|\hat{P}|_{r-\delta,s_+} \le \left(\frac{4}{31} + \frac{1}{40} + \frac{13}{33} + \frac{1}{16}\right) M \le \frac{8}{13}M$$

as wanted in (24). The inductive lemma is proved.

5. The iteration process

5.1 The ν-th step of the iteration.

Replacing the symbols $r, \delta,\ s, \varepsilon,\ P, H,\ a, X,\ Y, Z\ ,\ f, p, M$ in 4.1 and 4.2 by $r_\nu, \delta_\nu,\ s_\nu, \varepsilon_\nu,\ P_\nu, H_\nu,\ a_\nu, X_\nu,\ Y_\nu, Z_\nu,\ f_\nu, p_\nu, M_\nu$ and the symbols $r_+, s_+, \varepsilon_+, P_+, H_+, a_+, M_+$ by $r_{\nu+1}, s_{\nu+1},\ \varepsilon_{\nu+1}, P_{\nu+1},\ H_{\nu+1}, a_{\nu+1}, M_{\nu+1}$, respectively, the ν-th step of an iteration process is established for $\nu = 0, 1, \dots$ provided that the relations

$$0 < r_\nu, \tag{1a}$$

$$0 < \varepsilon_\nu \leq 1, \tag{1b}$$

$$0 < M_\nu \leq \frac{\varepsilon_\nu^2}{10^3|A|^3}, \tag{1c}$$

$$|H_{\nu yy} - A|_{r_\nu, s_\nu} \leq \frac{1}{5} \tag{2}$$

are satisfied for $\nu = 0, 1, \dots$ where we have to put

$$s_\nu = \frac{1}{6|A|}\varepsilon_\nu, \quad s_{\nu+1} = \frac{7}{8}s_\nu, \tag{3a}$$

$$M_{\nu+1} = \frac{8}{13}M_\nu, \tag{3b}$$

$$r_{\nu+1} = r_\nu - 1.002\delta_\nu, \quad \delta_\nu = n(5.55 + \log n)\Phi(\varepsilon_\nu). \tag{4}$$

In what follows the index $\nu = 0$ will be in general suppressed.

5.2 Result after ν steps:.

Under the conditions 4.1.1-3, 4.1.5-7,

$$0 < r' < r, \quad 0 < \varepsilon \leq \frac{7}{8}, \quad \int_0^{\frac{8}{7}\varepsilon} \Phi(t)\frac{dt}{t} \leq \frac{r - r'}{n(42 + 8\log n)}, \tag{5}$$

and

$$|H_{yy} - A|_{r,s} \leq \frac{1}{120} \tag{6}$$

there exists for $\nu = 0, 1, \dots$ a canonical transformation

$$W^{(\nu)} : \begin{cases} x = U^{(\nu)}(\xi) = \xi + U_\nu(\xi), & U_\nu \in \mathcal{P}^n(r_\nu), \\ y = V^{(\nu)}(\xi, \eta) = \eta + V_\nu(\xi, \eta), & V_\nu \in \mathcal{P}_*^n(r_\nu, s_\nu), \\ \quad = (\eta + g_{\nu\xi}(\xi))(E + U_{\nu\xi}(\xi))^{-1}, & g_\nu \in \mathcal{P}(r_\nu) \end{cases}$$

where

$$r' \leq r_\nu = r - 1.002\sum_{j=0}^{\nu-1}\delta_j, \quad \delta_\nu = n(5.55 + \log n)\Phi(\varepsilon_\nu) \tag{7}$$

$$s_\nu = \left(\frac{7}{8}\right)^\nu s, \quad \varepsilon_\nu = \left(\frac{7}{8}\right)^\nu \varepsilon \tag{8}$$

such that the estimates

$$|U_\nu|_{r_\nu} \leq \frac{r-r'}{501}, \tag{9a}$$

$$|U_{\nu\xi}|_{r_\nu} \leq \frac{2}{21} \tag{9b}$$

$$|V^{(\nu)}|_{r_\nu, s_\nu} \leq \frac{15}{16} s \tag{10a}$$

$$|V_{\nu\eta}|_{r_\nu} \leq \frac{1}{11}|A|^{-2} \tag{10b}$$

and the equality

$$H_\nu(\xi,\eta) = H \circ W^{(\nu)}(\xi,\eta) = a_\nu + <\omega,\eta> + P_\nu(\xi,\eta) + \mathcal{O}(|\eta|^2) \tag{11}$$

with

$$a_\nu \in \mathbb{R}, \quad P_\nu \in \mathcal{P}_*(r_\nu, s_\nu), \quad |P_\nu|_{r_\nu,s_\nu} \leq M_\nu = \left(\frac{8}{13}\right)^\nu M \tag{12}$$

are valid.

Proof: 1. From (5), (8), and 3.2 we deduce

$$\begin{aligned} 1.002 \sum_{\nu=0}^\infty \delta_\nu &= 1.002 n(5.55 + \log n) \sum_{\nu=0}^\infty \Phi(\varepsilon_\nu) \\ &\leq \frac{1.002(5.55+\log n)}{(\log 8/7)(42 + 8\log n)}(r-r') \leq r - r' \end{aligned}$$

so that the numbers r_ν defined in (7) and satisfying (4) are bounded from below by the positive number r'. So (1a) holds for $\nu = 0, 1, \ldots$. From 4.1.5, (5), and (8) it follows that (3a) and (1b) are satisfied for all $\nu \geq 0$. (1c) for $\nu = 0, 1, \ldots$ is a consequence of 4.1.5, (8), and the definition of M_ν in (3b) which coincides with that in (12). The validity of (2) for $\nu = 0, 1, \ldots$ will be shown as a consequence of (6) in the last part of the proof.

2. We get by construction after ν steps $W^{(\nu)} = Z^{(0)} \circ Z^{(1)} \circ \ldots \circ Z^{(\nu-1)}$, hence, writing $Z^{(\nu)} = (X^{(\nu)}, Y^{(\nu)})$,

$$U^{(\nu)} = X^{(0)} \circ X^{(1)} \circ \ldots \circ X^{(\nu-1)}, \tag{13a}$$

$$V^{(\nu)} = Y^{(0)} \circ Z^{(1)} \circ \ldots \circ Z^{(\nu-1)}. \tag{13b}$$

By definition we have $X^{(\nu)}(\xi) = \xi + X_\nu(\xi), Y^{(\nu)}(\xi, \eta) = \eta + Y_\nu(\xi, \eta)$. Therefore we infer from (13) and the defintion of $W^{(\nu)}$

$$U_\nu = \sum_{j=0}^{\nu-1} X_j \circ X^{(j+1)} \circ \ldots \circ X^{(\nu+1)}, \tag{14}$$

$$V_\nu = \sum_{j=0}^{\nu-1} Y_j \circ Z^{(j+1)} \circ \ldots \circ Z^{(\nu+1)}. \tag{15}$$

All these compositions are well defined because from $4.2.1_\nu$, $4.2.2_\nu$ (the index ν indicates that we have changed the symbols as described in 5.1), (3a), and (4) we see that for $\nu = 0, 1, \ldots$

$$X^{(\nu)}(\mathcal{S}(r_{\nu+1})) \subseteq \mathcal{S}(r_\nu - \delta_\nu) \subseteq \mathcal{S}(r_\nu),$$
$$Y^{(\nu)}(\mathcal{S}(r_{\nu+1}) \times \mathcal{B}(s_{\nu+1})) \subseteq \mathcal{B}\left(\frac{15}{16} s_\nu\right) \subseteq \mathcal{B}(s_\nu).$$

As a consequence (13b) implies (10a). Using (7), (14), and $4.2.1_j$ we get

$$|U_\nu|_{r_\nu} \le \sum_{j=0}^{\nu-1} |X_j|_{r_{j+1}} \le \frac{1}{500} \sum_{\nu=0}^{\nu-1} \delta_\nu \le \frac{r - r'}{501}$$

as wanted in (9a). For the proof of (9b) and (10b) we differentiate (14) and (15) in order to obtain the equalities

$$U_{\nu\xi} = \sum_{j=0}^{\nu-1} X_{j\xi}(E + X_{j+1\xi}) \cdots (E + X_{\nu-1\xi}),$$
$$V_{\nu\eta} = \sum_{j=0}^{\nu-1} Y_{j\eta}(E + Y_{j+1\eta}) \cdots (E + Y_{\nu-1\eta})$$

from which, with the aid of $4.2.1_j$ and $4.2.2_j$, we deduce the estimates

$$|U_{\nu\xi}|_{r_\nu} \le \sum_{j=0}^{\nu-1} \frac{p_j}{1 - p_j} \cdot \frac{1}{1 - p_{j+1}} \cdots \frac{1}{1 - p_{\nu-1}} \le \frac{1}{1 - b} - 1,$$
$$|V_{\nu\eta}|_{r_\nu} \le \sum_{j=0}^{\nu-1} p_j(1 + p_{j+1}) \cdots (1 + p_{\nu-1}) \le e^b - 1$$

where $b = \sum_{\nu=0}^{\infty} p_\nu$ and, using (8), (11), and 4.1.5,

$$p_\nu = 17|A| \frac{M_\nu}{\varepsilon_\nu^2} = 17|A| \frac{M}{\varepsilon^2} = \left(\frac{8}{13} \cdot \frac{8}{7} \cdot \frac{8}{7}\right)^\nu \le \frac{17}{10^3 |A|^2} \left(\frac{512}{637}\right)^\nu.$$

Thus, by means of 4.3(7), we get

$$b \leq \frac{10829}{125000}|A|^{-2} \leq \frac{2}{23}|A|^{-2} \leq \frac{2}{23}$$

and consequently

$$\frac{b}{1-b} \leq \frac{2}{21}, \quad e^b - 1 \leq (e^{2/23} - 1)|A|^{-2} \leq \frac{1}{11}|A|^{-2}$$

such that (9b) and (10b) follow.

3. Finally we have to prove (2). Since $H_\nu = H \circ W^{(\nu)}$ we have

$$H_{\nu\eta\eta} - A = (E + V_{\nu\eta}^T)(H_{yy} \circ W^{(\nu)} - A)(E + V_{\nu\eta}) + V_{\nu\eta}^T A + AV_{\nu\eta} + V_{\nu\eta}^T AV_{\nu\eta}.$$

Hence, using 4.3(7), (6), and (10b), we obtain

$$\begin{aligned} |H_{\nu\eta\eta} - A|_{r_\nu, s_\nu} &\leq (1 + |V_{\nu\eta}|_{r_\nu})^2(|H_{yy} - A|_{r,s} + |A|) - |A| \\ &\leq \left(1 + \frac{1}{11}\right)^2 \frac{1}{120} + |A|\left(\left(1 + \frac{1}{11}|A|^{-2}\right)^2 - 1\right) \\ &\leq \frac{6}{5}\left(\frac{1}{11}\right)^2 + \left(1 + \frac{1}{11}\right)^2 - 1 = \frac{1}{5}. \end{aligned}$$

5.3 Proof of the Main Theorem 1.3.

First of all we assume $|A^{-1}| = 1$ so that the conditions 4.1.1-3, 4.1.5-7 (5), (6) required in 5.2 coincide with 1.3.1-7. The sequences

$$U_\nu,\, U_{\nu\xi},\, V^{(\nu)}(\cdot, 0) = V_\nu(\cdot, 0),\, V_{\nu\eta} = -U_{\nu\xi}^T(E + U_{\nu\xi}^T)^{-1},\; \nu = 0, 1, \ldots$$

are uniformly bounded in $S(r')$ by (7), (9), and (10). Therefore there are subsequences converging uniformly in any compact subset of $\mathcal{S}(r')$. Using for the index of these subsequences again $\nu = 0, 1, \ldots$ we get

$$U_\nu \to X \in \mathcal{P}^n(r'), \quad U_{\nu\xi} \to X_\xi \in \mathcal{P}^{n\times n}(r'),$$

$$V_\nu(\cdot, 0) \to \overset{0}{Y} \in \mathcal{P}^n(r'), \quad V_{\nu\eta} \to \overset{1}{Y} = -X_\xi^T(E + X_\xi^T)^{-1}, \tag{16}$$

$$|X|_{r'} \leq \frac{r - r'}{501}, \quad |X_\xi|_{r'} \leq \frac{2}{21}, \tag{17}$$

$$|\overset{0}{Y}|_{r'} \leq \frac{15}{16}s, \quad |\overset{1}{Y}|_{r'} \leq \frac{1}{11}, \tag{18}$$

where for the last inequality we refer to 4.3(7). The definition of $W^{(\nu)}$ yields

$$g_{\nu\xi} = V_\nu(\cdot,0)(E+U_{\nu\xi}) \to Q = \overset{0}{Y}(E+X_\xi) \in \mathcal{P}^n(r')$$

with $Q_\xi^T = Q_\xi$ so that there is an $f \in \mathcal{P}(r')$ with $f_\xi = Q$. Therefore we have

$$\overset{0}{Y} = f_\xi(E+X_\xi)^{-1}, \quad f \in \mathcal{P}(r'). \tag{19}$$

We conclude from (11) and (12)

$$\begin{aligned} H_\nu(\xi,\eta) &= H \circ W^{(\nu)}(\xi,\eta) = H(\xi + U_\nu(\xi), V^{(\nu)}(\xi,\eta)) \\ &= a_\nu + <\omega,\eta> + P_\nu(\xi,\eta) + \mathcal{O}(|\eta|^2) \end{aligned}$$

hence

$$\begin{aligned} H(\xi + U_\nu(\xi), V_\nu(\xi,0)) &= a_\nu + P_\nu(\xi,0), \\ H_y(\xi + U_\nu(\xi), V_\nu(\xi,0))(E + V_{\nu\eta}(\xi)) &= \omega + P_{\nu\eta}(\xi) \end{aligned}$$

with the estimates

$$|P_\nu|_{r_\nu,s_\nu} \le M_\nu = \left(\frac{8}{13}\right)^\nu M, \quad |P_{\nu\eta}|_{r_\nu} \le \left(\frac{64}{91}\right)^\nu \frac{M}{s}$$

following from (12), (8), and 4.3(8). Going to the limit $\nu \to \infty$ we obtain

$$\begin{cases} H(\xi + X(\xi), \overset{0}{Y}(\xi)) = a \in \mathbb{R}, \\ H_y(\xi + X(\xi), \overset{0}{Y}(\xi))(E + \overset{1}{Y}(\xi)) = \omega. \end{cases} \tag{20}$$

Now we define $Y(\xi,\eta) = \overset{0}{Y}(\xi) + \eta\overset{1}{Y}(\xi)^T$. Then we infer from (16), (17), (18), and (19)

$$Y \in \mathcal{P}_*^n(r',s'), \quad s' = \frac{s}{18}, \quad |Y|_{r',s'} \le \frac{17}{18}s,$$

$$|Y_\eta|_{r'} \le \frac{1}{11}, \quad Y(\xi,\eta) = (\eta + f_\xi(\xi))(E + X_\xi(\xi))^{-1} - \eta,$$

moreover,

$$\xi + X(\xi) \in \mathcal{S}(r), \quad \eta + Y(\xi,\eta) \in \mathcal{B}(s) \quad \forall\, (\xi,\eta) \in \mathcal{S}(r') \times \mathcal{B}(s'),$$

and finally with (20)

$$H(\xi + X(\xi), \eta + Y(\xi,\eta)) = a + <\omega,\eta> + \mathcal{O}(|\eta|^2).$$

Thus the existence of the canonical transformation

$$(\xi,\eta) \mapsto Z(\xi,\eta) = (\xi + X(\xi), \eta + Y(\xi,\eta))$$

required in Theorem 1.3 is proved in the case $|A^{-1}| = 1$.

The general case can easily be reduced to the case $|A^{-1}| = 1$ by means of the substitution $y \mapsto |A^{-1}|y$, $H \to H/|A^{-1}|$.

References

[1] Akhiezer, N.I.: *Theory of Approximation*, Ungar, New York; Constable, London (1956).

[2] Arnol'd, V.I.: Proof of a theorem of A.N. Kolmogorov on the invariance of quasi-periodic motions under small pertubations of the Hamiltonian, Uspehi Mat. Nauk 18 (113), 13–40 (1963) [Russian]. Russ. Math. Surveys 18 (5), 9–36 (1963).

[3] Bang, T.: Une inégalité de Kolmogoroff et les fonctions presque-périodiques, Danske Vid. Selsk. Math.-Fys. Medd. 19, no. 4, 3–28 (1941).

[4] Bruno, A.D.: The analytic form of differential equations. Tr. Mosk. Mat. O-va 25, 119–262 (1971); 26, 199–239 (1972) [Russian]. Trans. Mosc. Math. Soc. 25, 131–288 (1971); 26, 199–239 (1972).

[5] Bruno, A.D.: *Local Methods in Nonlinear Differential Equations*, Springer, Berlin Heidelberg 1989.

[6] Perez Marco, R.: Sur la structure des germes holomorphes non-linearisables, C.R. Acad. Sci. Paris Sér. I Math. 312, no. 7, 533–536 (1991).

[7] Moser, J.: On the construction of almost periodic solutions for ordinary differential equations, Proc. Int. Conf. Funct. Anal. and Rel. Top., Tokyo (1969).

[8] Rüssmann, H.: On an Inequality for Trigonometrical Polynomials in Several Variables, "Analysis, et cetera", Acad. Press Inc. 545–562 (1990).

NEW RESULTS IN THE REVERSIBLE KAM THEORY

MIKHAIL B. SEVRYUK

1. REVERSIBLE SYSTEMS AND THE KAM THEORY

Consider a mechanical system of s particles with the interaction forces which are independent of velocities or even functions in velocities. Such a system ruled by the Newton equation $d^2r/dt^2 = F(r,v)$, $r \in \mathbb{R}^{3s}$, $v = dr/dt$, $F(r,-v) \equiv F(r,v)$, is time reversible, i.e., reversing all the velocities v reverses all the trajectories in the configuration space $\mathbb{R}^{3s}$. More generally, an autonomous differential equation $du/dt = V(u)$ and the corresponding vector field V are said to be *reversible* if there exists a phase space involution G (a mapping for which $G^2 = \mathrm{Id}$) that reverses the direction of time: $TG \circ V = -V \circ G$, where TG is the differential of G, i.e., G transforms the field V into the opposite field $-V$. This means that with $u(t)$, also $G(u(-t))$ is a solution of the equation. In the above example, $G : (r,v) \mapsto (r,-v)$. A system

$$dx/dt = f(x,y), \quad dy/dt = g(x,y), \quad x \in \mathbb{R}^p, \quad y \in \mathbb{R}^q \tag{1}$$

is reversible with respect to the involution

$$G : (x,y) \mapsto (-x,y) \tag{2}$$

if and only if f is even in x and g is odd in x.

The concept of reversibility has been discussed in detail in [1–6]. Side by side with reversible vector fields, there are reversible diffeomorphisms. A mapping A is said to be *reversible* if there exists an involution G that conjugates the A with its inverse A^{-1}, i.e., $AGA = G$. The flow map of a reversible vector field for each fixed time is reversible with respect to the same involution, and vice versa. A number of important examples of reversible differential equations and mappings is presented in [6]. The relation between reversible vector fields and reversible diffeomorphisms is analogous to that between Hamiltonian vector fields and exact symplectic diffeomorphisms.

Reversible dynamical systems have turned out to be very similar to Hamiltonian ones in a lot of aspects [1, 3–6]. In particular, one can develop *the reversible KAM theory.*

The Kolmogorov — Arnol'd — Moser theory is often treated as a branch of the perturbation theory, but it seems more natural to hold that the KAM theorems describe the generic phenomena connected with quasiperiodic motion in symmetric (Hamiltonian or reversible) systems.

Let us confine ourselves to vector fields, then, e.g., the KAM theory guarantees that in the phase space of a generic Hamiltonian system with S degrees of freedom, there are m-parameter Cantor families of invariant m-tori with quasiperiodic motions for each $0 \le m \le S$. The union of these tori has positive $2m$-dimensional Lebesgue measure. The quasiperiodic motion frequencies on the tori are strongly incommensurable. Moreover, these tori are isotropic (Lagrangian for $m = S$) and reducible. Isotropicity means that the restriction of the symplectic structure vanishes on the torus. Reducibility means that near the torus one can choose such a coordinate system (X, Y), $X \in (\mathbb{R}/2\pi\mathbb{Z})^m$, $Y \in \mathbb{R}^N$ (here $N = 2S - m$), in which the torus in question is $\{Y = 0\}$ and the equations of the motion take the form

$$dX/dt = \omega + \mathcal{O}(|Y|), \quad dY/dt = KY + \mathcal{O}(|Y|^2) \tag{3}$$

with some matrix $K \in gl(N, \mathbb{R})$ independent of X ($\omega \in \mathbb{R}^m$ being the frequency vector).

For $m < S$ these tori are called *lower dimensional.* Among recent works containing lower dimensional Hamiltonian KAM results one should mention [7–15] where references to earlier papers are also presented (see as well [6] for a long list of relevant references).

Remark. Here and henceforth, the words "a generic system possesses the property $\mathcal{P}$" mean "in the functional space of all systems endowed with an appropriate topology, the systems with the property $\mathcal{P}$ constitute an open set".

The reversible setting is more diverse than the Hamiltonian one. Whereas all symplectic structures in a given dimension are locally equivalent (the Darboux theorem [16]), involutions differ in their *types* [3–6]. An involution of a $(p+q)$-dimensional manifold is said to have type (p, q) if its submanifold of fixed points is of dimension q. Near a fixed point of a type-(p, q) involution G, one can always introduce local coordinates $x \in \mathbb{R}^p$, $y \in \mathbb{R}^q$ in which G takes the form (2) (the Bochner theorem [16]).

In most cases involutions encountered are "isosceles", i.e., of types (p, p) [2, 6] but involutions of types (p, q) with $p < q$ are also often met with [3–6]. Now the essence of the reversible KAM theory can be formulated as follows.

Theorem 0. *In the $(2p+\nu)$-dimensional phase space of a generic vector field reversible with respect to an involution of type $(p, p+\nu)$ with $\nu \ge 0$, there are $(m+\nu)$-parameter Cantor families of invariant m-tori with quasiperiodic motions for each $0 \le m \le p$. The union of these tori has positive $(2m+\nu)$-dimensional Lebesgue measure. The quasiperiodic motion frequencies on the tori are strongly incommensurable. Moreover, these tori are also invariant under the reversing involution and reducible.*

This principle was first reported by the author at the 2nd Soviet — American Chaos Conference held in the town of Tarusa (Russia) in August 1990 and published in [6] as a conjecture. *Now Theorem 0 has been proven.* Various results concerning the particular case $\nu = 0$ (for arbitrary $2 \le m \le p$) were obtained or discussed in [7, 8, 14, 17–24], and those concerning the particular case $m = p$ (for arbitrary $\nu \ge 0$) in [3–5, 9]. The purpose of this paper is to announce precise statements which imply Theorem 0 as well as to sketch the proofs.

Note that the cases $m = 1$ (closed trajectories) and $m = 0$ (equilibrium points) for arbitrary $\nu \ge 0$ are very simple and not of the KAM character, since they involve no small divisors. The families of invariant tori in these cases are smooth rather than Cantor.

The KAM theory also embraces assertions on invariant m-tori of Hamiltonian systems with S degrees of freedom for the $m > S$ case [25], as well as on invariant p-tori of systems reversible with respect to an involution of type (p, q) for the $p > q$ case [9, 26]. To the author's knowledge, there are no results on invariant m-tori of systems reversible with respect to a type-(p, q) involution for $p > q$ and $m < p$. In this paper we will not touch upon all these problems. However, one should mention a simple reason [3–6] for why type-(p, q) involutions with $p < q$ are more "natural" than involutions with $p > q$. The point is that involutions of types $(p, p + \nu)$ with $\nu > 0$ appear in studying periodic solutions of reversible differential equations. Given a vector field V reversible with respect to an involution G of type (S, S), consider a G-invariant closed trajectory ξ of this vector field and a G-invariant Poincaré section Σ for ξ. The restriction G_1 of G to Σ is an involution of type $(S - 1, S)$. The corresponding Poincaré mapping $A: \Sigma \to \Sigma$ is reversible [2–5] with respect to G_1.

Under the hypotheses of Theorem 0, for each invariant torus, the matrix $K \in gl(2p + \nu - m, \mathbb{R})$ in the definition (3) of reducibility possesses $m + \nu$ zero eigenvalues and $2(p - m)$ simple eigenvalues other than zero. In the hyperbolic $m < p$ case, where none of these $2(p - m)$ eigenvalues is purely imaginary, one may try to find two invariant surfaces asymptotic to the torus in question, one of them being stable (asymptotic as $t \to +\infty$) and the other unstable (asymptotic as $t \to -\infty$). These surfaces ("whiskers") definitely exist if $\nu = 0$ (and are of dimension p). In this paper we will not discuss tori's whiskers although they are of great importance for transport (e.g., the Arnol'd diffusion) in the phase space of the system (see [27] for a lucid exposition in the case of Hamiltonian dynamics). Moreover, we will not distinguish the hyperbolic case at all.

By now, all the reversible KAM theorems have been proven in the analytic situation only (apart from the "classical" case $\nu = 0$, $m = p$ [28]), but their C^∞ and finitely differentiable versions are believed to hold. In [9] there is a declaration that the KAM results for invariant p-tori in systems reversible with respect to involutions of type (p, q) for arbitrary p and q can be obtained in the C^ℓ framework for any ℓ sufficiently large.

In fact, there are used two main approaches to prove that families of quasi-periodic motions are generic (i.e., structurally stable) in Hamiltonian or reversible systems. The *global* approach proposes constructing invariant tori in nearly integrable systems (invariant tori in integrable systems constitute a smooth family rather than a Cantor one), while the *local* approach is to look for invariant tori near an equilibrium point or a closed trajectory (see a detailed discussion in [6]). Of course, two concrete theorems within the same approach may well be drastically different. E.g., if one studies lower dimensional m-tori in Hamiltonian systems with $S > m$ degrees of freedom, it is natural to perturb a system possessing an m-parameter smooth family of invariant m-tori [9–11, 13], but it is also possible to consider perturbations of a completely integrable system whose phase space is foliated into invariant S-tori [12, 15]. In the latter case the desired m-tori of a perturbed system are generated from resonant S-tori of the unperturbed one. As a rule, local statements can be easily reduced to global ones. The inverse reduction is also often possible.

All the results presented below for reversible vector fields can be *mutatis mutandis* carried over to reversible diffeomorphisms. The case $\nu = 0$ for diffeomorphisms was considered in [23], some applications in dimensions $\nu = 0$, $p = 2m = 2$ are presented in [29–31]. The case $m = p$ for diffeomorphisms was considered in [3–5].

2. The global theorem

We fix nonnegative integers m, k, and ν (k being even). In the sequel, we will closely follow [23] where the particular case $\nu = 0$ was considered. Indices j, μ, σ, p, τ, and t range respectively in the intervals $1 \le j \le m$, $1 \le \mu \le k$, $1 \le \sigma \le k$, $1 \le p \le \nu$, $1 \le \tau \le 4$, and $1 \le t \le 3$. Symbols $|a|$ and $\|a\|$ denote respectively the ℓ_1-norm and the ℓ_2-norm of a vector $a \in \mathbb{C}^n$:

$$|a| = |a_1| + \dots + |a_n|, \qquad \|a\|^2 = |a_1|^2 + \dots + |a_n|^2.$$

We use as well the $\| \ \|$-norm of an arbitrary $n \times n'$ matrix $A = (A_{\alpha\alpha'}) \in \mathbb{C}^{nn'}$:

$$\|A\|^2 = \sum_{\alpha=1}^{n} \sum_{\alpha'=1}^{n'} |A_{\alpha\alpha'}|^2.$$

The letter q will always be for a vector in $\mathbb{Z}^m$ and if $a \in \mathbb{C}^m$ then

$$(q, a) = q_1 a_1 + \dots + q_m a_m.$$

By E the unit $k \times k$ matrix will be denoted, and by mes_n the n-dimensional Lebesgue measure in $\mathbb{R}^N$, $N \ge n$. A dot over a letter means differentiating with respect to time.

Theorem 1. *Let U be a complex neighborhood of a point $y^0 \in \mathbb{R}^m$, W a neighborhood of the origin in $\mathbb{C}^k$, $\widetilde{U}$ a complex neighborhood of a point $\eta^0 \in \mathbb{R}^\nu$, and $0 < r_0 \leq 1$. Suppose that on the domain*

$$\begin{aligned} D =& \{x \in \mathbb{C}^m \mid |\mathrm{Im}\, x_j| < r_0,\ j = 1,\ \ldots,\ m\} \times \{y \in \mathbb{C}^m | y \in U\} \\ & \times \{w \in \mathbb{C}^k | w \in W\} \times \{\eta \in \mathbb{C}^\nu | \eta \in \widetilde{U}\} \subset \mathbb{C}^{2m+k+\nu}, \end{aligned} \tag{4}$$

a vector field V determining the system of differential equations

$$\begin{aligned} &\dot{x} = \varphi + \gamma y + \gamma^3 f^1(x, y, w, \eta), \quad \dot{y} = \gamma^3 f^2(x, y, w, \eta), \\ &\dot{w} = [X + \gamma Y(y, \eta)]w + \gamma^3 f^3(x, y, w, \eta), \quad \dot{\eta} = \gamma^3 f^4(x, y, w, \eta), \end{aligned} \tag{5}$$

and a mapping $G: \ D \to \mathbb{C}^{2m+k+\nu}$,

$$G: \ (x, y, w, \eta) \mapsto (-x, y, Rw, \eta) \tag{6}$$

are defined, where $\varphi \in \mathbb{R}^m$, $0 < \gamma \leq 1$, X and R are matrices in $gl(k, \mathbb{R})$,

$$Y: \ U \times \widetilde{U} \to gl(k, \mathbb{C})$$

is a holomorphic function real-valued on $(U \times \widetilde{U}) \cap \mathbb{R}^{m+\nu}$, and

$$f^\tau: \ D \to \mathbb{C}^{2m+k+\nu}, \quad \tau = 1,\ \ldots,\ 4$$

are holomorphic functions 2π-periodic in x_j and real-valued on $D \cap \mathbb{R}^{2m+k+\nu}$.

Let the involutivity condition $R^2 = E$ be satisfied and the following reversibility conditions:

$$XR + RX = 0, \tag{7}$$

$$[X + \gamma Y(y, \eta)]R + R[X + \gamma Y(y, \eta)] = 0 \tag{8}$$

everywhere in $U \times \widetilde{U}$, and

$$TG \circ V = -V \circ G \tag{9}$$

everywhere in $\{(x, y, w, \eta) \in D | Rw \in W\}$ be satisfied. Let the eigenvalues $\lambda_1,\ \ldots,\ \lambda_k$ of the matrix X be simple and other than zero.

Below we fix y^0, η^0, D, φ, X and R as well as a matrix $M \in GL(k, \mathbb{C})$ which diagonalizes X over $\mathbb{C}$:

$$MXM^{-1} = \mathrm{diag}(\lambda_1,\ \ldots,\ \lambda_k),$$

a closed ball $B_0 \subset (U \cap \mathbb{R}^m)$ centered at y^0 and a closed ball $\widetilde{B}_0 \subset (\widetilde{U} \cap \mathbb{R}^\nu)$ centered at η^0.

Suppose that

$$\|Y\| < T_*$$

in $U \times \widetilde{U}$ *and*

$$|f^\tau| < T_*, \quad \tau = 1, \ldots, 4$$

in D *for some constant* $T_* > 0$,

$$|(M[Y(y^2,\eta) - Y(y^1,\eta)]M^{-1})_{\mu\mu}| \le T_\mu \|y^2 - y^1\|, \quad \mu = 1, \ldots, k,$$

$y^1, y^2 \in U$, $\eta \in \widetilde{U}$, *for some constants* $T_1 > 0, \ldots, T_k > 0$, *and the nonresonance conditions*

$$i(q,\varphi) \ne \lambda_\mu \qquad \forall q \in \mathbb{Z}^m,\ \|q\| \le T_\mu,\ 1 \le \mu \le k; \tag{10}$$

$$i(q,\varphi) \ne \lambda_\mu - \lambda_\sigma \qquad \forall q \in \mathbb{Z}^m,\ \|q\| \le T_\mu + T_\sigma,\ 1 \le \mu < \sigma \le k \tag{11}$$

are satisfied.

Let $B \subset B_0$ *and* $\widetilde{B} \subset \widetilde{B}_0$ *be arbitrary closed balls centered at* y^0 *and* η^0 *respectively.*

Then there exists a constant $\gamma^* > 0$ *depending on* T_* *and* T_μ, $\mu = 1, \ldots, k$ *only such that if at least one of the following two conditions:*

1) $\gamma \le \gamma^*$;
2) $y^0 = 0$, $Y(y^0,\eta^0) = 0$ *and the radii of* B *and* $\widetilde{B}$ *do not exceed* γ^*

is satisfied then for any $\varepsilon > 0$ *there exist constants* $\delta > 0$ *and* $K > 1$ *depending on* $B, \widetilde{B}, T_*, T_1, \ldots, T_k, \varepsilon$, *independent of* γ *and such that the following holds.*

Assume

$$|f^\tau(x,y,0,\eta)| < \delta, \quad \tau = 1, \ldots, 4, \tag{12}$$

$$\left\| \frac{\partial f^3}{\partial w}(x,y,0,\eta) \right\| < \delta \tag{13}$$

for $|\mathrm{Im}\, x_j| < r_0$, $j = 1, \ldots, m$, $y \in U$, $\eta \in \widetilde{U}$. *Then for each* $\zeta \in \widetilde{B}$ *there exists a set* $\Omega_\zeta \subset (\varphi + \gamma B)$ *such that*

$$\frac{\mathrm{mes}_m \Omega_\zeta}{\gamma^m \mathrm{mes}_m B} > 1 - \varepsilon \tag{14}$$

and for every $\omega \in \Omega_\zeta$ *there exist a matrix* $Z_{\omega\zeta} \in gl(k,\mathbb{R})$ *and a mapping*

$$F_{\omega\zeta} : \{\widetilde{x} \in \mathbb{C}^m \,|\, |\mathrm{Im}\, \widetilde{x}_j| < r_0/2,\ j = 1, \ldots, m\} \times \{(\widetilde{y}, \widetilde{w}, \widetilde{\eta}) \in \mathbb{C}^{m+k+\nu}\} \to \{(x,y,w,\eta) \in \mathbb{C}^{2m+k+\nu}\} \tag{15}$$

with the following properties.

1) In the coordinate notation, $F_{\omega\zeta}$ has the form

$$x = \widetilde{x} + \Phi^1_{\omega\zeta}(\widetilde{x}, \widetilde{y}, \widetilde{w}, \widetilde{\eta}), \quad y = \frac{\omega - \varphi}{\gamma} + \widetilde{y} + \Phi^2_{\omega\zeta}(\widetilde{x}, \widetilde{y}, \widetilde{w}, \widetilde{\eta}),$$
$$w = \frac{1}{K}[\widetilde{w} + \Phi^3_{\omega\zeta}(\widetilde{x}, \widetilde{y}, \widetilde{w}, \widetilde{\eta})], \quad 8\eta = \zeta + \widetilde{\eta} + \Phi^4_{\omega\zeta}(\widetilde{x}, \widetilde{y}, \widetilde{w}, \widetilde{\eta}),$$

where $\Phi^\tau_{\omega\zeta}$, $\tau = 1, \dots, 4$, are holomorphic functions 2π-periodic in $\widetilde{x}_j$, real-valued on $\mathbb{R}^{2m+k+\nu}$ and affine in $\widetilde{y}$, $\widetilde{w}$, $\widetilde{\eta}$:

$$\Phi^\tau_{\omega\zeta}(\widetilde{x}, \widetilde{y}, \widetilde{w}, \widetilde{\eta}) = \Sigma^\tau_{\omega\zeta}(\widetilde{x}) + \Pi^{\tau 1}_{\omega\zeta}(\widetilde{x})\widetilde{y} + \Pi^{\tau 2}_{\omega\zeta}(\widetilde{x})\widetilde{w} + \Pi^{\tau 3}_{\omega\zeta}(\widetilde{x})\widetilde{\eta}.$$

2) The following estimates are valid:

$$|\Sigma^\tau_{\omega\zeta}| \le \varepsilon\gamma^2, \tag{16}$$
$$\|\Pi^{\tau t}_{\omega\zeta}\| \le \varepsilon\gamma, \tag{17}$$
$$|\Sigma^\tau_{\omega_2\zeta_2} - \Sigma^\tau_{\omega_1\zeta_1}| \le |\omega_2 - \omega_1|\varepsilon\gamma + |\zeta_2 - \zeta_1|\varepsilon\gamma^2, \tag{18}$$
$$\|\Pi^{\tau t}_{\omega_2\zeta_2} - \Pi^{\tau t}_{\omega_1\zeta_1}\| \le |\omega_2 - \omega_1|\varepsilon + |\zeta_2 - \zeta_1|\varepsilon\gamma \tag{19}$$

for $\tau = 1, \dots, 4$ and $t = 1, 2, 3$.

3) In coordinates $(\widetilde{x}, \widetilde{y}, \widetilde{w}, \widetilde{\eta})$ the vector field V determines near the surface $\{\widetilde{y} = 0, \ \widetilde{w} = 0, \ \widetilde{\eta} = 0\}$ a differential equation of the form

$$\dot{\widetilde{x}} = \omega + \gamma\widetilde{y} + g^1(\widetilde{x}, \widetilde{y}, \widetilde{w}, \widetilde{\eta}), \quad \dot{\widetilde{y}} = g^2(\widetilde{x}, \widetilde{y}, \widetilde{w}, \widetilde{\eta}),$$
$$\dot{\widetilde{w}} = \left[X + \gamma Y\left(\frac{\omega - \varphi}{\gamma}, \zeta\right) + Z_{\omega\zeta}\right]\widetilde{w} + g^3(\widetilde{x}, \widetilde{y}, \widetilde{w}, \widetilde{\eta}), \quad \dot{\widetilde{\eta}} = g^4(\widetilde{x}, \widetilde{y}, \widetilde{w}, \widetilde{\eta}), \tag{20}$$

where

$$g^\tau(\widetilde{x}, \widetilde{y}, \widetilde{w}, \widetilde{\eta}) = \mathcal{O}(|\widetilde{y}|^2 + |\widetilde{w}|^2 + |\widetilde{\eta}|^2), \quad \tau = 1, \dots, 4, \tag{21}$$

and the involution G is

$$G: \ (\widetilde{x}, \widetilde{y}, \widetilde{w}, \widetilde{\eta}) \mapsto (-\widetilde{x}, \widetilde{y}, R\widetilde{w}, \widetilde{\eta}). \tag{22}$$

4) The following estimates are valid:

$$\|Z_{\omega\zeta}\| \le \varepsilon\gamma^2, \tag{23}$$
$$\|Z_{\omega_2\zeta_2} - Z_{\omega_1\zeta_1}\| \le |\omega_2 - \omega_1|\varepsilon\gamma + |\zeta_2 - \zeta_1|\varepsilon\gamma^2. \tag{24}$$

Corollary 1. *The field V admits analytic reducible invariant m-tori*

$$T^m_{\omega\zeta} = \left\{\left(\widetilde{x} + \Sigma^1_{\omega\zeta}(\widetilde{x}),\ \frac{\omega-\varphi}{\gamma} + \Sigma^2_{\omega\zeta}(\widetilde{x}),\ \frac{1}{K}\Sigma^3_{\omega\zeta}(\widetilde{x}),\ \zeta + \Sigma^4_{\omega\zeta}(\widetilde{x})\right) \mid \widetilde{x} \in (\mathbb{R}/2\pi\mathbb{Z})^m\right\} \subset (\mathbb{R}/2\pi\mathbb{Z})^m \times \mathbb{R}^{m+k+\nu},$$

which are invariant under the reversing involution G as well. On torus $T^m_{\omega\zeta}$, the field V induces a quasiperiodic motion $\dot{\widetilde{x}} = \omega$ and the restriction of G on $T^m_{\omega\zeta}$ takes the form $\widetilde{x} \mapsto -\widetilde{x}$.

This corollary follows from (20)–(22).

Corollary 2. *Denote the union of all $T^m_{\omega\zeta}$ taken over $\zeta \in \widetilde{B}$, $\omega \in \Omega_\zeta$ by Ξ and the projection $(x, y, w, \eta) \mapsto (x, y, \eta)$ by P. Then*

$$\frac{\mathrm{mes}_{2m+\nu} P(\Xi)}{(2\pi)^m\, \mathrm{mes}_m B\, \mathrm{mes}_\nu \widetilde{B}} > \left(\frac{1-\kappa}{1+\kappa}\right)^{2m+\nu} (1-\varepsilon),$$

where $\kappa = 6\sqrt{2m+\nu}\,\gamma^2 r_0^{-1}\varepsilon$.

This corollary can be easily obtained from (14), (16) and (18).

Remark 1. Relation (7) together with the fact that the matrix X is nonsingular implies that k is even and the type of involution $w \mapsto Rw$ is equal to $(k/2, k/2)$. So we might have made no assumptions on the evenness of k beforehand. The type of the involution G (6) is equal to $(m+k/2, m+k/2+\nu)$.

Remark 2. Relations (8) and (9) imply that

$$f^1 \circ G = f^1,\ f^2 \circ G = f^2,\ f^3 \circ G = -Rf^3,\ f^4 \circ G = -f^4 \tag{25}$$

in $\{(x, y, w, \eta) \in D | Rw \in W\}$.

Remark 3. The parameters φ and γ are introduced here with the only purpose that one may reduce the local theorem (see Section 4) to Theorem 1.

Remark 4. The eigenvalues of the matrix X may be purely imaginary.

Remark 5. If all the eigenvalues of the matrix X are real then the set Ω_ζ is independent of ζ and f^τ and consists of all frequency vectors ω with sufficiently strongly incommensurable components. Otherwise Ω_ζ does depend on ζ and f^τ and there are additional resonances that take part in selecting ω. Note that in [23], where the particular case $\nu = 0$ was considered, the impression can be created that Ω is the same for all f^τ sufficiently small (due to some carelessness in the formulation of Theorem 2 therein). In reality, in the $\nu = 0$ case, Ω generally depends on f^τ also (if the matrix X possesses eigenvalues with nonzero imaginary parts).

Remark 6. In [6], while describing systems (27) and (30) (in the numeration of [6]), I required that none of the eigenvalues of the matrices $K(I)$ and $K(I,\eta)$ respectively was equal to 1 or -1 (those matrices are analogs of the matrix $X+\gamma Y(y,\eta)$ here, system (27) corresponding to the particular case $\nu=0$). This was, of course, a slip of the pen, in fact, $K(I)$ and $K(I,\eta)$ should be nonsingular.

3. The iterative procedure

One can prove Theorem 1 by the standard (Kolmogorov's) method of constructing an infinite rapidly convergent succession of coordinate changes whose definition domains shrink down to the desired invariant torus. The coordinate transformations are determined by a pair (ζ,ω). In this Section we describe very briefly (and omitting many important details) an iteration step. Each step is controlled by positive quantities $r,\ v,\ s,\ d,\ c,\ \theta,\ \chi,\ \beta$ subject to inequalities

$$\theta<r\le 1,\ 2\chi<v,\ C^0\beta<s,\ c\le 1,\ s<v<r-\theta,\ C_0\gamma^2 d<sc^2(r-\theta)^{N_0},$$

where C^0 and C_0 are certain constants greater than unity which depend on matrix R, matrix-valued function $X+\gamma Y(y,\eta)$ and vector ω only, while N_0 is a certain positive constant which depends on m only.

Let in the domain

$$\begin{aligned}D(r,v,s)=&\{x\in\mathbb{C}^m\,|\,|\mathrm{Im}\,x_j|<r\}\times\left\{y\in\mathbb{C}^m\,\middle|\,\left|y_j-\frac{\omega_j-\varphi_j}{\gamma}\right|<v\right\}\\&\times\{w\in\mathbb{C}^k\,|\,|w_\mu|<s\}\times\{\eta\in\mathbb{C}^\nu\,|\,|\eta_p-\zeta_p|<v\}\subset\mathbb{C}^{2m+k+\nu},\end{aligned}$$

a vector field V determine the system of differential equations (5) reversible with respect to the involution (6), the relations (7)–(9) being valid. We assume that

$$|f^\tau(x,y,w,\eta)|<d,\quad \tau=1,\ \ldots,\ 4$$

in $D(r,v,s)$ and that a vector $\omega\in\mathbb{R}^m$ and the eigenvalues $\Lambda_1,\ \ldots,\ \Lambda_k$ of the matrix

$$L=X+\gamma Y\left(\frac{\omega-\varphi}{\gamma},\zeta\right)$$

satisfy the arithmetical conditions

$$|i(q,\omega)-\Lambda_\mu|\ge\frac{\gamma c}{(|q|+1)^m}\qquad\forall q\in\mathbb{Z}^m,\ 1\le\mu\le k;\tag{26}$$

$$|i(q,\omega)-(\Lambda_\mu-\Lambda_\sigma)|\ge\frac{\gamma c}{|q|^m}\qquad\forall q\in\mathbb{Z}^m\backslash\{0\},\ 1\le\mu\le\sigma\le k.\tag{27}$$

Note that $LR+RL=0$.

Now consider linear functional differential equations

$$(\mathfrak{A}\psi)(x,y,w,\eta) = \frac{\partial\psi(x,y,0,\eta)}{\partial w}Lw + \frac{\partial\psi(x,y,w,\eta)}{\partial x}\omega = f(x,y,w,\eta), \tag{28}$$

$$(\mathfrak{B}\psi)(x,y,w,\eta) = \frac{\partial\psi(x,y,0,\eta)}{\partial w}Lw + \frac{\partial\psi(x,y,w,\eta)}{\partial x}\omega - L\psi(x,y,w,\eta) = f(x,y,w,\eta), \tag{29}$$

where $f : D(r,v,s) \to \mathbb{C}^\ell$ is the known function and $\psi : D(r',v,s) \to \mathbb{C}^\ell$ is the function sought for $(0 < r' < r)$, ℓ is arbitrary in (28) and $\ell = k$ in (29). Functions f and ψ are supposed to be holomorphic and 2π-periodic in x_j.

The operators $\mathfrak{A}$ and $\mathfrak{B}$ were studied in [23] for the particular case $\nu = 0$, but the only change needed for the case $\nu > 0$ is the replacement of y by (y,η). Define the functions ψ^τ, $\tau = 1, \dots, 4$ by the following relations:

$$\begin{aligned}
\mathfrak{A}\psi^2 &= \gamma^3(f^2 - \langle f^2\rangle + [f^2]), & \langle\psi^2\rangle - [\psi^2] &= \gamma^2([f^1] - \langle f^1\rangle),\\
\mathfrak{A}\psi^1 &= \gamma^3 f^1 + \gamma\psi^2, & \langle\psi^1\rangle - [\psi^1] &= 0,\\
\mathfrak{B}\psi^3 &= \gamma^3(f^3 - [f^3]), & [\psi^3] &= 0,\\
\mathfrak{A}\psi^4 &= \gamma^3(f^4 - \langle f^4\rangle + [f^4]), & \langle\psi^4\rangle - [\psi^4] &= 0.
\end{aligned}$$

Here $\langle f^\tau\rangle$ denotes the mean value of f^τ over x and $[f^\tau]$ the linear part of $\langle f^\tau\rangle$ with respect to w:

$$\langle f^\tau\rangle(y,w,\eta) = \frac{1}{(2\pi)^m}\int\!\cdots\!\int_{(\mathbb{R}/2\pi\mathbb{Z})^m} f^\tau(x,y,w,\eta)\,\mathrm{d}x,$$

$$[f^\tau](y,w,\eta) = \frac{\partial\langle f^\tau\rangle(y,0,\eta)}{\partial w}w,$$

and the analogous notations are employed for ψ^τ. Set

$$\Psi : (x,y,w,\eta) \mapsto (x + \psi^1(x,y,w,\eta),\ y + \psi^2(x,y,w,\eta),\ w + \psi^3(x,y,w,\eta),\ \eta + \psi^4(x,y,w,\eta)).$$

It easily follows from (25) that

$$\psi^1 \circ G = -\psi^1,\ \psi^2 \circ G = \psi^2,\ \psi^3 \circ G = R\psi^3,\ \psi^4 \circ G = \psi^4, \tag{30}$$

i.e., the mapping Ψ commutes with the involution G. Now one can verify that in the narrower domain $D(\theta,\chi,\beta)$ the vector field $T\Psi^{-1}\circ V\circ\Psi$ determines the system of differential equations

$$\begin{aligned}
&\dot{x} = \varphi + \gamma y + \gamma^3 h^1(x,y,w,\eta), \quad \dot{y} = \gamma^3 h^2(x,y,w,\eta),\\
&\dot{w} = [X + \gamma Y(y,\eta) + \gamma\Delta(y,\eta)]w + \gamma^3 h^3(x,y,w,\eta), \quad \dot{\eta} = \gamma^3 h^4(x,y,w,\eta),
\end{aligned} \tag{31}$$

where

$$\Delta(y,\eta) = \gamma^2 \frac{\partial \langle f^3\rangle(y,0,\eta)}{\partial w}$$

(note that $\Delta(y,\eta)R + R\Delta(y,\eta) = 0$) and h^τ, $\tau = 1, \ldots, 4$, are holomorphic functions 2π-periodic in x_j and real-valued for $(x,y,w,\eta) \in (D(\theta,\chi,\beta) \cap \mathbb{R}^{2m+k+\nu})$, the inequalities

$$|h^\tau(x,y,w,\eta)| < \frac{C_1}{(r-\theta)^{N_1} c^2}\left(dv + \frac{\gamma^2 d^2}{s} + \frac{d\beta^2}{\gamma s^2}\right), \qquad \tau = 1, \ldots, 4,$$

$$\|\Delta(y,\eta)\| < \frac{C_3\gamma^2 d}{s}$$

holding. Moreover, in the domain $D((r+\theta)/2, v, s)$ the functions ψ^τ satisfy the inequality

$$|\psi^\tau(x,y,w,\eta)| < \frac{C_2\gamma^2 d}{(r-\theta)^{N_2} c^2}, \qquad \tau = 1, \ldots, 4.$$

Here C_1, C_2, and C_3 are certain positive constants depending on R, X, $Y(y,\eta)$ and L only, while N_1 and N_2 are certain positive constants depending on m only.

Let us also point out the values of parameters r, v, s, d, c, θ, χ, β at the nth iteration step, $n \geq 0$:

$$r_n = \frac{r_0}{2}\left(1 + \frac{1}{2^n}\right), \quad v_n = d_*^{b^n \alpha}\gamma, \quad s_n = d_*^{b^n a}\gamma^{n+1}, \quad d_n = d_*^{b^n}\gamma^n, \quad c_n = \frac{c_*}{2^n},$$

$$\theta_n = r_{n+1}, \quad \chi_n = v_{n+1}, \quad \beta_n = s_{n+1},$$

where r_0 is the constant entering the definition of the domain (4), d_* and c_* are sufficiently small positive constants depending on ε but not on γ, and a, α, b are arbitrary fixed numbers subject to inequalities $1/2 < a < 1$, $0 < \alpha < 1 - a$, $1 < b < 1 + \alpha$ (e.g., $a = 5/8$, $\alpha = 1/4$, $b = 9/8$).

Nevertheless, the calculations in the iterative procedure are very cumbersome.

4. The local theorem

In the sequel, we will closely follow [22, 23] where the particular case $\nu = 0$ was considered.

Lemma. *Let V be an analytic vector field defined near the origin in $\mathbb{R}^{2m+k+\nu}$ and reversible with respect to an analytic involution G. Suppose that $V(0) = 0$, $G(0) = 0$, zero is an eigenvalue of the linearization of the field V at 0* *of multiplicity ν and the remaining $2m+k$ eigenvalues are simple. Assume that there are $2m$ purely imaginary numbers $\pm i\varphi_1, \ldots, \pm i\varphi_m$ (here $\varphi_j > 0$, $j = 1, \ldots, m$) among those $2m+k$ eigenvalues and denote the remaining k eigenvalues by $\lambda_1, \ldots, \lambda_k$ (they also may be purely imaginary). Let the type of involution G be equal to $(m+k/2, m+k/2+\nu)$.*

Under these hypotheses, if for some integer $\ell > 0$ the nonresonance conditions2

$$(q,\varphi) \neq 0 \qquad \forall q \in \mathbb{Z}^m,\ 1 \leq |q| \leq 2\ell+2; \tag{32}$$

$$i(q,\varphi) \neq \lambda_\mu \qquad \forall q \in \mathbb{Z}^m,\ |q| \leq 4\ell+1,\ 1 \leq \mu \leq k; \tag{33}$$

$$i(q,\varphi) \neq \lambda_\mu - \lambda_\sigma \qquad \forall q \in \mathbb{Z}^m,\ |q| \leq 2\ell,\ 1 \leq \mu < \sigma \leq k \tag{34}$$

are satisfied then there exists a coordinate frame ($z \in \mathbb{C}^m$, $u \in \mathbb{R}^k$, $\xi \in \mathbb{R}^\nu$) in $\mathbb{R}^{2m+k+\nu}$ (with the same origin) in which the vector field V determines the system of differential equations

$$\begin{aligned} \dot z_j &= iz_j\left(\varphi_j + \sum_{n=1}^{\ell} Q_{jn}(\rho)\right) + I_j(z,\bar z,u,\xi),\\ \dot u &= \left(\sum_{n=0}^{\ell} S_n(\rho)\right)u + J(z,\bar z,u,\xi),\\ \dot\xi &= \Theta(z,\bar z,u,\xi), \end{aligned} \tag{35}$$

and the involution G takes the form

$$G:\ (z,u,\xi) \mapsto (\bar z, Ru, \xi), \tag{36}$$

where: 1) $\rho = (\rho_1, \ldots, \rho_m)$, $\rho_j = |z_j|^2$;

2) $Q_{jn}:\ \mathbb{R}^m \to \mathbb{R}$ and $S_n:\ \mathbb{R}^m \to gl(k,\mathbb{R})$ are homogeneous of degree n polynomial functions of ρ;

3) the series I_j are of order $2\ell+2$, while the components of the real-valued vector-series J and Θ are of order $4\ell+2$ with respect to the quasihomogeneous filtration of the space $\mathbb{C}[[z,\bar z,u,\xi]]$ defined by weights 1, 1, $2\ell+1$, and $2\ell+1$ of variables z_j, $\bar z_j$, u_μ, and ξ_p, respectively;

4) R is an involutive matrix in $GL(k,\mathbb{R})$.

One can easily prove this Lemma by the standard Normal Form technique [5].

Remark. It is clear that $\lambda_1, \ldots, \lambda_k$ are eigenvalues of the matrix S_0.

Theorem 2. *Let the hypotheses of the Lemma above be satisfied for $\ell = 3$ and assume a matrix $M \in GL(k,\mathbb{C})$ to diagonalize S_0 over $\mathbb{C}$:*

$$MS_0M^{-1} = \mathrm{diag}(\lambda_1, \ldots, \lambda_k).$$

Suppose that the linear operator

$$\Gamma = (Q_{11},\ \ldots,\ Q_{m1}) :\ \mathbb{R}^m \to \mathbb{R}^m$$

is nondegenerate ($\det \Gamma \neq 0$) *and consider linear operator*

$$\mathbb{R}^m \to gl(k, \mathbb{C}), \qquad \rho \mapsto M S_1(\Gamma^{-1}\rho) M^{-1}.$$

Set

$$T_\mu = \max_{\|\rho\|=1} |(M S_1(\Gamma^{-1}\rho) M^{-1})_{\mu\mu}|, \quad \mu = 1,\ \ldots,\ k,$$

and suppose that the additional nonresonance conditions (10) and (11) are satisfied.

Then in any neighborhood of the origin in $\mathbb{R}^{2m+k+\nu}$ *the vector field* V *and the involution* G *possess common analytic reducible invariant* m*-tori on which* V *induces quasiperiodic motions with strongly incommensurable frequencies close to* $\varphi_1,\ \ldots,\ \varphi_m$. *Moreover, if* A_ϵ *denotes the* ϵ*-neighborhood* ($\epsilon > 0$) *of the origin in the* $(2m + \nu)$*-dimensional subspace* $\{u = 0\}$ *and* Ξ_ϵ *the union of all invariant tori whose images under the projection* $P :\ (z, u, \xi) \mapsto (z, \xi)$ *lie in* A_ϵ, *then*

$$\lim_{\epsilon \to 0} \frac{mes_{2m+\nu} P(\Xi_\epsilon)}{mes_{2m+\nu} A_\epsilon} = 1.$$

One can reduce Theorem 2 to Theorem 1 in the following way. Fix a domain $U_1 \subset \mathbb{R}^m$ such that $(\Gamma^{-1}y)_j > 0$ for any $y \in \mathrm{Closure}(U_1)$, $j = 1\ \ldots,\ m$, a neighborhood W_1 of the origin in $\mathbb{R}^k$, and a neighborhood $\widetilde{U}_1$ of the origin in $\mathbb{R}^\nu$. The mapping

$$Q = (Q_{11} + Q_{12} + Q_{13},\ \ldots,\ Q_{m1} + Q_{m2} + Q_{m3}) :\ (\mathbb{R}^m, 0) \to (\mathbb{R}^m, 0)$$

is a polynomial (of degree ≤ 3) diffeomorphism. Let $\epsilon > 0$ be a small parameter. Introduce new coordinates $x \in (\mathbb{R}/2\pi\mathbb{Z})^m$, $y \in U_1$, $w \in W_1$, $\eta \in \widetilde{U}_1$ by the formulas

$$\begin{aligned} z_j &= ([Q^{-1}(\epsilon^2 y)]_j)^{1/2} \exp(i x_j), \quad j = 1,\ \ldots,\ m, \\ u &= \epsilon^7 w, \\ \xi &= \epsilon^7 \eta \end{aligned}$$

(here $7 = 2\ell + 1$, $\ell = 3$). In coordinates (x, y, w, η) the system (35) and the involution (36) get the forms (5) and (6) respectively with $\gamma = \epsilon^2$ and $f^\tau = \mathcal{O}(\epsilon)$, $\tau = 1,\ \ldots,\ 4$. The latter estimate will remain valid after the complex continuation, and for ϵ sufficiently small Theorem 1 will be applicable.

Acknowledgments

It is a great pleasure for me to thank V. I. Arnol'd who acquainted me with reversible systems, normal forms, and invariant tori filled with quasiperiodic motions. I am also grateful to J. K. Moser, H. Rüßmann, J. Pöschel, S. Wiggins, C. Simó, A. Lahiri, S. B. Kuksin, A. I. Neĭshtadt, V. F. Lazutkin, Yu. S. Il'yashenko, Yu. N. Bibikov, V. V. Kozlov, V. Aquilanti, D. V. Treshchëv, S. A. Dovbysh, N. G. Moshchevitin, and A. V. Borisov for a lot of useful discussions on generic structures constituted by quasiperiodic motions in Hamiltonian and reversible systems. I acknowledge a kind TEXnical* help by V. F. Lazutkin during preparation of the final version of the manuscript.

REFERENCES

1. J. K. Moser, *Stable and Random Motions in Dynamical Systems, with Special Emphasis on Celestial Mechanics,* Ann. Math. Stud. , Vol. 77, Princeton Univ. Press, Princeton, NJ, 1973.
2. R. L. Devaney, *Reversible diffeomorphisms and flows*, Trans. Am. Math. Soc. **218** (1976), 89–113.
3. V. I. Arnol'd, *Reversible systems*, in Nonlinear and Turbulent Processes in Physics (R. Z. Sagdeev, ed.), Vol. 3, Harwood, Chur, New York, 1984, pp. 1161–1174.
4. V. I. Arnol'd and M. B. Sevryuk, *Oscillations and bifurcations in reversible systems*, in Nonlinear Phenomena in Plasma Physics and Hydrodynamics (R. Z. Sagdeev, ed.), Mir, Moscow, 1986, pp. 31–64.
5. M. B. Sevryuk, *Reversible Systems,* Lecture Notes in Mathematics, Vol. 1211, Springer- Verlag, Berlin, 1986.
6. M. B. Sevryuk, *Lower-dimensional tori in reversible systems*, Chaos **1** (1991), no. 2, 160–167.
7. P. Moson, *Quasi-periodic solutions of differential equations depending on parameters*, Z. Angew. Math. Mech. **65** (1985), no. 4, 86–87.
8. P. Moson, *Quasiperiodic solutions of differential equations depending on parameters* I, Vestnik Leningrad. Univ. Mat. Mekh. Astronom. **1986**, no. 2, 16–22; II, **1986**, no. 3, 34–39 (Russian); English translation in Vestnik Leningrad Univ. , Math.
9. G. B. Huitema, *Unfoldings of Quasi-periodic Tori,* Proefschrift, Univ. Groningen, 1988.
10. L. H. Eliasson, *Perturbations of stable invariant tori for Hamiltonian systems,* Ann. Sc. Norm. Super. Pisa, Cl. Sci. , Ser. IV **15** (1988), no. 1, 115–147.
11. J. Pöschel, *On elliptic lower dimensional tori in Hamiltonian systems*, Math. Z. **202** (1989), no. 4, 559–608.

*this word seems to have become standard

12. D. V. Treshchëv, *A mechanism for the destruction of resonance tori in Hamiltonian systems*, Mat. Sb. **180** (1989), no. 10, 1325–1346 (Russian); English translation in Math. USSR, Sb.
13. H. W. Broer, G. B. Huitema, and F. Takens, *Unfoldings of quasi-periodic tori*, Mem. Am. Math. Soc. **83** (1990), no. 421, 1–81.
14. Yu. N. Bibikov, *Multifrequency Nonlinear Oscillations and their Bifurcations*, Leningrad Univ. Press, Leningrad, 1991. (Russian)
15. R. de la Llave and C. E. Wayne, *Whiskered and low dimensional tori in nearly integrable Hamiltonian systems,* preprint, 1991.
16. K. R. Meyer, *Hamiltonian systems with a discrete symmetry*, J. Diff. Equat. **41** (1981), no. 2, 228–238.
17. Yu. N. Bibikov, *The existence of conditionally periodic solutions of differential equation systems*, Differential Equations **7** (1971), no. 8, 1347–1356 (Russian); English translation in Differ. Equat. **7** (1971), no. 8, 1021–1027.
18. J. Scheurle, *Bifurcation of a stationary solution of a dynamical system into n-dimensional tori of quasiperiodic solutions*, in Functional Differential Equations and Approximation of Fixed Points, Lecture Notes in Mathematics, Vol. 730 (H. -O. Peitgen and H. -O. Walther, eds.), Springer-Verlag, Berlin, 1979, pp. 442–454.
19. J. Scheurle, *Über die Konstruktion invarianter Tori, welche von einer stationären Grundlösung eines reversiblen dynamischen Systems abzweigen*, in Constructive Methods for Nonlinear Boundary Value Problems and Nonlinear Oscillations, International Series of Numerical Mathematics, Vol. 48 (J. Albrecht, L. Collatz, and K. Kirchgässner, eds.), Birkhäuser-Verlag, Basel, 1979, pp. 134–144.
20. J. Scheurle, Verzweigung quasiperiodischer Lösungen bei reversiblen dynamischen Systemen, Habilitationsschrift, Univ. Stuttgart, 1980.
21. J. Scheurle, *Bifurcation of quasi-periodic solutions from equilibrium points of reversible dynamical systems*, Arch. Rat. Mech. Anal. **97** (1987), no. 2, 103–139.
22. M. B. Sevryuk, *Invariant tori of reversible systems in a neighborhood of an equilibrium state*, Uspekhi Mat. Nauk **42** (1987), no. 4, 191–192 (Russian); English translation in Russ. Math. Surveys **42** (1987), no. 4, 147–148.
23. M. B. Sevryuk, *Invariant m-tori of reversible systems whose phase space dimension is greater than* $2m$, Trudy Sem. Im. I. G. Petrovskogo **14** (1989), 109–124 (Russian); English translation in J. Sov. Math. **51** (1990), no. 3, 2374–2386.
24. M. B. Sevryuk, *On the dimensions of invariant tori in the KAM theory*, in Mathematical Methods in Mechanics (V. V. Kozlov, ed.), Moscow Univ. Press, Moscow, 1990, pp. 82–88. (Russian)
25. I. O. Parasyuk, *On the preservation of multidimensional invariant tori of Hamiltonian systems*, Ukrain. Mat. Zh. **36** (1984), no. 4, 467–473 (Russian); English translation in Ukrain. Math. J.
26. I. O. Parasyuk, *Conservation of quasiperiodic motions in reversible multifrequency systems*, Dokl. Akad. Nauk Ukrain. SSR, Ser. A **1982**, no. 9, 19–22. (Russian)
27. S. Wiggins, *Global Bifurcations and Chaos. Analytical Methods,* Appl. Math. Sciences, Vol. 73, Springer-Verlag, New York, 1988.
28. J. Pöschel, *Integrability of Hamiltonian systems on Cantor sets*, Comm. Pure Appl. Math. **35** (1982), no. 5, 653–696.
29. M. B. Sevryuk, *Bifurcations of Cantor families of invariant circles for reversible mappings,* preprint no. 1, ÈLNI, Moscow, 1990. (Russian)

30. M. B. Sevryuk and A. Lahiri, *Bifurcations of families of invariant curves in four-dimensional reversible mappings*, Phys. Lett. A **154** (1991), no. 3–4, 104–110.

31. T. K. Roy and A. Lahiri, *Reversible Hopf bifurcation in four-dimensional maps*, Phys. Rev. A (3) **44** (1991), no. 8, 4937–4944 (to appear).

INSTITUTE OF ENERGY PROBLEMS OF CHEMICAL PHYSICS, THE USSR ACADEMY OF SCIENCES, LENIN PROSPECT 38, BLDG.2, 117829 MOSCOW, RUSSIA

E-mail address: RUSIN@IEPCP.MSK.SU

Part II
Infinite dimensional dynamical systems

MAXIMAL ALMOST-PERIODIC SOLUTIONS FOR LAGRANGIAN EQUATIONS ON INFINITE DIMENSIONAL TORI

LUIGI CHIERCHIA† AND PAOLO PERFETTI

1. INTRODUCTION

We shall briefly discuss the generalization to infinite dimensions of the existence of *maximal quasi-periodic* solutions for the following Euler-Lagrange equations on $\mathbf{T}^N \equiv (\mathbf{R}/2\pi\mathbf{Z})^N$:

$$\ddot{x}_i = V_{x_i}(x) \ , \qquad i = 1, \dots , N \tag{1.1}$$

associated to the Lagrangian

$$L(\dot{x}, x) = \frac{1}{2} \sum_{i=1}^{N} \dot{x}_i^2 + V(x) \tag{1.2}$$

$V(x) = V(x_1, \dots , x_N)$ being a smooth function 2π-periodic in x_i; $(\cdot)_{x_i}$ denotes partial differentiation: $V_{x_i} \equiv \frac{\partial V}{\partial x_i}$. If $\omega \in \mathbf{R}^N$ is a "Diophantine vector" and if V is small enough it follows from KAM theory (see e.g. [SZ], [CC1], [CC2] for Lagrangian KAM theory) that (1.1) admits *quasi-periodic* solutions $x(t) = \omega t + u(\omega t)$ where $u\colon \mathbf{T}^N \to \mathbf{R}^N$ is a smooth function. We recall that a vector $\omega \in \mathbf{R}^N$ is called (γ, τ)-Diophantine if

$$\Big|\sum_{i=1}^{N} \omega_i n_i\Big| \geq \frac{1}{\gamma |n|^\tau}, \qquad \forall\, n \in \mathbf{Z}^N \backslash \{0\} \tag{1.3}$$

for some positive numbers γ and τ; $|n| \equiv \sum_{i=1}^{N} |n_i|$.

A simple rescaling argument ($\omega \to \omega/\epsilon, \quad 0 < \epsilon << 1$) shows that *for any* potential (smooth enough) there always exist plenty of quasi-periodic solutions with *large* frequencies.

---

† Partially supported by CNR–GNFM grant, n. 2398/91

In this note we present some results concerning the existence of many *maximal almost-periodic* solutions in infinite dimensions. Such results are, in a suitable sense, a generalization to infinite dimensions of [CZ] and complete proofs will appear elsewhere.

Before introducing the precise infinite dimensional set-up that generalizes the Lagrangian system (1.1)–(1.2), let us consider two examples to which our techniques will apply. The first is a so-called "finite-range system of infinitely many coupled rotators", which can be viewed as an infinite system of coupled second order differential equations:

$$\frac{d^2}{dt^2}x_i(t) = a_i \cos(x_i - x_{i-1}) - a_{i+1}\cos(x_{i+1} - x_i) \tag{1.4}$$

where $i \in \mathbf{Z}$; the a_i's are real constants with $\sup_{i\in\mathbf{Z}} |a_i| < \infty$.

Systems of this kind (and their finite dimensional approximations) are of interest in statistical mechanics (from which the above terminology has been borrowed) and have been extensively studied by many authors; see e.g. [VB], [W], [FSW], [P].

The second example involves a "*long-range* interaction" and is given by the following equations:

$$8\frac{d^2}{dt^2}x_i(t) = \cos x_i \sum_{n\in\mathbf{Z}} a_n \prod_{0\neq m\in\mathbf{Z}} (1 + a_{n+m}\sin x_{i+m}) \tag{1.5}$$

where $a_n \in \mathbf{R}$ and $\sum_{n\in\mathbf{Z}} |a_n| < \infty$. Notice that *formally* (1.4) and (1.5) are the Euler-Lagrange equations associated to the *formal* Lagrangians

$$L(x,\dot{x}) = \frac{1}{2}\sum_i \dot{x}_i^2 + \sum_i a_i \sin(x_i - x_{i-1})$$

and

$$L(x,\dot{x}) = \frac{1}{2}\sum_i \dot{x}_i^2 + \sum_i \prod_j [1 + a_j \sin x_{i+j}].$$

2. Set up

As "configuration space" we shall consider the Cartesian product

$$\mathbf{T}^{\mathbf{Z}^d} \equiv \bigotimes_{i\in\mathbf{Z}^d} \mathbf{T}_i \equiv \mathcal{T}, \qquad \mathbf{T}_i \equiv \mathbf{T} \equiv \mathbf{R}/2\pi\mathbf{Z}$$

endowed with the standard weak (compact) topology. Such a topology is induced by metrics: given a *weight* w (i.e. $w_i > 0$ for all i and $\sum_{i\in\mathbf{Z}^d} w_i < \infty$)

we introduce on $\mathcal{T}$ the metric

$$\rho_w(x,y) \equiv \sum_{i\in\mathbf{Z}^d} w_i\ \rho(x_i,y_i), \qquad (x,y\in\mathcal{T})$$

where $\rho(x_i,y_i)$ is the standard flat metric on $\mathbf{T}$. The tangent space of $\mathcal{T}_w \equiv (\mathcal{T},\rho_w)$ is the Banach space, $\mathcal{B}_w$, of vectors $a\in\mathbf{R}^{\mathbf{Z}^d}$ with finite norm:

$$\|a\|_w = \sum_{i\in\mathbf{Z}^d} w_i\,|a_i| < \infty.$$

Given a continuous map $f\colon\mathcal{T}_w \to \mathcal{B}_w$ we can now consider the *second order system*

$$\ddot{x}_i = f_i(x(t)) \ , \qquad\qquad i\in\mathbf{Z}^d \tag{2.1}$$

and a *continuous map* $t\in\mathbf{R}\to x(t)\in\mathcal{T}_w$ will be called a *solution* of (2.1) if (for any $i\in\mathbf{Z}^d$) $x_i(t)$ belongs to $\mathrm{C}^2(\mathbf{R})$ and satisfy (2.1).

Equation (2.1) is an equation in $\mathcal{B}_w$ (having identified the tangent space of $\mathcal{B}_w$ with $\mathcal{B}_w$ itself). However for a solution of (2.1) it might (and will) happen that $\dot{x}(t)$ *does not* belong to $\mathcal{B}_w$ (e.g., it may happen that $\dot{x}_i(t)=\omega_i+\partial_t u_i(t)$ with ω_i growing arbitrarily fast as $|i|\to\infty$ and $|u_i|+|\partial_t u_i|$ bounded).

With standard contraction arguments one can prove the following elementary

Proposition. *Let $f\colon\mathcal{T}_w\to\mathcal{B}_w$ be a Lipschitz map (i.e. $\exists C$ s.t. $\|f(x)-f(y)\|_w\le C\rho_w(x,y)$, $\forall x,y\in\mathcal{T}_w$). Given any $x^o\in\mathcal{T}_w$ and any $y^o\in\mathbf{R}^{\mathbf{Z}^d}$, there exists a unique solution, global in time, of the Cauchy problem*

$$\begin{cases} \ddot{x}_i(t) = f_i(x(t)), & i\in\mathbf{Z}^d \\ x_i(0)=x_i^o, \qquad \dot{x}_i(0)=y_i^o. \end{cases} \tag{2.2}$$

We remark that the initial "velocity" y^o is arbitrary and is *not* required to belong to the tangent space $\mathcal{B}_w$.

Notice that the examples (1.4) and (1.5) in the introduction have a Lipschitz right hand side, *provided* one chooses suitably the weight w.

In this context the "Lagrangian structure" will be reflected by f being, in a suitable sense, a *gradient.*

As it is clear even from the "finite-range" example above we need a *generalized* notion of gradient. Such a notion will use *averages.*

The Haar measure $d\mu_i \equiv (2\pi)^{-1} dx_i$ on $\mathbf{T}_i \equiv \mathbf{T}$ induces, in a natural way, a product measure $d\mu \equiv \bigotimes_{i\in\mathbf{Z}^d} d\mu_i$ on $\mathcal{T}_w$. More precisely $d\mu$ is the unique extension on the σ-algebra generated by the cylinders,

$$\mathcal{R}_I \equiv \bigotimes_{i\in I} A_i \bigotimes_{j\in\mathbf{Z}^d\backslash I} \mathbf{T}_j, \qquad A_i \equiv \text{ open subset of } \mathbf{T}_i, \quad |I| < \infty$$

($|I| \equiv$ cardinality of I), satisfying

$$\mu(\mathcal{R}_I) = \prod_{i\in I} \mu_i(A_i).$$

Fubini's theorem holds and one can use integrations as projection operators on finite dimensional function spaces. If $g\colon \mathcal{T}_w \to \mathbf{R}$ is a bounded measurable function and I is a finite subset of $\mathbf{Z}^d$, we define $g^{[I]}(x^{(I)})$ as the bounded measurable function of $x^{(I)} \in \mathbf{T}^{|I|} \equiv \bigotimes_{i\in I} \mathbf{T}_i$ obtained by integrating over $\bigotimes_{i\notin I} \mathbf{T}_i$:

$$g^{[I]} \equiv \int g \bigotimes_{i\notin I} d\mu_i \equiv \lim_{j\to\infty} \int g \bigotimes_{k=1}^{j} d\mu_{n_k}$$

where $k \to n_k$ is any one-to-one map from $\mathbf{N}$ onto $\mathbf{Z}^d\backslash I$. By Fubini's theorem the function $g^{[I]}$ does not depend on the choice of the sequence $\{n_k\}$.

Definition 2.1 *A continuous function $f\colon \mathcal{T}_w \to \mathcal{B}_w$ is a g-gradient if for any finite $I \subset \mathbf{Z}^d$ there exists a $C^1(\mathbf{T}^{|I|}, \mathbf{R})$ function $V^{(I)}(x)$ so that*

$$f_i^{[I]}(x) = \partial_{x_i} V^{(I)}(x), \quad \forall\, i \in I \quad \forall\, x \in \mathbf{T}^{|I|}$$

We remark that the right hand side of (1.4), (1.5) are *g-gradients* .

3. Results

To state our main results we need some more definitions.

Definition 3.1. *A vector $\omega \in \mathbf{R}^{\mathbf{Z}^d}$ is said to be rationally independent if*

$$\sum_{i\in I} \omega_i n_i = 0 \ \text{ for some finite } I \subset \mathbf{Z}^d \Rightarrow n_i = 0 \quad \forall\, i \in I.$$

A rationally independent vector ω will be also called a $\mathcal{T}$-frequency vector.

Definition 3.2. *Given a $\mathcal{T}$-frequency vector ω, a continuous function $q(t)$ is called ω-almost-periodic if there exists a function $Q \in C(\mathcal{T}_w, \mathbf{R})$ such that $q(t) = Q(\omega t)$. A solution $x(t)$ of (2.1) is called maximal almost-periodic (with frequencies $\omega \in \mathbf{R}^{\mathbf{Z}^d}$) if $x_i(t) - \omega_i t$ is ω-almost-periodic for all $i \in \mathbf{Z}^d$.*

Remarks:
1) The word *maximal* refers to the rational independence property of ω.
2) An *ω-almost-periodic* function q is just an *almost-periodic* function in the sense of H. Bohr with frequency modulus

$$\sigma(q) = \left\{ \sum_{i\in I} \omega_i n_i \,:\, I \subset \mathbf{Z}^d,\ |I| < \infty,\ n_i \in \mathbf{Z} \right\}.$$

Finally we introduce the smoothness properties we shall consider.

Definition 3.3. *A g-gradient f is called uniformly weakly real-analytic if there exists a real number $\xi > 0$ such that for any finite set $I \subset \mathbf{Z}^d$, $V^{(I)}(x)$ is real-analytic on $\mathbf{T}^{|I|}$ and can be analytically continued to the set $\{z \in \mathbf{C}^{|I|},\ |\mathrm{Im}\, z_i| \le \xi\}$.*

The *g-gradients* of the examples in the introduction are uniformly weakly real-analytic and as parameter ξ one can take any positive number.

Theorem 1. *Let f be a uniformly weakly real analytic g-gradient. Then there exist uncountably many maximal almost-periodic solutions of (2.1).*

This Theorem is an immediate corollary of the following more detailed statement.

Theorem 2. *Let f as in* **Theorem 1** *(recall Definition 2.1) and assume that for some finite $I \subset \mathbf{Z}^d$ the equation*

$$\ddot{x}^{(I)} = \partial_{x^{(I)}} V^{(I)}(x^{(I)}), \qquad (x^{(I)} \in \mathbf{T}^{|I|}) \tag{3.1}$$

admits a non-degenerate real-analytic quasi-periodic solution with a (γ,τ)-Diophantine frequency $\omega^{(I)} \in \mathbf{R}^{|I|}$ (i.e. $x^{(I)}(t) = \omega^{(I)}t + u^{(I)}(\omega^{(I)}t)$ for a suitable real-analytic function $u^{(I)} : \mathbf{T}^{|I|} \to \mathbf{R}^{|I|}$ such that $\det(Id + \partial u^{(I)}) \neq 0$). Then there exist uncountably many ω-almost-periodic solutions with $\omega_i = \omega_i^{(I)}, \forall i \in I$. All such frequencies ω are "γ-Diophantine" in the sense that for all $J \supset I$ with $|J\backslash I| = m$ it is:

$$\Big|\sum_{j\in J} \omega_j n_j\Big| \ge \frac{1}{\gamma(\sum_{j\in J} |n_j|)^{\tau+m}}, \qquad \forall\ (\{n_j\}_{j\in J}) \in \mathbf{Z}^{|J|}\backslash\{0\}. \tag{3.2}$$

Moreover for a suitable (small) constant $\epsilon > 0$ one has

$$\|x_i - x_i^{(I)}\|_{C^2} \le \epsilon \quad (i \in I) \qquad , \qquad \|x_i - \omega_i t\|_{C^2} \le \epsilon \quad (i \notin I)$$

where $\|\cdot\|_{C^2}$ is the standard C^2 norm.

The frequencies in the above theorems will be such that $|\omega_j|$ grows rapidly as $|j| \to \infty$. In fact rough estimates based on the technique used to prove the above results, indicate the behaviour $|\omega_j| \sim (|j|!)^c$. Of course better estimates can be obtained by softening the numerical properties (3.2) of the frequencies. Establishing the existence of maximal almost-periodic solutions with slowly growing frequencies is an interesting (and difficult) problem especially in view of more "realistic" models such as perturbed integrable P.D.E.'s (where, typically, the integrable frequencies grow as $|j|^c$ compare [K]).

The reason for the abundance of maximal almost-periodic solutions with $|\omega_j|$ growing rapidly may be justified as follows. Imagine that a subsystem of our model admits a quasi-periodic solution (see the assumption of Theorem 2), and imagine to "turn on one mode at time". Then, intuitively speaking, if the "turned–on mode" rotates fast enough, its effect will be mostly "averaged out" and it will weakly interact with the pre-existing motion.

In the rest of this note we present the main ideas beyond the proof of the above theorems.

4. Sketch of proofs

Theorems 1 is an immediate corollary of Theorem 2: for example one could take $I = \{i_o\}$ (with any $i_o \in \mathbf{Z}^d$) in Theorem 2: in this case (3.1) becomes trivial and it always admits non-degenerate quasi-periodic (in this case simply periodic) solutions.

The proof of Theorem 2 is based on a recursive argument.

Fix once for all a one-to-one map, j_n, from $\mathbf{N}$ onto $\mathbf{Z}^d \backslash I$ and let $I_o \equiv I$, $I_1 \equiv I_o \cup \{j_1\}$, $I_{n+1} \equiv I_n \cup \{j_{n+1}\}$, (so that $|I_n| = |I| + n$ and $I_o \subset I_1 \subset \dots I_n \uparrow \mathbf{Z}^d$).

The **main step** consists in showing how, assuming to have a non-degenerate quasi-periodic solution of

$$\ddot{x} = \partial_x V^{(I_n)}(x), \qquad (x \in \mathbf{T}^{|I_n|}) \tag{4.1$_n$}$$

with frequencies $\omega \equiv \omega^{(n)} \equiv (\{\omega_j\}_{j \in I_n})$, one can construct, via a "KAM theorem", a quasi-periodic non-degenerate solution of of $(4.1)_{n+1}$ with frequencies

$\omega' \equiv \omega^{(n+1)} \equiv (\omega, \alpha) \equiv (\{\omega_j\}_{j \in I_{n+1}})$ provided $\alpha \equiv \omega_{j_{n+1}}$ is large enough and suitably chosen.

Once this step is carried out and *made quantitative* a solution $x(t)$ of (2.1) (with f as in Theorem 2) will be easily obtained by taking, in a suitable (but natural) sense the limit

$$x_j(t) \equiv \lim_{n\to\infty} x_j^{(n)}(t) \tag{4.2}$$

where $x_j^{(n)}(t) \equiv \omega_j^{(n)} t + u_j^{(n)}(\omega^{(n)} t)$ is the quasi-periodic solution of $(4.1)_n$.

The abundance of (rapidly oscillating) almost-periodic solutions is related to the choice of $\omega_{j_{n+1}}$ *given* $\omega^{(n)}$: $\omega_{j_{n+1}}$ can be *arbitrarily chosen* in a Cantor set $\Omega^{(n+1)} \subset [\overline{\alpha}, \infty)$ (for a suitable $\overline{\alpha} = \overline{\alpha}(\omega^{(n)})$ large enough) having the property that

$$\lim_{R\to\infty} \ell(\Omega^{(n+1)} \cap [R, R+1]) = 1 \tag{4.3}$$

where ℓ denotes Lebesgue measure. We shall not work out here the straightforward details necessary to give meaning to (4.2), while we shall concentrate on the main step.

As already mentioned the main technical tool comes from KAM theory: we shall use a minor modification (see [Pe]) of the "configurational KAM theorem" given in [CC1] (see also [SZ] and [CC2]).

Consider (1.1) with V real-analytic on $\mathbf{T}^N$ admitting a holomorphic extension to

$$\Delta^N_{\xi_o} \equiv \{x \in \mathbf{C}^N : |\mathrm{Im} x_j| \le \xi_o \ j = 1, \dots, N\}.$$

It is easy to see that having a non-degenerate quasi-periodic solution $x(t) = \omega t + u(\omega t)$ (with $u\colon \mathbf{T}^N \to \mathbf{R}^N$ and $\omega \in \mathbf{R}^N$ rationally independent) is *equivalent* to require that u satisfies

$$D^2 u(\theta) = V_x(\theta + u(\theta)) \tag{4.4}$$

where $Du \equiv \omega \cdot \partial_\theta u \equiv \sum_{k=1}^N \omega_k \partial_{\theta_k} u$; "non-degenerate" means that $\det(\mathrm{Id} + u_\theta) \neq 0$.

Theorem K (cfr. [CC1]). *Let ω verify (1.3) and let $v\colon \mathbf{T}^N \to \mathbf{R}^N$ be a holomorphic function on $\Delta^N_{\xi_*}$, with $\xi_* < \xi_o$, such that:*

i) $\{\theta + v(\theta) : \theta \in \Delta^N_{\xi_*}\} \subset \Delta^N_{\xi_o}$,   ii) $\sup_{\Delta^N_{\xi_*}} \|(Id + v_\theta)^{-1}\| \equiv \widetilde{M} < \infty$.

Finally let $0 < \xi' < \xi_*$. Let be a constant $K = K(\|V\|_{C^3, \Delta^N_{\xi_o}}, \widetilde{M}, \gamma, \tau, \xi_* - \xi') > 1$ such that if

$$K \, \|D^2 v - V_x(\theta + v)\|_{\Delta^N_{\xi_*}} \equiv KE \le 1 \tag{4.5}$$

then there exists a solution $u\colon \mathbf{T}^N \to \mathbf{R}^N$ of (4.4) with a holomorphic extension to $\Delta^N_{\xi'}$; such a solution is (locally) unique if we require that $\int u d\theta = \int v d\theta$. The *constant K can be taken to be*

$$K \equiv \lambda\gamma^2 \frac{\overline{M}^{10}\widetilde{M}^8 (N!)^4\, 2^{34N+12}}{(\xi_* - \xi')^{8N+1}} \tag{4.6}$$

with

$$\lambda \equiv \max\Big\{1\ ,\gamma^2\,\|V_{xxx}\|_{\Delta^N_{\xi_o}}\Big\},\quad M \equiv \sup_{\Delta^N_{\xi_*}} \|Id + v_\theta\|. \tag{4.7}$$

The solution u is close to v in the following sense:

$$\begin{aligned}&\max\Big\{\|u\ -\ v\|_{\Delta^N_{\xi'}}\ ,\ \|u_\theta\ -\ v_\theta\|_{\Delta^N_{\xi'}}\Big\} \le KE\\ &\max\Big\{\gamma\,\|Du\ -\ Dv\|_{\Delta^N_{\xi'}}\ ,\ \gamma^2\,\big\|D^2u\ -\ D^2v\big\|_{\Delta^N_{\xi'}}\Big\} \le KE\Lambda\end{aligned} \tag{4.8}$$

where $\quad \Lambda = \max\Big\{1,\ \|V_{xx}\|_{\Delta^N_{\xi_o}}/\|V_{xxx}\|_{\Delta^N_{\xi_o}}\Big\}.$

Remarks:
1) In other words: near any (non-degenerate) *approximate* solution of (4.4) there is a true (non-degenerate) solution, provided the approximate solution solves equation (4.4) up to a small *enough* error.
2) The (minor) changes with respect to the version in [CC1] are the estimates in (4.6), (4.8) and the introduction of the parameter ξ' (the domain of holomorphy of u) which, here, is left free.

Assume now to have a non-degenerate solution of $(4.1)_n$, $x^{(n)}(t) = \theta' + \omega^{(n)}t + u'(\theta' + \omega^{(n)}t)$, $\theta' \in \mathbf{T}^{|I|+n}$, $u'\colon \mathbf{T}^{|I|+n} \to \mathbf{R}^{|I|+n}$. Let $N \equiv |I| + n + 1$ and let ξ_o be the parameter measuring the analyticity of the *g-gradient* f (see Definition 3.3: $\xi_o \equiv \xi$). The function $u'\colon \mathbf{T}^{|I|+n} \to \mathbf{R}^{|I|+n}$ is assumed to be such that $|\mathrm{Im}(\theta'_i + u'_i(\theta'))| \le \xi_o$ for any $i \in I_n$, for any $\theta' \in \Delta^{N-1}_\xi$, for a suitable ξ; the non-degeneracy of $x^{(n)}(t)$ means that $\|(\mathrm{Id} + u'_{\theta'})^{-1}\|_{\Delta^{N-1}_\xi} < \infty$. To attack the problem with one more degree-of-freedom on $\mathbf{T}^N$ we shall look directly at the P.D.E. (4.4) for a new quasi-periodic function $x^{(n+1)}(t) = \omega^{(n+1)}t + u(\omega^{(n+1)}t)$, u and $\alpha \equiv \omega_{j_{n+1}}$ being the *unknowns*: of course V in (4.4) is now $V^{(I_{n+1})}$ (recall that $V^{(I_n)} = \int_0^{2\pi} V^{(I_{n+1})} d\theta_{j_{n+1}}/2\pi$ up to a constant playing no role).

The new frequency $\alpha = \omega_{j_{n+1}}$ is taken to be in the (Cantor) set

$$\Omega_{\alpha_o} \equiv \Big\{\alpha \in \mathbf{R} : |\omega^{(n)}\cdot n + \alpha m| \ge \frac{\alpha_o}{|n|^N},\ \alpha \ge \alpha_o,\ \forall\, n \in \mathbf{Z}^{N-1},\ \forall\, m \in \mathbf{Z}\backslash\{0\}\Big\}$$

where α_o is (at the moment) an arbitrary parameter larger than $1/\gamma$ (γ, τ are the Diophantine constants associated to $\omega^{(o)}$: cfr. hypotheses of Theorem 2).

It is not difficult to see that $\ell([\alpha_o,\infty)\backslash\Omega_{\alpha_o}) \leq c|\omega^{(n)}|$ with a suitable constant c depending only on N,τ. Thus the set Ω_{α_o} verifies (4.3).

The idea now is to try to construct out of $u'(\theta')$ an approximate solution $v\colon \mathbf{T}^N \to \mathbf{R}^N$ for (4.4) with $V = V^{(I_{n+1})}$ and to use Theorem K to show the existence of a solution, u, close to u'. The job is done by setting ($\theta \equiv (\theta', \theta_{j_{n+1}}) \in \mathbf{T}^N$):

$$\begin{aligned} v(\theta) \equiv & D^{-2}_{\omega^{(n+1)}} V_x^{(I_{n+1})}(\theta' + u'(\theta'), \theta_{j_{n+1}}) \\ = & - \sum_{\substack{n\in\mathbf{Z}^{N-1}, m\in\mathbf{Z} \\ (n,m)\neq(0,0)}} e^{(in\cdot\theta' + m\theta_{j_{n+1}})} \frac{C_{n,m}}{(\omega^{(n)}\cdot n + \alpha m)^2} \end{aligned} \tag{4.9}$$

where $x \in \mathbf{T}^N$ ($x = \{x_i\}_{i\in I_{n+1}}$), $C_{n,m}$ denotes the Fourier coefficient of the (vector-valued) function $C(\theta) = V_x^{(I_{n+1})}(\theta' + u'(\theta'), \theta_{j_{n+1}})$, $D_{\omega^{(n+1)}} \equiv (\omega^{(n)}, \alpha)\cdot \partial_\theta \equiv \omega^{(n)} \cdot \partial_{\theta'} + \alpha \partial_{\theta_{j_{n+1}}}$ and if $g(\theta)$ is a function with zero average we denote by $D^{-2}g$ the *unique* solution of $D^2 f = g$ with vanishing mean value.
Notice that in (4.9) it is implicitly stated that

$$\int_{\mathbf{T}^N} V_x^{(I_{n+1})}(\theta' + u'(\theta'), \theta_{j_{n+1}}) \frac{d\theta}{(2\pi)^N} = 0, \tag{4.10}$$

a fact that is deduced by recalling that u' solves equation (4.4) with $V = V^{(I_n)}$ and that

$$\int_0^{2\pi} V_x^{(I_{n+1})}(\theta' + u'(\theta'), \theta_{j_{n+1}}) \frac{d\theta_{j_{n+1}}}{(2\pi)} = V_{x'}^{(I_n)}(\theta' + u'(\theta')).$$

This fact justify the application of the operator D^{-2}.

Now, notice that since u' solves (4.4) with $V = V^{(I_n)}$, it is

$$u'(\theta') = D^{-2}_{\omega^{(n)}}[V_{x'}^{(I_n)}(\theta' + u')]$$

thus

$$v = -\sum_{m\neq 0} e^{(in\cdot\theta' + m\theta_{j_{n+1}})} \frac{C_{n,m}}{(\omega^{(n)}\cdot n + \alpha m)^2} + (u', 0) \equiv \tilde{v} + (u', 0).$$

But recalling the definition of Ω_{α_o} it is easy to see that the norm of $\tilde{v}$ is $O(1/(\alpha_o)^2)$ and it can be made arbitrarily small by choosing the free parameter α_o large enough. How large one has to choose α_o is dictated by the conditions (4.5) in Theorem K. In fact it is not difficult to show that also $\|D^2 v - V^{(I_{n+1})}(\theta + v)\|$ is of size $O(1/(\alpha_o^2))$; thus if one takes $\alpha_o = O(K^{1/2})$ one can apply Theorem K obtaining in such a way, a quasi-periodic solution $x^{(n+1)}(t)$. This concludes our discussion of the main step.
Complete detailed proofs will appear elsewhere.

References

[CC1] A. Celletti, L. Chierchia, *Construction of Analytic KAM Surfaces and Effective Stability Bounds,* Commun. Math. Phys. **118** (1988) 119–161

[CC2] A. Celletti, L. Chierchia, *A constructive theory of Lagrangian tori and computer-assisted applications,* Carr Reports in Mathematical Physics December 1990 n.27/90

[CZ] L. Chierchia, E. Zehnder, *Asymptotic Expansion of Quasiperiodic Solutions,* Ann. Sc. Norm. Sup. Pisa cl. Sci. IV **XVI**. Fasc. 2 (1989)

[FSW] J. Frölich, T. Spencer, C. E. Wayne, *Localization in Disordered Nonlinear Dynamical Systems,* Jour. of Stat. Phys., **42**, Nos.3/4 (1986) pp. 247–274

[K] S. B. Kuksin, *Perturbation of quasi-periodic solutions of infinite dimensional Hamiltonian systems,* Math. USSR Izvestiya Vol. 32 No. 1 (1989)

[P] J. Pöschel, *Small Divisors with Spatial Structure in Infinite Dimensional Hamiltonian Systems,* Commun. Math. Phys. **127** (1990) 351–393

[Pe] P. Perfetti, *Soluzioni quasi-periodiche massimali per sistemi Lagrangiani infinito dimensionali,* Ph. Doct. Thesis, Physics Department, University of Rome "La Sapienza" (1991)

[SZ] D. Salamon, E. Zehnder, *KAM theory in configuration space,* Comment. Math. Helv. **64** (1989) 84–132

[VB] M. Vittot, J. Bellissard, *Invariant tori for an infinite lattice of coupled rotators,* Preprint Centre de Physique Théorique CNRS-Luminy, Marseille (1985)

[W] C. E. Wayne, *The KAM Theory of Systems with Short Range Interactions,* I *and* II, Commun. Math. Phys. **96** (1984) 311–329 and 331–344

NONPERSISTENCE OF BREATHER SOLUTIONS UNDER PERTURBATION OF THE SINE-GORDON EQUATION

JOCHEN DENZLER

1. INTRODUCTION

This note deals with a question on partial differential equations that has however several connections with infinite dimensional dynamical systems. The present state of knowledge on it is only very limited.

A solution u (not vanishing identically) to some wave equation is called a *breather* if it is periodic in time t and decays as $|x| \to \infty$, x the space variable. This definition is reasonable for $x \in \mathbb{R}^n$ for every n, but we shall restrict ourselves to the case $n = 1$, which already poses enough interesting and unresolved questions. The sine Gordon equation

$$u_{tt} - u_{xx} + \sin u = 0 \tag{1}$$

has a well-known family of breather solutions

$$u^*(x,t;m) = 4 \arctan \frac{m \sin \omega t}{\omega \cosh mx} \quad , \qquad m, \omega > 0 \, , \; m^2 + \omega^2 = 1 \tag{2}$$

Our result is a non-existence result. A bold conjecture would be that among all equations of the form $u_{tt} - u_{xx} + g(u) = 0$, $g(0) = 0$ there is essentially only one, namely the sine Gordon equation, $g(u) = \mu \sin \lambda u$, which permits breather solutions. We are far from proving or disproving such a conjecture. Theorem 1 below is only a local non-persistence result for perturbations of the sine Gordon equation, namely

$$u_{tt} - u_{xx} + \sin u = \varepsilon \Delta(u) + O(\varepsilon^2) \tag{3}$$

Such a type of result has first been proved by Birnir, McKean, and Weinstein [1] under the assumption that $\Delta(\cdot)$ is analytic in the strip $|\operatorname{Re} u| \leq \pi$. By improving their method, we can weaken this assumption and need only that $\Delta(\cdot)$ is analytic in an arbitrarily small neighbourhood of $u = 0$. This improvement is not a mere technicality, since there is some degeneracy (to be described below) in the family of breathers at $u = 0$. Weakening the assumptions on Δ in the indicated way forces one to work in a neighbourhood of this degeneracy.

Before continuing the discussion, let us mention a heuristic common sense argument against the existence of breathers. Asking for a breather solution means posing a boundary value problem to a wave equation. Such problems are typically ill-posed since wave equations possess characteristics, connecting different parts of the boundary, i.e. the equation itself propagates information from one part of the boundary to the other. A solution can exist only if the boundary data on the latter part coincide with those propagated from the former part. So there are a lot of conditions to satisfy.

Physicists consider breathers as particle-like solutions of some (classical) field theory. Non-existence of breathers for $u_{tt} - u_{xx} + u - u^3 = 0$ has been claimed and discussed in a physical context by H. Segur and M. Kruskal [11], but not proved rigorously. The sine Gordon breather can be viewed as a bound state of a soliton-antisoliton pair.

2. The Problem and its Connections to Dynamical Systems

We consider the sine Gordon equation (1) and the family of breather solutions (2). While the integrability of (1) is behind the fact that such an explicit solution can be obtained, integrability is certainly not sufficient for the existence of breathers. The Korteweg-de-Vries equation $u_t + uu_x + u_{xxx} = 0$, which is also integrable, can be easily seen not to admit any breather by the following argument: the time average $v(x) := \int u(t,x)\,dt$ over the period of a supposed breather u satisfies the boundary value problem $(\frac{1}{2}\int u^2\,dt)+v'' = \text{const}$, $v \to 0$ as $x \to \pm\infty$. The boundary conditions imply const $= 0$, thus $v'' \leq 0$. Again the boundary conditions give $v \equiv 0$, hence $u \equiv 0$. For the purpose of comparison, we shall occasionally refer to a model problem, which is a linear equation constructed so as to admit an easy breather solution:

$$u_{tt} - u_{xx} - \frac{2}{\cosh^2 x} u + 2u = 0 \quad , \quad u^*(x,t) = m\frac{\sin t}{\cosh x} \tag{4}$$

We may wish to view the problem (1) as a dynamical system on some space of periodic functions (of the variable t). The dynamical variable is then x. The sine Gordon equation becomes

$$\partial_x U = \begin{bmatrix} 0 & 1 \\ \partial_t^2 + \sin(\cdot) & 0 \end{bmatrix} U \quad , \quad U(x) = \begin{bmatrix} u(x,\cdot) \\ u_x(x,\cdot) \end{bmatrix}$$

The linearization of this equation about its trivial solution $U \equiv 0$ has the matrix $\left[\begin{smallmatrix} 0 & 1 \\ \partial_t^2+1 & 0 \end{smallmatrix}\right]$. It has pure point spectrum: finitely many eigenvalues on the real axis, infinitely many on the imaginary axis. In this setting, a breather solution is a homoclinic orbit to the fixed point $U = 0$. This point of view has been stressed by [13], [5]. If a breather exists, this means that miraculously a finite dimensional stable and unstable manifolds coincide (or at least have a one dimensional orbit in common) in an infinite dimensional space. These manifolds may split under perturbation of the equation. A non-persistence result means that they do actually split. We shall consider some obstructions whose vanishing is a necessary condition for the persistence of breathers under the perturbation. These obstructions should therefore be related somehow to some geometrical object like splitting distance or splitting angle. No such connection is established by now. But one fact is remarkable: The obstructions to be considered will turn out to be exponentially small with respect to the amplitude of the unperturbed breather. This situation reminds one of the results on exponentially small splitting of separatrices established recently [4], [6], [8], [10]. Probably the analogy is not too close, because the problems with the exponentially small terms (which are notoriously difficult) turn out to be comparatively easy in our setting.

Let us now consider the same equation, but with t as the dynamical variable, as a dynamical system on some space of decaying functions (of the variable x). Then a breather is simply a periodic solution. We want to compare the situation with Lyapunov's center theorem. It says: Let $\dot{u} = Au + O(u^2)$ be an ordinary differential equation having an integral of motion, and let $\pm i\lambda$ be a pair of simple imaginary eigenvalues of A. (It gives therefore rise to a 2 dimensional linear space Σ fibred by periodic solutions to the linear equation $\dot{u} = Au$.) Now, if $\pm in\lambda$ $(n = 2, 3, \dots)$ are not contained in the spectrum of A, then locally a 2 dimensional manifold S fibred by periodic solutions to the nonlinear equation exists, and it is tangential to Σ in 0. Without the last nonresonance condition, S might not exist.

Even if our equation is not an ODE, let us look at the linearization about 0 and see whether the nonresonance conditions ar satisfied. This is what (1) looks like:

$$\partial_t U = \begin{bmatrix} 0 & 1 \\ \partial_x^2 - \sin(\cdot) & 0 \end{bmatrix} U \quad , \quad U = \begin{bmatrix} u \\ u_t \end{bmatrix}$$

The linearization about 0 has the matrix $A = \begin{bmatrix} 0 & 1 \\ \partial_x^2 - 1 & 0 \end{bmatrix}$ with continuous spectrum all on the imaginary axis: $\operatorname{spec} A = \pm i \cdot [1, \infty[$. We haven't even an eigenvalue to start with! What has happened?

The breather (2) is a genuinely nonlinear phenomenon, not visible in the linearization about 0. u^* spreads out on the real axis as $m \to 0$, and the shape ceases to decay for $|x| \to \infty$ in the limit $m \to 0$. This is the sort of degeneracy near $u = 0$ mentioned above. It will be the culprit for the exponential smallness of the obstructions discussed below. At this point, the model problem (4) is useful: it lacks the degeneracy, but still displays the spectral phenomenon. Its matrix $\begin{bmatrix} 0 & 1 \\ \partial_x^2 + 2/\cosh^2 x - 2 & 0 \end{bmatrix}$ has a simple pair of eigenvalues $\pm i$ and continuous spectrum $\pm i \cdot [\sqrt{2}, \infty[$. All multiples of the eigenvalues fall into the continuous spectrum, so we have infinitely many resonances. They lead to conditions on the persistence of a breather u^* under perturbation of (4) by a nonlinearity $f(u) = O(u^2)$ on the right hand side. They come from the first order in

m and stipulate that $\int f(u^*)v\,dt\,dx = 0$ for all generalized eigenfunctions v of $\partial_t^2 - \partial_x^2 - 2/\cosh^2 x + 2$ corresponding to the resonant values $\pm in$ ($n = 2, 3, \ldots$). We can show that no analytic perturbation f can satisfy all these conditions, and that for any energy small enough, the equation

$$u_{tt} - u_{xx} + u - \frac{2}{\cosh^2 x} u = f(u) \quad , \quad f(u) = O(u^2) \text{ analytic near } 0$$

has no C^2 breather solution (weighted C^1)-near the periodic solutions of the linear equation (4). In principle the same argument (first order in the perturbation, interaction of the nonlinearity with the continuous spectrum) lies also behind the result in [1], and behind ours.

The problem with the continuous spectrum could be relaxed by working on a finite x-interval with some boundary conditions. This would result in a pure point spectrum on the imaginary axis. However, even if the countably many non-resonance conditions should be satisfied in this case, they will be so in a non-uniform way. In fact, in this situation small divisor problems occur, and Craig and Wayne [3] can show, using Nash-Moser arguments, that for a full measure open set of x-intervals (with Dirichlet or periodic boundary conditions) and a given family of time periodic solutions to the linear equation, for a generic set of perturbation functions $g(x, u) = O(u^2)$, a lot of (= a positive measure set of amplitudes) solutions persist under the perturbation. In contrast, our result shows that in a (large) neighbourhood of 0 at most finitely many breathers can persist under any perturbation analytic near the origin, if x is on the infinite real line. In other words, none can persist in a small enough neighbourhood of 0.

3. Formulation and Proof of the Theorem

Theorem 1. *Consider the perturbed sine Gordon equation*

$$u_{tt} - u_{xx} + \sin u = \varepsilon\Delta(u, \varepsilon) \quad , \quad \Delta(0, \varepsilon) = 0 \tag{5}$$

Suppose that $\Delta(\cdot, \cdot)$ is analytic in a neighbourhood of $(0, 0)$, say $|\tan \frac{u}{4}| < \rho \leq 1$, $|\varepsilon| < \varepsilon_0$, and moreover that $\frac{\partial^2}{\partial u^2}\Big|_{u=0} \Delta(u, \varepsilon) = 0$.

Consider the family of breathers which solves the unperturbed sine Gordon equation:

$$u^*(x, t) = u^*(x, t, m) = 4 \arctan \frac{m \sin \omega t}{\omega \cosh mx}, \quad (m^2 + \omega^2 = 1), \quad m, \omega > 0 \tag{6}$$

Suppose that for infinitely many values of m satisfying $0 < \frac{m}{\omega} \leq \rho' < \rho$ there exists a breather solution $u_m(x, t, \varepsilon)$ of time period $T(\varepsilon) = \frac{2\pi}{\omega(\varepsilon)}$ to (5) for $0 < \varepsilon < \varepsilon_{max}(m)$ which depends analytically on ε as a function of ε with values in the Banach space $\mathbf{X}$ (defined below) of functions depending on (x, t), such *that the period $T(\varepsilon)$ also depends analytically on ε, and which is $u^*(x,t,m)$ for $\varepsilon = 0$.*

X *consists of all $C^2(\mathbb{R} \times S^1)$-functions v satisfying estimates of the form*

$$|v(x,t)| + |v_x(x,t)| + |v_t(x,t)| \leq \frac{c}{1+x^2}$$

Then, the perturbation function is necessarily of the form:

$$\varepsilon\Delta(u,\varepsilon) = \sin u - \frac{\mu^2(\varepsilon)}{\lambda(\varepsilon)} \sin \lambda(\varepsilon) u$$

for some functions λ, μ satisfying $\lambda(0) = \mu(0) = 1$. In this case, the perturbed sine Gordon equation (5) is merely a rescaled version of the sine Gordon equation itself, namely for $\check{x} = \mu x$, $\check{t} = \mu t$, $\check{u} = \lambda u$, it reduces to $\check{u}_{\check{t}\check{t}} - \check{u}_{\check{x}\check{x}} + \sin \check{u} = 0$.

Proof.

First Step: Normalizations

The assumption that u_m is analytic in ε means that one can write

$$u_m(x,t,\varepsilon) = u^*(x,t,m(\varepsilon)) + \varepsilon v_m(x,\tau) + \varepsilon^2 v_m^{[2]}(x,\tau) + \ldots$$

$$\tau = t\frac{T(0)}{T(\varepsilon)} \quad , \quad m(\varepsilon) = \sqrt{1 - \left(\frac{2\pi}{T(\varepsilon)}\right)^2}$$

Note that t, not τ enters in u^*, because the 0th order should be an *exact* solution to the unperturbed equation; an ansatz with $u^*(x,\tau,m)$ instead would be equivalent, but mess up the orders of the perturbation.

First we argue that one may assume with no loss of generality that $\Delta(u,\varepsilon)$ contains no first or third order terms in u. This effect is connected with the scaling property. It is a straightforward calculation to check that the scaling with λ, μ given in the theorem indeed absorbs the perturbation function $\sin u - \frac{\mu^2}{\lambda} \sin \lambda u$. Choosing λ, μ one can tune the $O(u)$ and $O(u^3)$ terms arbitrarily.

Next take care of the translation invariance of the equation (5). The unperturbed breather (6) can be distinguished from its translates in time and space by the normalization condition $u^*(0,0,m) = u_x^*(0,\frac{\pi}{2\omega},m) = 0$. By means of the implicit function theorem one can impose the analogous condition on u_m thus breaking the translation invariance. The consequence of this normalization is $v(0,0) = v_x(0,\frac{\pi}{2\omega}) = 0$ with the analogous equations being also true for $v^{[2]}, \ldots$.

Second Step: The Obstructions

For fixed m, a necessary condition for the persistence of a breather is that (5) should be verified to order ε, i.e.

$$\mathcal{L}v := v_{tt} - v_{xx} + (\cos u^*)v = \Delta(u^*), \quad v \ \frac{2\pi}{\omega}\text{-periodic in } t, \quad u^* = u^*(\cdot,\cdot,m) \tag{7}$$

where $\Delta(u) := \Delta(u,0)$. The equation $\mathcal{L}w = 0$ has countably many bounded solutions w_n that are $\frac{2\pi}{\omega}$-periodic in t. These solutions are explicitly known [9]. They give rise to necessary conditions for the solvability of (7), namely

$$\int_{-\infty}^{\infty}\int_0^{2\pi/\omega} w_n\Delta(u^*)\,dt\,dx = 0 \quad , \quad (n = 2,3,4,\dots) \tag{8}$$

Indeed, these conditions are also sufficient for the solvability of (7), but we do not need this here. Let us write $z := \frac{m}{\omega}$, then $m = z(1+z^2)^{-1/2}$, $\omega = (1+z^2)^{-1/2}$. Then w_n is a function of x, t, and $z = \frac{m}{\omega}$, and so is $\Delta(u^*)$; the integrand of (8) is holomorphic in $t \in \mathbb{C}$, $|z| < \rho \le 1$ and meromorphic in $x \in \mathbb{C}$, but is integrable only for real z. One can consider the left hand side of (8) as a function of z:

$$\mathcal{R}_n(z) := \int_{-\infty}^{\infty}\int_0^{2\pi} \Phi\left(z\frac{\sin t}{\cosh x}\right) T_n(x,t,z)e^{int}e^{i\frac{\sqrt{n^2\omega^2-1}}{m}x}\,dt\,dx \tag{9}$$

where $\Phi(z) := \Delta(4\arctan z)/(1+z^2)$ and ω and m have been absorbed into t and x respectively. The exponentials are 2π-periodic solutions to the linearization of (1) about 0, the Klein-Gordon equation $\omega^2 v_{tt} - m^2 v_{xx} + v = 0$, and are one of the factors in w_n. T_n also stems from w_n. Here, we only need that it tends to a constant as $x \to \pm\infty$ and is holomorphic in $|z| < 1$, $t \in \mathbb{C}$, $x \in \mathbb{C}$, $\cosh x \ne 0$. The conditions (8) now simply read $\mathcal{R}_n(z) = 0$, $(n = 2,3,\dots)$.

The following results have essentially been obtained in [1] by means of a Taylor expansion of Φ:

Theorem [Birnir, McKean, Weinstein]. *If $\Phi(z)$ is analytic for $|z| < 1$, then $\mathcal{R}_n$ is of the form $\mathcal{R}_n(z) = \mathcal{R}_n^\circ(z)g_n(z)$ where $\mathcal{R}_n^\circ(z)$ is analytic for $|z| < 1$ and $g_n(z)$ is independent of Φ, non-vanishing and given by a closed formula. Up to some factors that don't teach anything $g_n(z)$ is $\left(\cosh\frac{\pi\sqrt{n^2\omega^2-1}}{2m}\right)^{-1}$ for n odd, and $\left(\sinh\frac{\pi\sqrt{n^2\omega^2-1}}{2m}\right)^{-1}$ for n even. There is the following series expansion* *for $\mathcal{R}_n^\circ$ in terms of the power series coefficients Δ_n of Φ, valid for $|z| < 1$:*

$$\mathcal{R}_n^\circ(z) = \sum_{q=0}^{\infty} \left(\frac{m^2}{\omega^2}\right)^q \binom{n+2q}{q} [(n+2q-1)!]^{-1} \cdot \prod_{r=0}^{q-1} \left[r(n+r) + \frac{n^2-1}{4m^2}\right]$$
$$\times \left\{\Delta_{n+2q}\left(\frac{n^2+1}{2}\omega^2 - 1 - \frac{n^2\omega^2-1}{n+2q}\right) + \Delta_{n+2q-2}\left(\frac{n^2+1}{2}\omega^2 + \frac{n^2\omega^2}{n+2q}\right)\right\}$$
$$(n = 2,3,4,5,\dots)$$
$$\frac{m}{\omega} = z\,,\ m = z/\sqrt{1+z^2}\,,\ \omega = 1/\sqrt{1+z^2} \tag{10}$$

In particular, the value of $\mathcal{R}_n^\circ(z)$ for $z^2 = -\frac{n^2-1}{(n+2\tilde{q})^2-1}$ $(\tilde{q} = 1,2,3,\dots)$ only depends on finitely many of the coefficients Δ_p.

Now, Birnir, McKean, and Weinstein argue that if $\mathcal{R}_n$ (and hence $\mathcal{R}_n^\circ$ vanishes in a set of points that accumulate in the interior of the unit circle, $\mathcal{R}_n^\circ$ vanishes identically, and this fact can be exploited at the special points mentioned to get *manageable* conditions on the coefficients.

Looking at (9), one already sees that $\mathcal{R}_n(z)$ is exponentially small as $z \to 0$ (i.e. $m \to 0$), $z, m > 0$, due to the fast oscillation of the last exponential. The be st one could hope for in such a situation, given the experiences from [8] (and references therein), [6], [10], [4] would be an asymptotic expansion like $\mathcal{R}_n(z) \sim e^{-c/z}z^{-k}(a_0 + a_1 z + a_2 z^2 + \dots)$ with quite some difficulties even to get a_0. The factoring actually makes the situation much better; without it, no analytic continuation argument would be possible.

There is another reason why $\mathcal{R}_n$ must be exponentially small as $m \to 0$. In fact, a *formal* breather, i.e. a formal power series in m satisfying the boundary conditions term by term and solving the equation to any order in m, *does* exist [7]. Inserting this formal expansion instead of the hypothetical exact breather into (5) immediately shows $\mathcal{R}_n(\frac{m}{\omega}) = O(m^k)$ for any k.

Note also that there is another modification of the problem which gives rise to existence rather than nonexistence of solutions: Boyd [2] allows time periodic solutions which have a central "core" and are exponentially small with respect to the amplitude of this core as x becomes large. They need however not tend to zero as x tends to infinity. He gives numerical estimates (no formal proof) that *such* solutions *do* exist.

The vanishing of the $\mathcal{R}_n^\circ$ at the special points mentioned yields conditions that can be viewed as recursions for the coefficients Δ_p. With our weaker assumption of a possibly small analyticity domain G of $\Delta(\cdot)$, lots of these recursions are not feasible, because their corresponding values z are not in G. See Figure 1 for an overview of the recursions (additional information displayed there will be explained later).

general obstruction

$$0 = \sum_{q=0}^{\infty} \frac{\mathrm{A}_{n+2q}}{q!(n+q)!} \left(\frac{-1}{\omega^2}\right)^q \prod_{r=0}^{q} \left[\frac{n^2-1}{4} + r(n+r)m^2\right]$$

recursion $(n, \tilde{q})$

$$0 = \sum_{q=0}^{\tilde{q}-1} \frac{\mathrm{A}_{n+2q}}{q!(n+q)!} \left(-\frac{n^2-1}{(n+2\tilde{q})^2-1}\right)^q \prod_{r=0}^{q} [\tilde{q}(n+\tilde{q}) - r(n+r)]$$

lattice points:

recursions

$\mathcal{R}_n^\circ(\frac{m}{\omega}) = 0$

$$\boxed{\frac{m^2}{\omega^2} = -\frac{(n-1)(n+1)}{(n+2\tilde{q}-1)(n+2\tilde{q}+1)}}$$

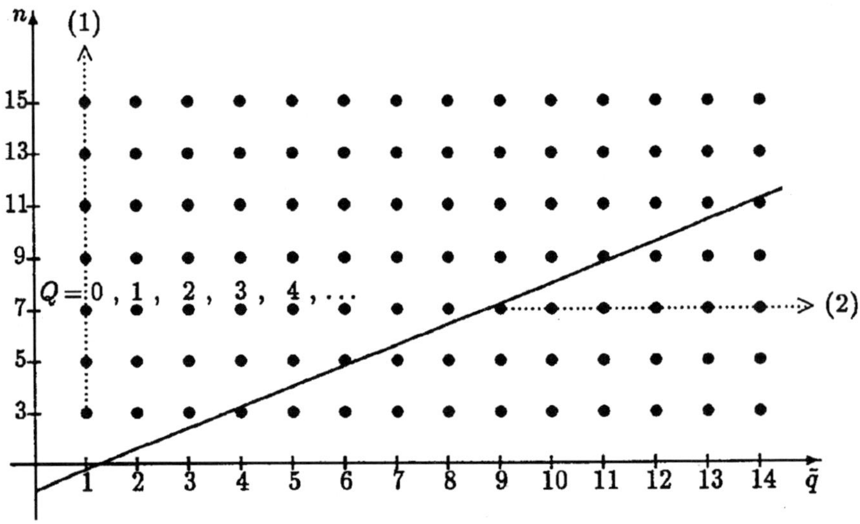

small ρ = small slope
below line $\Rightarrow |\frac{m}{\omega}| < \rho$
(recursion feasible)
$(n, \tilde{q})$ involves: $\Delta_{n-2}, \Delta_n, \ldots, \Delta_{n+2(\tilde{q}-1)}, \Delta_{n+2\tilde{q}}$
or equivalently: $\mathrm{A}_n, \ldots, \mathrm{A}_{n+2(\tilde{q}-1)}$

(1) recursive calculation of coefficients selects scaling solutions (feasible only for $\rho = 1$)

(2) recursive calculation of coefficients selects solutions to $\mathcal{R}_n^\circ \equiv 0$ for $|\frac{m}{\omega}| < \rho$ (any ρ; ill-conditioned; no problem due to surprising *explicit formula*)

Figure 1: The finite recursions

The scaling solutions are the odd solutions calculated from given initial conditions Δ_1, Δ_3 recursively by means of from the obstructions $(n, 1)$ for $n = 3, 5, \ldots$. The even component of $\Delta(\cdot)$ has to vanish. This follows from the initial conditions $\Delta_0 = \Delta_2 = 0$ and the vanishing of the obstructions $(n, 1)$ for $n = 2, 4, \ldots$. These obstructions are 3-term recursions (dotted direction (1) in the figure). The higher order recursions $(n, \tilde{q})$ are consequences of the 3-term recursions, in fact linear combinations of them. This must be the case, because their solution space contains the solution space of the 3-term recursions (namely the scaling solutions). Indeed, $\mathcal{R}_n^\circ \equiv 0$ can further be deduced from the recursions $(n, \tilde{q})$ by the analytic continuation argument.

Third Step: How to treat the small Analyticity Domain

It is much more difficult to work with the higher recursions; this is what is necessary if $\Delta(\cdot)$ has small domain of analyticity. More insight is gained by working not with the sequence (Δ_p), a coordinate on the space of perturbations, but with the sequence (A_p), a coordinate on the quotient space of perturbations modulo scalings. A_p is defined by

$$\Gamma_n := (-1)^{(n-1)/2} \frac{\Delta_n}{(n+1)^2} \qquad \mathrm{B}_n := n(\Gamma_n - \Gamma_{n-2}) \qquad \mathrm{A}_n := \mathrm{B}_{n+2} - \mathrm{B}_n \quad (11)$$

This reduction "kills" the scaling solutions, reducing all recursions by an order 2. It is constructed so as to simplify the original 3-term recursion

$$n \frac{\Delta_{n-2}}{(n-1)^2} + 2(n+1) \frac{\Delta_n}{(n+1)^2} + (n+2) \frac{\Delta_{n+2}}{(n+3)^2} = 0$$

to the trivial condition $\mathrm{A}_n = 0$.

By partial summation, (10) is transformed into the new coordinates; this gives the formulas displayed at the top of Figure 1.

Now, the key step is that the recursions $(3, \tilde{q})$, which are all feasible for $\tilde{q}$ large enough, determine a solution space for which *explicit* formulas can be found. This, again, is a surprising miracle not really accounted for. Note that the length of the recursions is $\tilde{q}$ in the A_p coordinates, and this goes to ∞.

All we need from this formula is the asymptotic behaviour of a solution sequence (A_p). Doing the same thing with all recursions $(n, \tilde{q})$ for n fixed and $\tilde{q}$ running (dotted direction (2) in figure 1) gives different asymptotics for different n, leaving only the zero solution. We give the explicit formula in the following lemma. It is proved by writing the obstruction $(n, \tilde{q})$ in a way similar to the Horner scheme for polynomials and inserting the formula. Checking it is an induction along the depth of the parentheses in the Horner scheme. More details will appear in a future paper.

Lemma 3. *Let n be fixed and consider the finite recursions displayed in Figure 1 for variable $\tilde{q}$. For any nonnegative integer Q, the following sequence A_{n+2q}*

is the "Greens function" at Q for these recursions, i.e. when inserted it gives 0 for any $\tilde{q} \neq Q+1$, but something different from 0 if $\tilde{q} = Q+1$.

$$\mathrm{A}_{n+2q}^{(Q)} = \mathit{rational}(n,q,Q)\,\alpha^{2q} \quad , \quad \alpha^2 = \frac{(n+2Q+1)(n+2Q+3)}{n^2-1}$$

$$\mathit{rational}(n,q,Q) = \frac{q(q-1)\cdots(q-Q+1)\cdot(n+2q+1)(n+2q+3)}{(q+n+1)(q+n+2)\cdots(q+n+Q+2)}$$

For $Q=0$, the term $q(q-1)\cdots(q-Q+1)$ is to be interpreted as the empty product, 1. In particular, for n fixed, it follows $\mathrm{A}_{n+2q}^{Q} \sim \mathit{const}\,\alpha^{n+2q}$ as $q \to \infty$ with const depending on n, Q.

Now, any solution A_p to the recursions $(n,\tilde{q})$, n fixed, $\tilde{q} > \tilde{q}_0$, must be a linear combination of the solutions displayed in the lemma ($Q = 0, \ldots \tilde{q}_0 - 1$) and therefore be asymptotic to const α^p for one of the possible values of α. This holds for all n, but no real number α is of the form given in the lemma for *every* n at once. Hence $\mathrm{A}_p \equiv 0$.

Fourth Step: Proof Completed

The above arguments show the theorem as far as the leading order in ε is concerned, i.e. that $\Delta(\cdot,\varepsilon)$ vanishes for $\varepsilon = 0$ under the normalization assumptions on $\Delta(\cdot)$. Using the normalization assumptions for the solution v of (7) and the completeness of solutions to the linearized sine Gordon equation [9], one has $v = 0$. Now the next order of the perturbation ansatz leads to exactly the same equations as the first order, and the argument can be repeated to any order.

4. More about the Recursions; some Conjectures

There seems to be some geometric meaning behind the recursions which to my knowledge is only scarcely understood.

First, the values of $z = \frac{m}{\omega}$ corresponding to the recursions (see Figure 1) are exactly the values where the factor split off from $\mathcal{R}_n$ (and also $\mathcal{R}_n$ itself has single poles. They accumulate at $z = 0$ creating the essential singularity there. None of these singularities is present in $\mathcal{R}_n^\circ$ any more.

The same values reappear in the formula for the explicit solutions (Lemma 3). Whereas the exact structure of the recursions is a feature of the power series expansion argument [1] (they contain the coefficients of such a power series), the special points are not. Indeed, we can show that $\mathcal{R}_n^\circ(\cdot)$ can be continued analytically to (the universal cover $\tilde{G}$ of) the domain of analyticity G of $\Phi(\cdot)$. The proof is by replacing the integrals in (9) with contour integrals in the complex x- and t-planes. More details will follow in a subsequent publication.

It is quite conceivable that some converse holds: I conjecture that every single $\mathcal{R}_n^\circ(\cdot)$ (n fixed) cannot be analytically continued further than to $\tilde{G}$, except for the special points corresponding to the recursions $(n,\tilde{q})$. One must allow for this exception, because the functions Φ given by the explicit solutions in Lemma 3 branch logarithmically at these points, whereas $\mathcal{R}_n^\circ$ vanishes identically for them. If this conjecture could be proved, it would give global function theoretical obstructions for the persistence of breathers that would not rely on surprising explicit formulas and would certainly give deeper insight.

If for fixed n, the recursion $(n, \tilde{q})$ is satisfied, $\mathcal{R}_n^\circ$ vanishes at the corresponding point (equivalently: $\mathcal{R}_n$ has no pole there). Since these points accumulate at 0 for $\tilde{q} \to \infty$, analytic continuation shows that if infinitely many of these recursions are satisfied for a sequence (A_p) corresponding to an analytic function germ, all but finitely many are satisfied. In other words, a sequence (A_p) satisfying infinitely many of these recursions, but also not satisfying another infinitely many (by an arbitrarily small error), must grow faster than any sequence α^p in order not to represent an analytic function germ. This shows that the calculation of the sequence by means of the recursions is ill-conditioned. Nothing short of giving the exact solution could have proved the asymptotics that was crucial in the proof.

There is also some connection between the possible poles of $\mathcal{R}_n$ and the possible poles of Kichenassamy's [7] ansatz functions for the formal breather as described in the proof of his Theorem 3. His ε is our m, and his poles are at the same places in the $\frac{m}{\omega}$-plane as ours, even though they are poles of quite different objects! His conditions are genuinely nonlinear, and it looks like their linearization about the coefficients for the nonlinearity $\sin u$ are equivalent to the recursions coming from Birnir's, McKean's and Weinstein's [1] arguments.

Kichenassamy also determines the coefficients along direction (2) in our Figure 1 ($n = 3$), but with no need for an explicit formula since he can start all the way at the left (our $\tilde{q} = 1$) due to the large analyticity domain for m he assumes. I conjecture that there may be an explicit solution also to his conditions, allowing again to reduce the assumption on the domain of analyticity. However, as long as no reduction analogous to (11) is found in that setting, such a formula may be extremely hard even to detect by contemplation.

Acknowledgement:

This work will become part of my PhD thesis. It has profited much from discussions with my advisor Prof. J. Moser who asked the right questions. Also, this exposition would have been much less readable without his valuable critics.

References

[1] **B. Birnir, H. McKean, A. Weinstein:** Nonexistence of breathers; private communication of draft 1990, publication being prepared.

[2] **J. P. Boyd:** A numerical calculation of a weakly non-local solitary wave: the ϕ^4 breather, Nonlinearity **3** (1990), 177–195..

[3] **W. Craig, C.E. Wayne:** Newton's Method and Periodic Solutions of Nonlinear Wave Equations, preprint 1991.

[4] **A. Delshams, M.T. Martinez-Seara:** An Asymptotic Expression for the Splitting of Separatrices of the Rapidly Forced Pendulum, to appear in Comm. Math. Phys..

[5] **V. M. Eleonskii, N. E. Kulagin, N. S. Novozhilova, V. P. Zilin:** Asymptotic Expansions and Qualitative Analysis of Finite-Dimensional Models in Nonlinear Field Theory, Teor. i Mat. Fizika, **60**,3 (1984), 395–403.

[6] **P. Holmes, J. Marsden, J. Scheurle:** Exponentially Small Splittings of Separatrices with Applications to KAM Theory and Degenerate Bifurcations, Contemp. Math. **81** (1988), 213–244.

[7] **S. Kichenassamy:** Breather Solutions of the Nonlinear Wave Equation, Comm. Pure Appl. Math. **44** (1991), 789–818.

[8] **V. F. Lazutkin, I. G. Schachmannski, M. B. Tabanov:** Splitting of Separatrices for Standard and Semistandard Mappings, Physica D 40 (1989), 235–248.

[9] **D. W. McLaughlin, A. C. Scott:** Perturbation analysis of fluxon dynamics, Physical Review A, **18**, 4 (1978), 1652–1680.

[10] **J. Scheurle:** Splitting of Separatrices and Chaos, Lect. in Appl. Math. **26** (1990), 561–571.

[11] **H. Segur, M. D. Kruskal:** Nonexistence of Small Amplitude Breather Solutions in ϕ^4 Theory, Phys. Review Letters, **58** (1987), 747–750.

[12] **I.M. Sigal:** Non-linear Wave and Schrödinger Equations I., Instability of Periodic and Quasiperiodic Solutions, preprint 1991.

[13] **A. Weinstein:** Periodic Nonlinear Waves on a Half-Line, Commun. Math. Phys. **99** (1985), 385–388; erratum **107** (1986), 177.

Part III
Miscellania

ATTRACTORS, INTEGRABLE HAMILTONIAN SYSTEMS AND THE REIDEMEISTER TORSION

A. L. Fel'shtyn

Abstract. In this paper we consider the flow with a circular chain-recurrent set. The Reidemaister torsion of a level surface of a Lyapunov function and of the attraction domain of an attractor is calculated as a special value of the twisted Lefschetz zeta function build via closed orbits in the attractor. We show that, for the integrable Hamiltonian system on the four-dimensional simplectic manifold, the Reidemaister torsion of the isoenergetic surface counts the critical circles (closed trajectories of the system) of the second independent Bott integral on this surface.

§1. Introduction

Assume that on a smooth compact manifold M of dimension n there is given a tangential vector field F of class C^1, and consider the corresponding system of differential equations

$$\frac{dx}{dt} = F(x). \tag{1}$$

Denote the trajectory passing through the point x under $t = 0$ by $\varphi(t, x)$. We shall say that the set I is the attractor for (1) or the asymptotically stable compact invariant set if for any neighborhood U of I there is the neighborhood W, $I \subset W \subset U$, such that

1) for any $x \in W$ $\quad \varphi(t, x) \in U$ if $t \in [0, +\infty)$,
2) for any $x \in W$ $\quad \varphi(t, x) \xrightarrow[t \to +\infty]{} I$.

By a Lyapunov function $V(x)$ for I we mean a function that satisfies the following conditions

1) $V(x) \in C^1(U - I)$, $V(x) \in C(U)$,
2) $V(x) > 0$, $x \in U - I$; $V(x) = 0$, $x \in I$,
3) $\dfrac{dV(x)}{dt} < 0$ on $U - I$.

Such a function $V(x)$ always exists [1]. Suppose that S is a level surface of $V(x)$. The condition 3) and the Implicit-Function theorem together imply that S is a compact smooth $(n-1)$-dimensional manifold transverse to the trajectories of (1). Any two level surfaces of $V(x)$ are diffeomorphic. Let $N \supset I$, $\dim N = n$, be a compact smooth manifold with the boundary $\partial N = S$. In this article we continue to study the dependence of the topology of the attraction domain $D = \{x \in M - I : \varphi(t,x) \xrightarrow[t \longrightarrow +\infty]{} I\}$ of the attractor I and of the level surface S of the Lyapunov function $V(x)$ on the dynamical properties of the system (1) on the attractor I. Note that the attraction domain D is diffeomorphic to $S \times R$ since each trajectory of (1) in D crosses S exactly once.

The investigation of the topological structure of the level surfaces of the Lyapunov function was initiated by Wilson [1]. Assume that the system (1) is a Morse-Smale system, i.e. the following conditions are satisfied:

1) the set of nonwandering trajectories of (1) is the union of a finite number of hyperbolic stationary points and hyperbolic closed traectories,

2) stable $W^s(p)$ and unstable $W^u(p)$ manifolds of stationary points and closed trajectories p intersect transversally.

For the Morse-Smale flow the topology of D and S are studied in [2–5]. In article [3] the following analog of Morse inequalities for D and S is obtained. Let a_k be the number of stationary points p of system (1) in I such that $\dim W^u(p) = k$, b_k is the number of closed orbits q of (1) in I such that $\dim W^u(q) = k$, $M_k = a_k + b_k + b_{k+1}$, $B_k = \dim H_k(D,Q) = \dim H_k(S,Q)$, $\chi(D) = \chi(S)$ is the Euler characteristic of D and S.

Theorem 1 [3].

$$B_0 \leq M_0 + M_{n-1} - M_n$$
$$B_1 - B_0 \leq M_1 - M_0 + M_{n-2} - M_{n-1} + M_n$$
$$B_2 - B_1 + B_0 \leq M_2 - M_1 + M_0 + M_{n-3} - M_{n-2} + M_{n-1} - M_n$$

....

$$\sum_{i=0}^{n-1}(-1)^i B_i = \chi(S) = \chi(D) = (1 + (-1)^{n-1}) \sum_{i=0}^{n}(-1)^i M_i$$

In the case of arbitrary autonomous system (1) with a finite number of rest points in I the Euler characteristic equals $\chi(D) = \chi(S) = ((-1)^n - 1) \times \sum_{p \in I, F(p)=0} \operatorname{ind}(p)$ [3, 4].

In §2 we consider the flow (1) with circular chainrecurrent set $R \subset I$. This means that there is a smooth map $\theta : U \longrightarrow R^1/Z$, U a neighborhood of R in N, on which $\frac{d}{dt}(\theta \cdot \varphi(t,x)) > 0$. For instance if R is finite (i.e. consists of finitely many closed orbits) then R is circular. More generally, if R has no stationary points and topological dimension of R is one then R is circular. For example, if flow is a nonsingular Smale flow on N so $R \subset I$ is hyperbolic and one-dimensional then R is circular. For the flow (1) with the circular chain-recurrent set $R \subset I$ the Reidemeister torsion of the attraction domain D and of the level surface S is the relevant topological invariant of D and S which is calculated in Theorem 2 and Corollary 1 via closed orbits of (1) in the attractor I.

In §3 we assume that the system (1) is a Hamiltonian system on a four-dimensional symplectic manifold which possesses, besides the Hamiltonian, an additional smooth Bott integral, that is, one whose critical points on a surface of constant energy (isoenergetic surface) are organised into nondegenerate critical submanifolds. In this connection A. T. Fomenko [6] has had to develop a specific Morse-type theory of integrable Hamiltonian systems and proved theorem on the topological classification of three-dimensional isoenergetic surfaces of integrable systems. A. T. Fomenko raised the problem of finding periodic solutions of integrable systems proceeding from the data on the topology of a surface of constant energy. In this direction in Theorem 3 we prove that the Reidemeister torsion of the isoenergetic surface counts the critical circles (corresponding to the closed trajectories of (1)) of the second independent Bott integral on this surface.

This article is a continuation of the previous papers [7, 13, 14] on the dynamical zeta functions and the Reidemeister torsion.

Acknowledgements. The author is grateful to V. G. Turaev, A. T. Fomenko, V. F. Lasutkin, V. B. Pilyugina, Th. Fidler for very helpful discussions and support. This article was completed while the author was the member of the Sonderforschungsbereich 170 “Geometrie und Analysis” at Göttingen. I wish to thank the SFB 170 for its hospitality and support.

§2. The Reidemeister torsion of the attraction domain and the dynamic on the attractor

2.1 The Reidemeister torsion. Like Euler characteristic, the definition of the Reidemeister torsion is based on algebra. Rougly speaking Euler characteristic is a graded version of dimension, extending dimension from a single vector space to a complex of vector spaces. In a similar way the Reidemeister torsion is a graded version of the absolute value of the determinant of an isomorphism of vector spaces. Let $d^i : C^i \longrightarrow C^{i+1}$ be a cochain complex C^* of finite dimensional vector spaces over C with $C^i = 0$ for $i < 0$ or i large. If cohomology $H^i = 0$ for all i we say that C^* is acyclic. If one is given positive densities Δ_i on C^i then the Reidemeister torsion $\tau(C^*, \Delta_i) \in (0, +\infty)$ for acyclic C^* is defined as follows. Consider a chain contraction $\delta^i : C^i \longrightarrow C^{i-1}$, i.e. a linear map with $d\delta + \delta d = id$. Then $d + \delta$ determines a map $(d+\delta)_+ : C^+ = \oplus C^{2i} \longrightarrow C_- = \oplus C^{2i+1}$ and map $(d+\delta)_- : C^- \longrightarrow C^+$. As $(d+\delta)^2 = id + \delta^2$ is unipotent, $(d+\delta)_+$ is an isomorphism. One define $\tau(C^*, \Delta_i) = |\det(d+\delta)_+|$ (see [7]). The Reidemeister torsion is defined in the following geometric setting. Suppose K is a finite complex and E is a flat complex acyclic vector bundle of finite dimension with base K. We recall that a flat vector bundle over K is essentially the same as a representation of the fundamental group $\pi_1(K)$, when K is connected. Denote by $C^*(K; E)$ the cochain complex of K with coefficients in E. One defines the Reidemeister torsion of K and E

as $\tau(K;E) = \tau(C^*(K;E),\Delta_i) \in (0,+\infty)$. The Reidemeister torsion of an acyclic bundle E on K has many nice properties. Suppose that A and B are subcomplexes of K. Then we have a multiplicative law:

$$\tau(A\cup B;E)\cdot\tau(A\cap B;E) = \tau(A;E)\cdot\tau(B;E) \tag{2}$$

Author property is the simple homotopy invariance of the Reidemeister torsion.

2.2. The Reidemeister torsion both of the level surface of a Lyapunov function and of the attraction domain of the attractor. Now consider the system (1) with circular chain-recurrent set $R\subset I$ on manifold N (see §1). According to Conley [8] there is a continuous function $G : N \longrightarrow R^1$ such that G is decreasing on $N - R$ and $G(R)$ is nowhere dense in R^1. There are finitely many points $x_i < x_{i+1}$ in $R^1 - G(R)$ such that $G^{-1}[x_i, x_{i+1}]$ isolated an invariant set J_i so that the isolated invariant set $J = \cup J_i$ is close as we please to chain-recurrent set R [7]. In particular we can make J circular. For further we need the isolating blocks [8]. Compact isolating neighborhood B_i of J_i is said to be isolating block if:

1) B_i is a smooth manifold with corners,
2) $\partial B_i = {b_i}^+\cup {b_i}^-\cup b_i^0$ where each term is compact manifold with boundary,
3) the trajectories $\varphi(t,x)$ is tangent to b_i^0 and $\partial b_i^0 = b_i^0\cap({b_i}^+\cup {b_i}^-)$,
4) the trajectories $\varphi(t,x)$ is transverse to ${b_i}^+$ and ${b_i}^-$, enters B_i on ${b_i}^+$ and exists on ${b_i}^-$.

Since J_i is circular there is a smooth map $\theta_i : B_i \longrightarrow R^1/Z$ such that $\frac{d}{dt}(\theta_i\cdot\varphi(t,x)) > 0$ on B_i. By perturbing θ_i, we can make θ_i transverse to $0\in R^1/Z$ on $B_i, {b_i}^+, {b_i}^-, b_i^0, \partial {b_i}^+, \partial {b_i}^-, \partial {b_i}^0$. Now let $Y_i = {\theta_i}^{-1}(0)\cup b_i^-$, $Z_i = {b_i}^-$. Then (Y_i, Z_i) is a simplicial pair. We define a continuous map $r_i : Y_i \longrightarrow Y_i$ as follows. If $y\notin Z_i$ then $r_i(y) = \varphi(\tau,y)$ where $\tau=\tau(y)>0$ is the smallest positive time t for which $\varphi(t,y)\in Y_i$. Since $\varphi(t,x)$ is transverse out on ${b_i}^- = Z_i$, we see that $\tau(y)$ is near 0 for y near Z_i. Thus τ extends continuously to Z_i if we set $\tau/Z_i = 0$. Now let E be a flat complex vector bundle of finite dimension on B_i. There is a bundle map $\alpha_i : {r_i}^*(E/Y_i) \longrightarrow E/Y_i$ defined by pulling back along the trajectory from y to $r_i(y)$, using the flat connection on E. This determines an endomorphism $(\alpha_i)_* : H^*(Y_i,Z_i;{r_i}^*E) \longrightarrow H^*(Y_i,Z_i;E)$. Since there is a natural induced map ${r_i}^* : H^*(Y_i,Z_i;E) \longrightarrow H^*(Y_i,Z_i;{r_i}^*E)$, we obtain the endomorphism $\beta_i = (\alpha_i)_*\cdot {r_i}^* : H^*(Y_i,Z_i;E) \longrightarrow H^*(Y_i,Z_i;E)$. So the relative Lefschetz number $L(\beta_i) = \sum_{k=0}^{n-1}(-1)^k\cdot \operatorname{Trace}(\beta_i)_k$ is defined. According to Atiyah and Bott [9] the numbers $L(\beta_i)$ can be computed from the fixed point set of r_i in $Y_i - Z_i$. If $\operatorname{Fix}(r_i) - Z_i$ is a finite set of points p with the Lefschetz index $\operatorname{ind}_L(r_i,p)$ and $(\alpha_i)_p : E_p \longrightarrow E_p$ is the endomorphism of the fiber at p then one has the relative Lefschetz formula $L(\beta_i) = \sum_p \operatorname{ind}_L(r_i,p)\cdot\operatorname{Trace}(\alpha_i)_p$. We see that $L(\beta_i^n)$, $n\geqslant 1$, counts the points of period n for β_i not in Z_i, i.e. the closed orbits of system (1) that wrap n times around R^1/Z under θ_i, with a weight coming from the holonomy of E around these closed orbits. Now, consider the twisted Lefschetz zeta function [7] for E and $(B_i, b_i{}^-)$: $L_i(z) = L_{\beta_i}(z) = \exp(\sum_{n=1}^{\infty}(L(\beta_i^n)/n) \cdot z^n$. Let $\rho_E : \pi_1(N,p) \longrightarrow GL(E_p)$ is holonomy reprezentation for acyclic bundle E on orientable manifold N, $n = \dim N$; ρ_E^* is the contragredient reprezentation of ρ_E and E^* is a flat complex vector bundle with the holonomy ρ_E^*. We suppose that $\det \rho_E = 1$. Let $L_i^*(z)$ be the twisted Lefschetz zeta function for E^* and (B_i, b_i^-), and $L^*(z) = \prod_i L_i^*(z)$, $L(z) = \prod_i L_i(z)$.

Theorem 2.

$$\tau(D;E) = \tau(S;E) = |L(1)|^{-1} \cdot |L^*(1)|^{\varepsilon(n)}, \quad \textit{where} \quad \varepsilon(n) = (-1)^n.$$

Proof. Consider the function G. Smoothing the level set $G^{-1}(x_i)$ by sliding it along the flow, one obtains a smooth region $N_i \subset N$ with $G^{-1}((-\infty, x_i - \epsilon)) \subset N_i \subset G^{-1}((-\infty, x_i + \epsilon))$, such that the trajectories $\varphi(t,x)$ transverse to ∂N_i, for large i $N_i = N$ and $\partial N^- = \varnothing$). If ϵ is small one has that $N_{i+1} - N_i$ isolates J_i. Then by properties of the Reidemeister torsion [7] one finds: $\tau(N;E) = \prod_i \tau(N_{i+1}, N_i; E) = \prod_i \tau(B_i, b_i; E)$. D. Fried proved [7] that E is acyclic for (B_i, b_i^-) if $I - \beta_i$ is invertible and then $\tau(B_i, b_i; E) = |L_i(z)|_{z=1}^{-1}$. So we have

$$\tau(N;E) = \prod_i |L_i(1)|^{-1} = |L(1)|^{-1}. \tag{3}$$

From the multiplicative law (2) for the Reidemeister torsion it follows:

$$\tau(N;E) = \tau(N, \partial N = S; E) \cdot \tau(\partial N = S; E) \tag{4}$$

Using Milnor's duality theorem for the Reidemeister torsion [10] we have:

$$\tau(N, \partial N = S; E) = \tau(N; E^*)^{(-1)^n} \tag{5}$$

From formula (3) it follows that

$$\tau(N;E^*) = \prod_i |L_i^*(1)|^{-1} = |L^*(1)|^{-1} \tag{6}$$

Since the attraction domain D is diffeomorphic to $S \times R^1$ then $\tau(D;E) = \tau(S;E)$ by the simple homotopy invariance of the Reidemeister torsion. Now from (3), (4), (5), (6) we have:

$$\begin{aligned}\tau(D;E) &= \tau(S = \partial N; E) = \tau(N;E) \cdot \tau^{-1}(N, \partial N = S; E) \\ &= \tau(N;E) \cdot \tau(N;E^*)^{(-1)^{n+1}} = |L(1)|^{-1} \cdot |L(1)|^{-1} \cdot |L^*(1)|^{(-1)^n}.\end{aligned}$$

Suppose now that the system (1) on N is a nonsingular almost Morse-Smale. This means that (1) has finitely many hyperbolic prime periodic orbits γ and no other chain-recurrent points. Over γ lies a strong unstable bundle $E^u(\gamma)$ of some dimension $u(\gamma)$. Let $\Delta(\gamma)$ be $+1$ if E^u is orientable and -1 if it is not. Let $\epsilon(\gamma) = (-1)^{u(\gamma)}$.

Corollary 1.

$$\tau(D;E) = \tau(S;E)$$
$$= \prod_{\gamma} |\det(I - \Delta(\gamma)\cdot\rho_E(\gamma))|^{\epsilon(\gamma)} \cdot \left(\prod_{\gamma} |\det(I - \Delta(\gamma)\cdot\rho_E^*(\gamma))|^{\epsilon(\gamma)}\right)^{(-1)^{n+1}}$$

Proof. According to D. Fried [7] if J_i is a prime hyperbolic closed orbit γ, then $|L_i(1)|^{-1} = |\det(I - \Delta(\gamma)\cdot\rho_E(\gamma))|^{\epsilon(\gamma)}$. Now, the statement follows from Theorem 2.

§3. The integrable Hamiltonian systems and the Reidemeister torsion

Let M be a four-dimensional smooth symplectic manifold and the system (1) be a Hamiltonian system with a smooth Hamiltonian H. In the Darboux coordinates such system has the form: $\dot{p}_i = \frac{\partial H}{\partial q_i}$; $\dot{q}_i = -\frac{\partial H}{\partial p_i}$. As the Hamiltonian H is the integral of the system (1), then three-dimensional level surface $Q = \{H = \text{const}\}$ is invariant for the system (1). The surface Q is called the isoenergetic surface or the constant-energy surface. Since M is orientable (as a symplectic manifold), the surface Q is automatically orientable in all cases. Suppose that the system (1) is complete integrable (in Liouville's sense) on the surface Q. This means, that there is the smooth function f (the second integral), which is independent with H and the Poisson bracket $\{H, f\} = 0$ in the neigborhood of Q. We shall call the integral f a Bott integral on the isoenergetic surface Q, if its critical points form critical nondegenerate smooth submanifolds in Q. This means that the Hessian $d^2 f$ of the function f is nondegenerate on the planes normal to the critical submanifolds of the function f. A. T. Fomenko [6] proved that a Bott integral on compact nonsingular isoenergetic surface Q can have only three types of critical submanifolds: circles, tori, Klein bottles. The investigation of the concrete systems shows [6] that it is a typical situation when the integral on Q is a Bott integral. In the classical integrable cases of the solid body movement (cases of the Kovalevskaya, Goryachev-Chaplygin, Clebsch, Manakov) the Bott integals are round Morse functions on the isoenergetic surfaces. The round Morse function is a Bott function all whose critical manifolds are circles. Note that critical circle of f is a periodic solution of the system (1) and the number of this circles is finite.

Suppose now that the Bott integral f is a round Morse function on the closed isoenergetic surface Q. Let us recall the concept of the separatrix diagram of the critical circle γ for a Bott function f. Let $x \in \gamma$ be an arbitrary point and $N_x(\gamma)$ be a disc of small radius normal to γ at x. The restriction of f to the $N_x(\gamma)$ is a normal Morse function wich the critical point x having a certain index $\lambda = 0, 1, 2$. The separatrix of the critical point x is the integral trajectory of the field grad f, which is entering or leaving x. The union of all the separatrices entering the point x gives a disc of dimension λ and is called the incoming separatrix diagram (disc). The union of outgoing separatrices gives a disc of additional dimension and is called the outgoing separatrix diagram (disc). Varing the point x and constructing the incoming and outgoing separatrix discs for each point x, we obtain the incoming and outgoing separatrix diagrams of circle γ. Let $u(\gamma)$ be the dimension of the outgoing separatrix diagram of γ, and $\Delta(\gamma)$ be $+1$ if this separatrix is orientable, and -1 if it is not. Let $\epsilon(\gamma) = (-1)^{u(\gamma)}$. Suppose that $\rho_E : \pi_1(Q,p) \longrightarrow GL(E_p)$ is holonomy representation for the acyclic bundle E over Q; E_p is a fiber at point p.

Theorem 3.

$$\tau(Q;E) = \prod_{\gamma} |\det(I - \Delta(\gamma) \cdot \rho_E(\gamma))|^{\epsilon(\gamma)}$$

Proof. As a Bott integral f on Q is a round Morse function then according to Thurston [11] Q has a round handle decomposition whose core circles are critical circles of f. According to Asimov [12] if Q has a round handle decomposition then Q has a nonsingular Morse-Smale flow whose closed orbits are exactly the core circles of the round handles, i.e. critical circles γ of f. Consider this nonsingular Morse-Smale flow. For a closed orbit γ of such flow the dimension $u(\gamma)$ of unstable manifold $W^u(\gamma)$ is exactly the dimension of the outgoing separatrix diagram of a critical circle of f. On can choose as isolating block B for γ to be a bundle over S^1 with fiber F a simplicial disc so that $F \cong I^u \times I^s$, $u = u(\gamma)$, $s = 4 - u(\gamma)$, and $F \cap b^- \cong \partial I^u \times I^s \subset F$. By collapsing I^s to a point one can produce a simple homotopy equivalence of (B, b^-) to $(X_\gamma, \partial X_\gamma)$ where X_γ is the unstable disc bundle over γ. Give Q its Smale filtration by compact submanifolds Q_i of top dimension so that $Q_i \subset \text{int} Q_{i+1}$, $Q_0 = \varnothing$, $Q_i = Q$ for large i, flow is transverse inward on ∂Q_i and $Q_{i+1} - Q_i$ is an isolating neighborhood for a hyperbolic closed orbit γ. Then (Q_{i+1}, Q_i) has the same homotopy type as $(X_\gamma, \partial X_\gamma)$ and by properties of the Reidemeister torsion [7] one finds: $\tau(Q;E) = \prod_i \tau(Q_{i+1}, Q_i; E) = \prod_\gamma \tau(X_\gamma, \partial X_\gamma; E) = \prod_\gamma |\det(I - \Delta(\gamma) \cdot \rho_E(\gamma))|^{\epsilon(\gamma)}$.

References

[1] F. W. Wilson, *The structure of the level surfaces of a Lyapunov function*, Jour. Diff. Equat., v.**3** (1967), pp. 323–329.

[2] S. Yu. Pilyugin, *A manifold that determines the type of an asymptotically stable invariant set*, Differ. Uravneniya, v.**16** (1980), pp. 2140–2147.

[3] I. B. Gontareva, A. L. Fel'shtyn, *An analog of Morse inequalities for domain of attraction*, Vestnik Leningr. Univ. Math., v.**17** (1984), pp. 15–20.

[4] A. L. Fel'shtyn, *On the Morse-smale systems without closed trajectories*, Izv. Vyssh. Uceb. Zaved. Math., v.**27** (1983), pp. 77–82.

[5] I. B. Gontareva, *Topological structure of attraction domain of an attractor for 3-dimensional Morse-smale system*, Izv. Vyssh. Uceb. Zaved. Math., v.**32**, n.**6**, pp. 32–37.

[6] A. T. Fomenko, *Symplectic geometry*, Advan. Stud. in Con. Math., v.**5** (1988), pp. 1–388.

[7] D. Fried, *Lefschetz formula for flows. The Lefschetz centennial conference*, Contempor. Math., v.**58**, part **3**, 1987, pp. 19–69.

[8] C. Conley, *Isolated invariant set and the Morse index*, C.B.M.S. Reg. conf. ser. v.**38** (1987).

[9] M. Atiyan, R. Bott, *A Lefschetz fixed point formula for elliptic complexes* II, Annals of Math., v.**88** (1968), pp. 451–491.

[10] J. Milnor. *A duality theorem for the Reidemeister torsion*, Annals of Math., v.**76** (1962), pp. 137–147.

[11] W. Thurston, *Existence of codimension one foliated manifolds*, Annals of Math., v.**104** (1976), pp. 249–268.

[12] D. Asimov, *Round handle and non-singular Morse-Smale flows*, Annals of math., v.**102** (1975), pp. 41–54.

[13] A. L. Fel'shtyn, *New zeta functions for dynamical systems and Nielsen fixed point theory*, Lecture Notes in Math., v.**1346** (1988), pp. 33–55.

[14] A. L. Fel'shtyn, *The Reidemeister, Nielsen zeta functions and the Reidemeister torsion in dynamical systems theory*, Mathematica Göttingensis, Heft **47**, october 1991, pp. 1–32, preprint.

LINEAR CONNECTIONS FOR HAMILTONIAN DYNAMICS OVER ISOTROPIC SUBMANIFOLD

Michael Karasev and Yurij Vorobjev

Appl. Math. Dep., MIEM, 109028 Moscow, Russia

Introduction

This paper was stimulated by the investigations in quantum spectral problems. We consider the systems having in a classical limit an isotopic (but non-Lagrangian) compact invariant submanifold, for example: a closed trajectory, low-dimensional torus or topologically more complicated object. To such a submanifold Λ one can try to assign a *series of eigenvalues of quantum problem*. It is well-known that for this purpose we need in investigation of the first variation equation in coordinates normal to Λ [1, 2].

From the viewpoint of ordinary differential equations the problems arising here are the following: reducibility, stability, calculation of Floquet multipliers and their analogues in the case $\dim \Lambda > 1$, analogues of the Gel'fand-Lidskiy and Kolmogorov–Arnold–Moser theories, etc., for linear systems with a complicated dependence of coefficients on time. In the case of quasi-periodical solutions, when Λ is a torus, a number of results along these lines is known (see [3–7] and also the review [8], and bibliography in [9]). Note that in the theory of semiclassical asymptotics important notions of a "complex germ" [2, 10] and "canonical basis" [11] where introduced for the first variation equation over isotropic Λ.

Independently from these themes the geometry of isotropic and coisotropic submanifolds was investigated carefully by symplectic and topological methods [12–18].

And there are some works where these problems were considered from the viewpoint of symplectic connections. It is known the work by V. S. Buslaev with pupils [19], where a symplectic connection was used for investigation of the first variation equation. Recently the paper by J. E. Marsden, T. Ratiu, G. Rangel [20] appeared, where the procedure of reduction for the first variation equation by means of parallel transport was studied in detail.There are also an important approach from the viewpoint of the Bott connection [21] for constructing the symplectic ones in the case of isotropic fibration (A. Weinstein [12], P. Dazord

[22–24], A. Lichnerowicz [25]). Similar ideas were used also in quantization theory [26–28].

Our approach to the problems mentioned above was stimulated by recently obtained integral representations for semiclassical and exact eigenfunctions, localized near the Lagrangian submanifolds [29–31]. Now we succeeded in a generalization of these representations for the case of isotropic submanifolds [32, 33]. Connections on the symplectic and Hermitian bundles over Λ are working here as a key technical means. They are used for the construction of quantum "Λ-coherent states".

In this way a number of purely geometric constructions arises. For example: an infinitesimal version of the Weinstein–Dazord–Lichnerowicz connection over isolated isotropic submanifold [34, 35], connection in the germ of Poisson structure [32, 33, 36], non-commutative integrability of the first variation equation [30] and an analog of the Maslov class over isotropic submanifold [30, 33]. In the present paper we continue the investigation of these constructions and consider their applications to the problems in reducibility and stability, in analogues of Floquet multipliers and the phase of a Jacobian (i.e., a solution of the Liouville equation).

So, our main objective is to replace the study of a variation equation on the normal symplectic bundle over Λ by the study of an adapted linear connection with zero curvature. Adaptation means that the dynamics of a variation equation coincides with the parallel transport by a connection along the Hamiltonian trajectory.

It seems that such an adapted connection with zero curvature is a more special object whose existence is a very hard demand on the system. But it turns out that this is exactly the object which permits to study the system by geometric and topological methods (not only by analytical ones). With respect to the solutions of the first variation equation an adapted connection plays the same role as an invariant Lagrangian or isotropic submanifold plays with respect to the individual Hamiltonian trajectories.

1. First variation on a normal symplectic bundle. Adaptatibility, ∇-reducibility and complete reducibility.

Let $\mathfrak{X}$ be a symplectic manifold with a closed nondegenerate 2-form ω. Let $\Lambda \subset \mathfrak{X}$ be an isotropic submanifold:

$$\omega|_\Lambda = 0, \quad \dim \Lambda = k < \frac{1}{2} \dim \mathfrak{X}.$$

Denote by $T_\Lambda \mathfrak{X}$ the bundle with the base Λ and the fibres $T_\alpha \mathfrak{X}$, $\alpha \in \Lambda$. Consider the isotropic subbundle $T\Lambda \subset T_\Lambda \mathfrak{X}$ and the coisotropic one $K \stackrel{\text{def}}{=} (T\Lambda)^\perp$ whose fibres are the skew-orthogonal complements to the fibres of $T\Lambda$.

Introduce the Lie algebra $\mathcal{A}^\Lambda$ of all Poissonian vector fields u on $\mathfrak{X}$ tangent to Λ:

$$L_u\omega = 0 \qquad \text{and} \qquad u_\alpha \in T_\alpha\Lambda \quad \forall\alpha \in \Lambda.$$

Here L_u is the Lie derivative.

For any $u \in \mathcal{A}^\Lambda$ the submanifold Λ is invariant with respect to the flow γ_u^t, and the bundle K is invariant with respect to the differential of this flow $d\gamma_u^t$. Of course locally there is the function H such that $u = \mathrm{ad}(H)$ is a *Hamiltonian field* and

$$dH|_K = 0.$$

Recall that symplectic structure, Hamiltonian fields and Poisson brackets correspond to each other by the formula

$$\omega(\mathrm{ad}(H_1),\, \mathrm{ad}(H_2)) = \{H_1,\, H_2\} = \mathrm{ad}(H_1)H_2.$$

Introduce the space $\mathcal{B}^\Lambda$ of all Poissonian fields v on $\mathfrak{X}$ such that

$$v_\alpha \in K_\alpha \qquad \forall\alpha \in \Lambda.$$

Locally we have $v = \mathrm{ad}(H)$, where

$$dH|_{T\Lambda} = 0.$$

It is evident that $\mathcal{B}^\Lambda \subset \mathcal{A}^\Lambda$ and the following statement holds.

Lemma 1.1. *$\mathcal{B}^\Lambda$ is an ideal in $\mathcal{A}^\Lambda$,i.e., for any $u \in \mathcal{A}^\Lambda$, $v \in \mathcal{B}^\Lambda$ $[u, v] \in \mathcal{B}^\Lambda$. If we fix u, then the restriction $[u, v]|_\Lambda$ depends on the restriction $v|_\Lambda$ only.*

Denote by $\Gamma^\infty(K)$ the space of all smooth sections of the bundle K. Locally in the neighbourhood $\mathcal{U} \subset \Lambda$ this space is generated by the restrictions on Λ of all fields from $\mathcal{B}^\Lambda$. Thus from Lemma 1.1 it follows that the commutator of the field $u \in \mathcal{A}^\Lambda$ and the section $s \in \Gamma^\infty(K)$ is correctly defined. Moreover, $[u, s] \in \Gamma^\infty(K)$.

Remark that there is a symplectic subbundle $E \subset K$ such that

$$K = T\Lambda \oplus E. \tag{1.1}$$

So for any $u \in \mathcal{A}^\Lambda$ we have a linear operator $\mathbb{D}_u\colon \Gamma^\infty(E) \to \Gamma^\infty(E)$ acting according to the formula

$$\mathbb{D}_u X \stackrel{\text{def}}{=} \pi([u, X]) \qquad \forall X \in \Gamma^\infty(E). \tag{1.2}$$

Here π is the projection of section generated by the projection of bundles

$$\pi\colon K \to E \quad \text{along} \quad T\Lambda.$$

Denote $\tilde{u} = u|_\Lambda$. The pair $(\tilde{u}, \mathbb{D}_u)$ generates the one-parameter group $\mathbb{S}_u^t$ of symplecic morphisms of the bundle E:

$$\mathbb{S}_u^t = (\gamma_u^t, \pi \cdot d\gamma_u^t) \colon E_\alpha \to E_{\gamma_u^t(\alpha)} \qquad (\alpha \in \Lambda,\ t \in \mathbf{R}).$$

Locally (and if E is trivial, then globally) this transformation is equivalent to the solution of the system of ordinary differential equations, namely, *first variation equations*:

$$\frac{dx}{dt} = V(\alpha(t))x.$$

Here $\alpha(t) = \gamma_u^t(\alpha(0))$ is the trajectory of the field u on Λ, $x = \{x^\sigma\}$ are the coordinates in the fibres E_α with respect to the local basis of sections $X_1(\alpha), \ldots, X_{2r}(\alpha) \in E_\alpha$. Matrix $V = ((V_\gamma^\sigma(\alpha)))$ is a *matrix of variations*:

$$\mathbb{D}_u X_\gamma = -\sum_{\sigma=1}^{2r} V_\gamma^\sigma X_\sigma.$$

Remark 1.1. Matrix V is only one block of the full matrix of variations on the whole tangent space $T\mathfrak{X}$. The study of this block is a first step. The second one deals with the "torsion" [5], which appears here when E is not invariant.

Remark 1.2. Note that there is a more invariant definition of V, which does not depend on the choice of symplectic subbundle E in (1.1). We can consider the factor-bundle

$$\overset{\circ}{E} \overset{\text{def}}{=} K/T\Lambda, \quad \overset{\circ}{E} \equiv \overset{\circ}{E}_\Lambda,$$

and the projection

$$E \ni X \to \overset{\circ}{X} \in \overset{\circ}{E}.$$

For each local basis $\{X_\gamma\}$ in E we have a local basis $\{\overset{\circ}{X}_\gamma\}$ in $\overset{\circ}{E}$ with respect to which the matrix of variation on $\overset{\circ}{E}$ is given by

$$\overset{\circ}{\mathbb{D}}_u \overset{\circ}{X}_\gamma = -\sum_\sigma V_\gamma^\sigma \overset{\circ}{X}_\sigma,$$

where $\overset{\circ}{\mathbb{D}}_u$ is the generator of the flow $d\overset{\circ}{\gamma}{}_u^t$ on $\overset{\circ}{E}$. The bundle $\overset{\circ}{E}$ is called a *normal symplectic bundle over* Λ. It controls the properties of the embedding $\Lambda \subset \mathfrak{X}$ (see [15]). Bellow we shall call the bundle E also "a normal symplectic".

Our purpose now is to define a notion of reducibility of the first variation equation on a normal symplectic bundle.

Introduce certain objects. Let ∇ be a symplectic connection on E. For any vector field $u \in \mathcal{A}^\Lambda$ denote by

$$\Xi = \nabla_{\tilde{u}} - \mathbb{D}_u, \qquad \tilde{u} \stackrel{\text{def}}{=} u|_\Lambda$$

the field of operators

$$\Xi(\alpha) \in \operatorname{sp}(E_\alpha; \mathbf{R}).$$

Locally with respect to the basis $\{X_\sigma\}$ on E the operator-field Ξ is given by a matrix which we shall denote by the same letter $\Xi = ((\Xi^\sigma_\gamma))$:

$$\Xi = \langle \theta, \tilde{u} \rangle + V. \tag{1.3}$$

Here θ is a *connection-form* and V is the matrix of variations. Recall a definition: $\nabla X_\sigma = \sum_\gamma \theta^\gamma_\sigma X_\gamma$.

Now consider the parallel transport by ∇ along the trajectory $\alpha(t) = \gamma^t_u(\alpha_0)$:

$$g_{\alpha(t),\alpha_0} \colon E_{\alpha_0} \ \rightarrow \ E_{\alpha(t)}.$$

We also have the flow

$$\pi \cdot d\gamma^t_u \colon E_\alpha \ \rightarrow \ E_{\alpha(t)}.$$

Introduce the family of operators $\mathbb{T}(t) \colon E_{\alpha_0} \ \rightarrow \ E_{\alpha_0}$ by the formula

$$\pi \cdot d\gamma^t_u = g_{\alpha(t),\alpha_0} \cdot \mathbb{T}(t). \tag{1.4}$$

We see that $\mathbb{T}(t) \in \operatorname{Sp}(E_{\alpha_0}, \mathbf{R})$ are linear symplectic transformations of the fixed fiber $E_{\alpha_0} \approx \mathbf{R}^{2r}$.

The family $\mathbb{T}(t)$ can be called a *reduction of a solution of the first variation equation along a connection.* We refer to [20] for details.

It is evident that

$$\frac{d}{dt}\mathbb{T} + \Xi^0(t) \cdot \mathbb{T} = 0, \qquad \mathbb{T}(0) = I, \tag{1.5}$$

where $\Xi^0(t) = g^{-1}_{\alpha(t),\alpha_0} \cdot \Xi(\alpha(t)) \cdot g_{\alpha(t),\alpha_0}$.

The two following definitions will deal with the situations

$$\Xi^0(t) = 0$$

or

$$\Xi^0(t) = \text{const}.$$

The first is the condition of adaptability, the second is the condition of ∇-reducibility.

More precisely. We shall say that the connection ∇ is *adapted* to the vector field $u \in \mathcal{A}^\Lambda$ on the bundle E (or a field is *adaptable* to connection) if

$$\Xi \equiv 0 \quad \text{or} \quad \nabla_{\tilde{u}} \equiv \mathbb{D}_u.$$

Then in (1.4) $\mathbb{T}(t) \equiv I$, i.e., the differential of the flow γ_u^t on the normal symplectic bundle E coincides with the parallel transport along the trajectory of vector field $\tilde{u}$.

Denote by ${}^{\mathbf{C}}E = E \otimes \mathbf{C}$ the complexification of the bundle E. All operators $\mathbb{D}$, Ξ, $\mathbb{T}$, ∇ are continued on $\Gamma^\infty({}^{\mathbf{C}}E)$.

We shall say that the first variation equation for the field $u \in \mathcal{A}^\Lambda$ is ∇-*reducible* on E (or on ${}^{\mathbf{C}}E$), if there is a symplectic connection ∇ on E (or on ${}^{\mathbf{C}}E$) such that

(i) a curvature of ∇ is zero;

(ii) an operator-field Ξ is covariantly constant:

$$\nabla \Xi = 0, \qquad \text{or} \qquad d\Xi + [\,\theta,\, \Xi\,] = 0. \tag{1.6}$$

Remark 1.3. The first condition (i) is a compatibility condition for equations (1.6) and for the equations of parallel transport

$$dg + \theta g = 0, \qquad g|_{\alpha_0} = I. \tag{1.7}$$

Also note that if a curvature is zero then (1.6) is equivalent to the invariance of a connection relative to the dynamical group $\mathbb{S}_u^t$; see [37].

If the variation equation is ∇-reducible, then there is a local ∇-parallel basis in which the matrix Ξ is constant, the matrix of variations is constant too: $V = \text{const}$, and the same can be said about the matrix $\Xi^0(t) = \text{const}$ in (1.5). So in this case we have $\mathbb{T}(t) = \exp(t\Xi^0)$.

Lemma 1.2. *(a) If there is a symplectic connection ∇ with zero curvature, adapted to the field $u \in \mathcal{A}^\Lambda$, then the first variation equation for the field u is ∇-reducible.*

(b) Let there be a closed 1-form μ on Λ such that $\langle \mu,\, u|_\Lambda \rangle = 1$. If the first variation equation for the field u is ∇-reducible then the connection

$$\tilde{\nabla} = \nabla - \Xi \otimes \mu$$

has zero curvature and is adapted to u.

Collorary 1.1. *If Λ is a torus and the vector field has constant frequencies on Λ, then its ∇-reducibility is equivalent to the existance of an adapted connection with zero curvature.*

Collorary 1.2. *Let Λ be a closed curve and the field u nodegenerate on Λ. Then the connection ∇ defined by*

$$\nabla_{\tilde{u}} \stackrel{\text{def}}{=} \mathbb{D}_u,$$

is adapted to u and has zero curvature. The field u is ∇-reducible (the Floquet theorem).

Remark 1.4. The notion of ∇-reducibility does not coincide with the notion of reducibility in the theory of differential equations. An ordinary definition is the following:

the first variation equation on the bundle E (or on ${}^{\mathbf{C}}E$) is *reducible* if there is a basis of sections in E (or in ${}^{\mathbf{C}}E$) relative to which a matrix of variations is constant.

A variation equation is called *completely reducible* on E (or on ${}^{\mathbf{C}}E$) if this basis is symplectic; see [7] .

For two-dimensional bundles ($\dim E = 2$) a complete reducibility is equivalent to an ordinary one.

If we have a completely reducible variation equation then we have the symplectic connection ∇ for which the basis, mentioned above, is parallel. The curvature is zero automatically. The form θ of the connection ∇ in the parallel basis is zero too. So $\Xi = V =$ const in this basis (see (1.3)). It means that an equation is ∇-reducible.

The inverse statement is not true because there is, in general, a non-trivial holonomy of the connection ∇ for a ∇-reducible variation equation. Thus the parallel transport g_{α,α_0} in (1.4) is not a global family of operators when α is running along Λ. But if the holonomy is trivial (and so the bundle E is symplectically trivial), then the ∇-reducible variation equation is completely reducible.

We shall formulate the sufficient conditions for a complete reducibility in Theorem 3.2.

2. Simplectic connection over isotropic submanifold and coisotropic continuality

We are interested in existance of a symplectic connection on the normal bundle over Λ. We introduce some notions which characterize the embedding $\Lambda \subset \mathfrak{X}$.

A submanifold $N \subset \mathfrak{X}$ will be called *coisotropic on* Λ, if

$$
\begin{aligned}
&(a) \qquad \Lambda \subset N,\\
&(b) \qquad \operatorname{Ker} \omega|_{TN} = T\Lambda,\\
&(c) \qquad \operatorname{codim} N = \dim \Lambda.
\end{aligned}
$$

If, in addition, N is a coisotropic submanifold in $\mathfrak{X}$, then we call it a *coisotropic continuation* of Λ, and we call Λ *coisotropically continual.*

Submanifold $\mathfrak{Y} \subset \mathfrak{X}$ will be called *symplectic on* Λ, if

$$\begin{aligned} &(a) \qquad \Lambda \subset \mathfrak{Y}, \\ &(b) \qquad \mathrm{Ker}\; \omega|_{T\mathfrak{Y}} = \{0\}, \\ &(c) \qquad \dim\, \mathfrak{Y} = 2 \dim\, \Lambda. \end{aligned}$$

If, an addition, $\mathfrak{Y}$ is simplectic in $\mathfrak{X}$, then we call it a *symplectic continuation* of Λ.

Both of these definitions can be understood as globally over Λ as locally over the neighbourhood of a given point in Λ.

Locally a symplectic continuation always exists. Let it be defined by independent functions:

$$\mathfrak{Y} = \{\Phi_1 = \dots = \Phi_{2r} = 0\}, \qquad 2r = \dim\, \mathfrak{X} - 2 \dim\, \Lambda$$

so that a matrix of the Poisson brackets

$$J_{\sigma\gamma} \stackrel{\mathrm{def}}{=} \{\Phi_\gamma, \Phi_\sigma\}|_\Lambda$$

is nondegenerate: $\det J \neq 0$. Hamiltonian fields $X_\gamma = \mathrm{ad}(\Phi_\gamma)|_\Lambda$ give a basis in the skew-orthogonal complement

$$E_{\mathrm{loc}} \stackrel{\mathrm{def}}{=} (T_\Lambda \mathfrak{Y})^\perp \subset K.$$

We stress that here the submanifold $\mathfrak{Y}$ and so the subbundle E_{loc} are defined locally. The sections $\{\overset{\circ}{X}_\gamma\}$ give a local basis in the factor-bundle $\overset{\circ}{E}$ (see Remark 1.2).

Now let N be coisotropic on Λ. Let it be locally defined by independent functions

$$N = \{\, f_1 = \dots = f_k = 0\,\}, \qquad k = \dim\, \Lambda.$$

Then the fields $\partial_j = \mathrm{ad}(f_j)|_\Lambda$ form a basis on Λ, and the Poisson brackets between functions f_i are the following:

$$\{\, f_i,\, f_j\,\} = \sum_{s=1}^{k} \lambda_{ij}^{s} f_s + O(f^2 + \Phi^2) \qquad \text{or} \qquad [\partial_i, \partial_j] = \sum_{s=1}^{k} \lambda_{ij}^{s} \partial_s,$$

where λ_{ij}^s are certain smooth functions.

Let $\{\eta^i\}$ be a basis of 1-forms, dual to the basis of vector fields $\{\partial_j\}$. Consider the matrix-valued 1-form on Λ:

$$\theta = \sum_{i=1}^{k} \theta_i \eta^i, \tag{2.1}$$

where

$$\theta_i \stackrel{\text{def}}{=} J^{-1}\{\Phi \overset{\otimes}{,} \{\Phi, f_i\}\}|_\Lambda.$$

Here we use the tensorial notations $(\Phi \otimes \Phi)_{\gamma\sigma} = \Phi_\gamma \Phi_\sigma$. Also consider the 2-form

$$\Omega = \frac{1}{2} \sum_{i,j=1}^{k} \Omega_{ij} \eta^i \wedge \eta^j, \tag{2.2}$$

where

$$\Omega_{ij} = -\sum_{s=1}^{k} \lambda_{ij}^s \theta_s + J^{-1}\{\Phi \overset{\otimes}{,} \{\Phi, \{f_i, f_j\}\}\}|_\Lambda.$$

Theorem 2.1. *Let the submanifold N be coisotropic on Λ. Then there is a linear connection on the normal symplectic bundle $\overset{\circ}{E}_\Lambda$. In the local basis $\{\overset{\circ}{X}_\gamma\}$ the form of this connection is given by formula (2.1), and the form of a curvature is given by formula (2.2). This connection is symplectic and adapted to the Hamiltonian fields of all functions, constant along N; there is a unique connection with these properties. A curvature of connection will be equal to zero iff for any two functions f', f'', constant along N, their Poisson brackets near Λ have a form*

$$\{f', f''\}|_N = O(d_\Lambda^3). \tag{2.3}$$

Here d_Λ denotes a distance from a point on N to Λ. If a curvature does not vanish then the right-hand side of (2.3) is $O(d_\Lambda^2)$.

Remark 2.1. Connection constructed, of course, depends on the choice of N. Two submanifolds N_1, N_2, both coisotropic on Λ, will be called equivalent $N_1 \sim N_2$, if corresponding connections coincide. The class of equivalent submanifolds will be called a "*coisotropic germ*" over Λ. The germ will be called *continual*, if it contains a coisotropic submanifold.

Theorem 2.1 states that curvature is an obstruction to continuality of the germ.

Coisotropic germ will be called *flat* if a curvature of the corresponding connection is equal to zero.

In the one-dimensional case $\dim \Lambda = 1$ any germ is flat and locally continual.

Hypothesis. *A flat coisotropic germ over an isotropic submanifold is locally continual.*

Global continuation meets the obstructions like those appeared in deformations of the Poisson brackets [36, 38]. We shall consider this question in the next paper.

Now we give a scheme of the proof of Theorem 2.1. Calculation will be local. It follows from [34, 35], where the statements of Theorem 2.1 were formulated in a similar situation.

From the definition of N, coisotropic on Λ, we have

$$\{ f_i, \Phi_\gamma \}|_{f=0} = \sum_{\sigma=1}^{2r} \theta_{i\gamma}^{\sigma} \Phi_\sigma + O(\Phi^2), \tag{2.4}$$

$$\{ f_i, f_j \}|_{f=0} = \frac{1}{2} \sum_{\gamma,\sigma=1}^{2r} \mathcal{R}_{ij}^{\gamma\sigma} \Phi_\gamma \Phi_\sigma + O(\Phi^3), \tag{2.5}$$

where $\theta_{i\gamma}^{\sigma}$, $\mathcal{R}_{ij}^{\gamma\sigma}$ are certain smooth functions. The Jacobi identities give the following correlations on Λ:

$$\theta_i^* J + J\theta_i - \partial_i J = 0, \tag{2.6}$$

$$\partial_i\theta_j - \partial_j\theta_i - \sum_{s=1}^{k} \lambda_{ij}^s \theta_s + [\theta_i, \theta_j] = -\mathcal{R}_{ij} J, \tag{2.7}$$

where we denote $\theta_i = ((\theta_{i\gamma}^{\sigma}))$.

It is easy to check that $\theta = \sum_i \theta_i \eta^i$ is the connection form in the basis $\{\overset{\circ}{X}_\gamma\}$. From (2.6) it follows that this connection is symplectic.

From (2.4) we have

$$[\,\mathrm{ad}(f_i),\, \mathrm{ad}(\Phi_\gamma)\,]\big|_\Lambda = \sum_{\sigma=1}^{2r} \theta_{i\gamma}^{\sigma} X_\sigma + (\text{vector field tangent to } \Lambda).$$

So this connection is adapted to the fields $\mathrm{ad}(f_i)$ on the factor-bundle $\overset{\circ}{E}$. And the covariant derivative can be defined by

$$\nabla_{\partial_j} X \overset{\mathrm{def}}{=} \mathbb{D}_{\mathrm{ad}(f_j)} X = \pi[\,\mathrm{ad}(f_j),\, X\,] \qquad \forall X \in \Gamma^\infty(E_{\mathrm{loc}}). \tag{2.8}$$

The curvature $\Omega = d\theta + \theta \wedge \theta$ is calculated from (2.7):

$$\Omega_{ij} = -\mathcal{R}_{ij} J.$$

From (2.5) it follows that the condition of zero curvature $\Omega = 0$ is equivalent to (2.3).

Remark 2.2. In formula (2.8) we cannot write any field $u \in \mathcal{A}^\Lambda$ instead of the basis fields $\partial_j = \mathrm{ad}(f_j)|_\Lambda$, i.e.,

$$\nabla_{\tilde{u}} X \neq \pi[\,u,\, X\,], \qquad \tilde{u} \equiv u|_\Lambda. \tag{2.9}$$

Thus our connection is analogous but not equal to the canonical Bott connection [21], which is defined similar to the right-hand side in (2.9). In particular, if N is coisotropic not only on Λ, but globally, and N possesses an isotropic fibration, then in (2.9) there will be an equality for all fields u tangent to the fibres. Thus in this case the connection ∇ can be obtained by the Lichnerowicz construction [25]. The case when $\mathfrak{X}$ is isotropically fibrated, was considered by Dazord [23]. The case of Lagrangian fibration was first investigated by Weinstein [12].

3. Sufficient conditions for reducibility over isotropic submanifold.

From Theorem 2.1 we immediately have the following

Theorem 3.1. *Let H be a real smooth function on the symplectic manifold $\mathfrak{X}$. Let $\Lambda \subset \mathfrak{X}$ be an isotropic compact submanifold, invariant with respect to the Hamiltonian flow of H and lying on the level $\{H = const\}$. Suppose that there is a submanifold $N \subset \{H = const\}$ coisotropic on Λ. Let coisotropic germ of N be flat (for example, N is coisotropic globally). Then, there is a symplectic connection ∇ with zero curvature on the normal symplectic bundle $\overset{\circ}{E}_\Lambda$ such that the first variation equation of the Hamiltonian field $ad(H)$ is ∇-reducible on $\overset{\circ}{E}_\Lambda$.*

And now we shall formulate sufficient conditions for a complete reducibility.

Theorem 3.2. *Let fundamental group $\pi_1(\Lambda)$ be commutative and have no torsion. Let the first variation equation be ∇-reducible on $\overset{\circ}{E}_\Lambda$. Then it is completely reducible on ${}^{\mathbf{C}}\overset{\circ}{E}_\Lambda$. If, in addition, the spectrum of ∇-holonomy does not contain negative numbers, then the first variation equation is completely reducible on $\overset{\circ}{E}_\Lambda$.*

The proof is the same as in the classical Floquet theory, but it is given in the language of linear connections [39].

Recall that $g = g_{\alpha,\alpha_0}$ is the parallel transport (1.7) on the bundle $\overset{\circ}{E}$ along the curve, connecting the point α_0 with the point $\alpha \in \Lambda$. Since the curvature is zero, then parallel transport does not depend on the choice of curve from a given homotopic class. Holonomy group for a connection with zero curvature is discrete [39].

Let Γ_j be a basic cycle in $\pi_1(\Lambda)$. Denote by $G_j \colon \overset{\circ}{E}_{\alpha_0} \to \overset{\circ}{E}_{\alpha_0}$ the operator from the holonomy group:

$$G_j = g_{\alpha,\alpha_0}|_{\alpha \quad \text{has run around} \quad \Gamma_j}.$$

We have $H_1(\Lambda) = \pi_1(\Lambda)$ and no torsion in $H_1(\Lambda)$. Thus [40]

(i) there is a basis of closed 1-forms $\{\mu^j\}$, dual to the basis of cycles $\{\Gamma_i\} \subset H_1(\Lambda)$:

$$\oint_{\Gamma_i} \mu^j = \delta_i^j, \qquad i,j = 1,\dots,m, \qquad m = \dim H_1(\Lambda);$$

(ii) the elements G_j of a holonomy group are commutative symplectic operators

$$G_j \in Sp(\overset{\circ}{E}_{\alpha_0}, \mathbf{R}), \qquad [\,G_i,\, G_j\,] = 0, \qquad i,j = 1,\dots,m \tag{3.1}$$

Consider the operator-fields over Λ:

$$F_j \overset{\text{def}}{=} g_{\alpha,\alpha_0} \cdot \ln(G_j) \cdot g_{\alpha,\alpha_0}^{-1} \in \mathrm{sp}(\overset{\circ}{E}_\alpha, \mathbf{C}).$$

Here we use the principal branch of the logarithm.

Then there is a connection on ${}^{\mathbf{C}}\overset{\circ}{E}$, namely

$$\tilde{\nabla} = \nabla + \sum_{j=1}^{m} F_j \otimes \mu^j.$$

It is symplectic, has zero curvature and trivial holonomy. If the first variation equation is ∇-reducible then this equation is $\tilde{\nabla}$-reducible also.

As we have seen in Remark 1.3, these conditions give a complete reducibility. More precisely, global $\tilde{\nabla}$-parallel basis $\{Y_\gamma\}$ in ${}^{\mathbf{C}}\overset{\circ}{E}$ (i.e. symplectical trivialization) is given by the formula

$$Y_\gamma(\alpha) = g_{\alpha,\alpha_0} \cdot \exp\Big\{ - \int_{\alpha_0}^{\alpha} \sum_{j=1}^{m} \ln(G_j) \otimes \mu^j \Big\} Y_\gamma^0.$$

Here $\{\, Y_\gamma^0 \,|\, \gamma = 1,\dots,2r\,\}$ is an arbitrary symplectic basis in $\overset{\circ}{E}_{\alpha_0}$.

Since $\ln(G_j)$ are complex (in general), then $Y_\gamma(\alpha)$ are complex and so the variation equation is reducible on ${}^{\mathbf{C}}\overset{\circ}{E}$. But if $(-\infty, 0) \cap \mathrm{spec}(G_j) = \varnothing$, then $\ln G_j$ are real (see [41]) and the variation equation is reducible on $\overset{\circ}{E}$.

Remark 3.1. There is a partial situation [7, 35], when the Hamiltonian field $\mathrm{ad}(H)$ has not one, but a hole family of invariant submanifolds (tori) Λ, fibrating a certain symplectic submanifold $\mathfrak{Y}$, and more over each Λ has a flat coisotropic germ. Then a normal bundle $E = (T\mathfrak{Y})^\perp$ is invariant with respect to $d\gamma^t_{\mathrm{ad}(H)}$ and the conditions of Theorem 3.2 are hold automatically.

4. Stability. Analogues of Floquet solutions.

Recall that isotropic subbundle $\tau \subset {}^{\mathbf{C}}T_\Lambda \mathfrak{X}$ is called *positive* if the form

$$i\omega(\cdot, \bar{\cdot}) \tag{4.1}$$

is positively defined on τ. In this case τ is the Hermitian bundle with respect to the inner product (4.1) on the fibres. Real subbundle $\varepsilon \subset \tau$ is called *Euclidean*, if this product is real on ε.

The symplectic operator $G \in \mathrm{Sp}(\mathbf{R}^{2m})$ is called *stable*, if G is diagonaliziable and the spectrum of G lies on the unit circle in $\mathbf{C}$ (see [15, 41]).

We shall say that the *first variation equation is stable*, if it possesses an adapted connection with zero curvature and with stable commutative basis elements G_j of the holonomy group (see (3.1)).

Lemma 4.1. *Let the first variation equation of a vector field from $\mathcal{A}^\Lambda$ be stable on the normal symplectic bundle E with respect to the connection ∇. Then there exist an expansion into a direct sum :*

$$\begin{aligned} E &= E_1 \oplus \cdots \oplus E_r, \qquad \dim E_j = 2, \quad E_j \quad \textit{is symplectic}, \\ {}^{\mathbf{C}}E_j &= \tau_j \oplus \bar{\tau}_j, \qquad \dim_{\mathbf{C}} \tau_j = 1, \quad \tau_j \quad \textit{is positive}, \end{aligned} \tag{4.2}$$

where each τ_j is invariant with respect to the connection ∇. The variation equation is stable on E_j with respect to the connection $\nabla|_{E_j}$.

The proof follows from such a statement: any set of commutative stable symplectic operators in a real symplectic space has common eigen-basis (in complexification of the space); half of vectors of this basis are positive with respect to the form (4.1).

We have to find such a basis for the holonomy operators G_j and transport the j-th positive vector by a connection to all fibres E_α, $\alpha \in \Lambda$. This procedure gives global complex one-dimensional subbundle τ_j. Intersections $(\tau_j \oplus \bar{\tau}_j) \cap E \overset{\text{def}}{=} E_j$ are symplectic. Since a connection is adapted, τ_j and E_j are invariant relative to connection and relative to variation equation. Restriction of a connection to E_j is adapted to this equation.

Now remark that if the first Chern class c_{1j} of E_j (or of the bundle τ_j) is equal to zero in half-integer numbers:

$$2c_{1j} = 0 \quad \text{in} \quad H^2(\Lambda, \mathbf{Z}),$$

then [40] there is a one-dimensional subbundle $l_j \subset E_j$ (or the Euclidean subbundle $\varepsilon_j \subset \tau_j$, $\dim \varepsilon_j = 1$). And vice versa.

In this case there is the real closed form β_j on Λ:

$$i\beta_j = \theta_j, \tag{4.3}$$

where θ_j is a form of connection $\nabla|_{\tau_j}$ relative to the basis in ε_j. (Recall that a connection ∇ is simplectic and has zero curvature. Thus its restriction to one-dimensional positive invariant subbundle τ_j is Hermitian, has zero curvature, and the form of connection θ_j is purely imaginary. Note that the form β_j depends on the choice of Euclidean subbundle $\varepsilon_j \subset \tau_j$).

Denote by w_{1j} the first Stifel-Whitney class of the bundle ε_j. Then $w_{1j} \in H^1(\Lambda, \mathbf{Z}_2)$ and $c_{1j} = 0$ in $H^2(\Lambda, \mathbf{Z}) \Leftrightarrow E_j$ is trivial $\Leftrightarrow \exists \varepsilon_j : w_{1j} = 0$.

Theorem 4.1. *Suppose that the first variation equation of the Hamiltonian field ad(H) on the normal symplectic bundle $E = E_\Lambda$ is stable with respect to the connection ∇.*

(a) Let the doubled Chern class $2c_{1j}$ of the j-th invariant subbundle $E_j \subset E$ from (4.2) be equal to zero in $H^2(\Lambda, \mathbf{Z})$. Then the spectrum of a holonomy of connection ∇ on E_j consists of the numbers

$$\lambda_{j1}, \bar{\lambda}_{j1}, \ldots, \lambda_{jm}, \bar{\lambda}_{jm},$$

where

$$\lambda_{js} \stackrel{\text{def}}{=} \exp\Big\{ -i \oint_{\Gamma_s} \beta_j - i\pi w_{1j}(\Gamma_s) \Big\}, \qquad \Gamma_s \in H_1(\Lambda),$$

$s = 1, \ldots, m,$ $\quad m = \dim H_1(\Lambda)$, *closed forms β_j are defined in (4.3).*

(b) Let in addition to (a)

$$c_{1j} = 0 \quad \text{in} \quad H^2(\Lambda, \mathbf{Z}) \qquad \text{for all} \quad j = 1, \ldots, \text{dim}E/2.$$

Then the first variation equation is completely reducible on E and has a basis of solutions along the trajectory $\alpha(t) = \gamma^t_{\text{ad}(H)}(\alpha_0)$:

$$X_j^{\pm}(t) = \exp\Big\{ \mp i \int_{\alpha_0}^{\alpha(t)} \beta_j \Big\} Y_j^{\pm}(\alpha(t)). \tag{4.4}$$

Here $Y_j^{\pm}(\alpha)$ are global positive and negative sections of the subbundles ${}^{\mathbf{C}}E_j$ (more precisely: Y_j^+ is a section of τ_j, Y_j^- is a section of $\bar{\tau}_j$, τ_j is defined in Lemma 4.1). Closed forms β_j in (4.4) are calculated by formula (4.3) with respect to Euclidean subbundles $\varepsilon_j = \{ yY_j^+ \mid y \in \mathbf{R} \}$.

Formula (4.4) gives an analogue of the Floquet solutions for a stable variation equation over general isotropic submanifold Λ. Note that in a general non-orientable case (a) in Theorem 4.1 we have no such analogue.

5. Liouville equation.

Let the field ad(H) satisfy the condition of Lemma 4.1. *Suppose that there is the Lagrangian subbundle $l^\#$* in the normal symplectic bundle $E = E_\Lambda$.

Denote $\tau = \tau_1 \oplus \cdots \oplus \tau_r$ (see Lemma 4.1) and introduce the Euclidean subbundle $\varepsilon^\# \subset \tau$: $\varepsilon^\#$ is the projection of $l^\#$ onto τ along $\bar{\tau}$. For any local Euclidean basis $\{e^j\}$ in $\varepsilon^\#$ we can calculate the matrix of variations $V^\#$:

$$\mathbb{D}_{\mathrm{ad}(H)} e^j = -\sum_{i=1}^{r} V_i^{\#j} e^i, \qquad j = 1, \ldots r.$$

Matrix $V^\#$ is anti-Hermitian and its trace does not depend on the choice of $\{e^j\}$. Thus we have the *global Liouville equation*:

$$\mathrm{ad}(H)\varphi = (\mathrm{tr} V^\#)\varphi, \tag{5.1}$$

where φ is a function over a universal covering of Λ.

In order to solve it we assume that the conditions of Theorem 4.1(a) hold for all $j = 1, \ldots, r$. Then we have the Euclidean subbundle

$$\varepsilon \stackrel{\mathrm{def}}{=} \varepsilon_1 \oplus \cdots \oplus \varepsilon_r \subset \tau$$

and the Lagrangian subbundle

$$l \stackrel{\mathrm{def}}{=} \mathrm{Re}\,\varepsilon = \left\{ \frac{z + \bar{z}}{2} \;\middle|\; z \in \varepsilon \right\} \subset E$$

Following [31] we define a closed 1-form on Λ for the pair $l, l^\#$ of Lagrangian subbundles in E_Λ:

$$\mu \stackrel{\mathrm{def}}{=} \frac{1}{2\pi i} d \ln \left(\frac{\mathcal{J}}{|\mathcal{J}|} \right)^2. \tag{5.2}$$

Here $\mathcal{J}$ is the Jacobian of projection

$$l \to {}^{\mathbf{C}} l^\# \qquad \text{along} \qquad \tau$$

with respect to any local bases in l and $l^\#$. We shall call μ the *Arnold form.* Cohomology class $[\mu] \in H^1(\Lambda, \mathbf{Z})$ is equal to the *Maslov class* of the pair $l, l^\#$.

Note that

$$[\mu] = w_1(l) + w_1(l^\#) \pmod 2,$$

where w_1 is the Stifel-Whitney class.

Theorem 5.1. *Let an isotropic Λ be invariant with respect to the Hamiltonian field ad(H). Let the first variation equation be stable on the normal symplectic bundle $E = E_\Lambda$. Let E have the Lagrangian subbundle, and the Liouville equation be defined with respect to this subbundle. Let double Chern classes of all invariant subbundles E_j from (4.2) be zero in $H^2(\Lambda, \mathbf{Z})$. Then the Liouville equation (5.1) has a solution*

$$\varphi(\alpha) = \exp\left\{ -i \int_{\alpha_0}^{\alpha} \left(\pi\mu + \sum_{j=1}^{r} \beta_j \right) \right\}, \qquad \alpha \in \Lambda,$$

where closed 1-forms β_j are defined by (4.3), and the closed Arnold form μ is defined by (5.2).

Acknowledgments

We are grateful to A. T. Fomenko, S. B. Kuksin, N. N. Nehoroshev, M. B. Sevryuk and V. V. Trofimov for useful discussion. Special thanks to Andre Lichnerowicz and Pierre Dazord for references on the results in symplectic connection theory. Also we express our gratitude to prof. V. F. Lazutkin and prof. V. P. Maslov for the attention to our work.

References

1. V. M. Babich, *Eigenfunctions locallized near closed geodesics*, Zapiski nauch. semin. LOMI, vol. 9, 1968. (Russian)
2. V. P. Maslov, *Complex WKB-method in nonlinear equations*, "Nauka", Moscow, 1977. (Russian)
3. R. A. Johnson, G. R. Sell, *Smoothness of spectral subbundles and reducibility of quasiperiodic linear differential systems*, J. Diff. Equat. **41** (1981), 262–288.
4. M. R. Herman, *Une méthode pour minores les exposants de Lapouniv et quelques exemples le caractére local d'un théoréme d'Arnold et de Moser sur le tore de dimension 2*, Comment. Math. Helv. **58** (1983), 453–502.
5. M. R. Herman, *Dinamics connected with indefined normal torsion*, Publ. Centre de Math. Ecole Polytechnique, 1990.
6. J. Pöschel, *On elliptic lower dimensional tori on Hamiltonian systems*, Math. Z. **202** (1989), 559–608.
7. S. B. Kuksin, *An infinitesimal Liouville-Arnold theorem as criterion of reducibility for Variational Hamiltonian equations*, Preprint Max-Planck-Institut für Math. (1991), Bonn.
8. V. I. Arnold, V. V. Kozlov, A. I. Neistadt, *Mathematical aspects of classical and celstial mechanics*, Current Problems of Mathematics. Results of Science and Technology, vol. 3, VINITI, Mockow, 1985, pp. 5–302. (Russian)
9. M. V. Sevryuk, *Lower-dimensional tori in reversible systems*, Chaos **1 N 2** (1991), 160–167.
10. S. Yu. Dobrokhotov, B. Valinjo, N. N. Nekhoroshev, *Complex germ in systems with one cyclic variable*, Uspehi Mat. Nauk **39 N 3** (1987), 233–234. (Russian)
11. V. V. Belov, S. Yu. Dobrokhotov, *Canonical Maslov operator on isotropic manifolds with a complex germ and its applications to spectral problems*, Dokl. Akad. Nauk USSR **298** No. 5 (1988), 1037–1042. (Russian)
12. A. Weinstein, *Symplectic manifolds and their lagrangian submanifolds*, Adv. in Math. **6** (1971), 329–346.
13. V. Guillemin, S. Sternberg, *Some problems in integral geometry and related problems in microlocal analysis*, Amer. J. Math. **101** (1979), 915–955.
14. M. J. Gotay, J. Sniatycki, *On the quantization of presymplectic dynamical systems via coisotropic imbedding*, Comm. Math. Phys **82** No. 3 (1981), 377–389.
15. V. J. Arnold, A. B. Givental, *Symplectic geometry*, Current Problems of Mathematics. Results of Science and Technology, vol. 4, VINITI, Mockow, 1985, pp. 5–178 (Russian); English transl. Encycl. of Math. Sci., vol. 4, Springer-Verlag, 1990.
16. A. T. Fomenko, *Symplectic geometry*, Moscow University, Moscow, 1988. (Russian)

17. N. N. Nekhoroshev, *Action-angle variables and their generalizations*, Trans. Moscow Math. Soc. **26** (1972), 180–198. (Russian)

18. A. S. Mishchenko, A. T. Fomenko, *Generalized Liouville method of integration for Hamiltonian systems*, Funct. Anal. Prilozhen **12** No. 2 (1978), 46–56. (Russian)

19. V. S. Buslaev, E. A. Nalimova, *Trace formula in general Hamiltonian mechanics*, Teor. Mat. Fiz. **60** No. 3 (1984), 344–355. (Russian)

20. J. E. Marsden, T. Ratiu, G. Rangel, *Symplectic Connections and the Linearization of Hamiltonian Systems*, Publ. Univ. of California, 1990.

21. R. Bott, *On a topological obstruction to integrability*, Proc. Symp. in Pure Math. A. M. S. **16** (1970), 127–131.

22. P. Dazord, *Sur la géométrie des sous-fibre's et des feuilletages lagrangiens*, Ann scient. Ec. Norm. Sup. No. 4 **13** (1981), 465–480.

23. P. Dazord, *Fenilletages en géométrie symplectique*, Comptes Rendus **294** (1982), 489–491.

24. P. Dazord, T. Delzant, *Le probleme general des variables actions-angles*, J. Diff. Geom. **26** (1987), 223–251.

25. A. Lichnerowicz, *Feuilletages, géométrie riemannienne et géométrie symplectique*, Riv. Mat. Univ. Parma **4** No. 10 (1984), 81–90.

26. A. Lichnerowicz, *Connexions symplectiques et $*$-produits invariants*, C. R. Acad. Sci. **291** (1980), 413–417.

27. H. Hess, *Connections on symplectic manifolds and geometric quantization*, Lect. Notes Math. **836** (1980), 153–166.

28. H. Omori, Y. Maeda, A. Yoshioka, *Global calculus on Weyl manifolds* (to appear).

29. M. V. Karasev, *Connections on Lagrangian submanifolds and certain problems of quasi-classical approximation*, Zapiski nauch. semin. LOMI **172** (1989), 41–54. (Russian)

30. M. V. Karasev, *To the Maslov theory of quasi-classical asymptotics. Examples of new global quantization formula application* **ITP-89-78E** (1989), Preprint Inst. Theor. Phys., Kiev.

31. M. V. Karasev, *Simple Quantization Formula*, Symplect. Geom. and Math. Phys . , Actes du colloque en l'honneur de J. -M. Souriau, Birkhäuser, Boston, 1991, pp. 234–244.

32. M. V. Karasev, Yu. M. Vorobjev, *Integral Representation of wave functions generated by connection in a germ of Poissonian structure*, Quantum field theory, quantum mechanics and quantum optics. Proc. 18th Intern. Coll. on Group Theor. Methods in Physics, N. -Y., 1991, pp. 193–195.

33. M. V. Karasev, Yu. M. Vorobjev, *Hermitian bundles over isotropic submanifolds and correction to Kostant-Souriau quantization rule* **ITP-90-85E** (1991), Preprint Inst. Theor. Phys., Kiev.

34. Yu. M. Vorobjev, *On quantization of isotropic tori in certain non-integrable cases*, Proc. Petrovski Confer. ; Uspehi Mat. Nauk **45 N 4** (1990), 126–127. (Russian)

35. Yu. M. Vorobjev, *The Maslov complex germ generated by linear connection*, Mat. Zametki **48** No. 6 (1990), 29–37 (Russian); English transl. in Math. Notes **48,** No. 6, 1191–1197.

36. M. V. Karasev, Yu. M. Vorobjev, *Deformation and cohomology of Poisson brackets*, Lect. Notes Math. **1453** (1990), 271–290.

37. S. Kobayashi, *Transformation groups in differential geometry*, Springer-Verlag, Berlin-Heidelberg-New York, 1972.

38. M. V. Karasev, V. P. Maslov, *Nonlinear Poisson brackets. Geometry and Quantization.*, Nauka, Moscow, 1991. (Russian)

39. A. Lichnerowicz, *Theo'rie Global des Connexions et de groupes d'holonomie*, Gremonese, 1955.

40. B. A. Dubrovin, S. P. Novikov, A. T. Fomenko, *Recent geometry. Methods in the theory of homologies*, "Nauka", Moscow, 1984. (Russian)

41. V. A. Yakubovich, V. M. Starzhinskiy, *Linear differential equations with periodic coefficients and their applications*, "Nauka", Moscow, 1972. (Russian)

FOUR-DIMENSIONAL INTEGRABLE HAMILTONIAN SYSTEMS WITH SIMPLE SINGULAR POINTS

L. M. LERMAN, JA. L. UMANSKII

The aim of this paper is to describe the structure of an integrable Hamiltonian vector field X_H on an invariant subset V of four-dimensional C^∞-smooth symplectic manifold M, the subset V containing a singular point p of X_H together with all of its orbits for which p is the limit set. Let $H : M \to \mathbb{R}$ be a C^∞-smooth function on M (*Hamiltonian*) and K be an additional (smooth) integral of the field X_H. The pair (X_H, K) is called an *integrable Hamiltonian vector field* (briefly, IHVF) if and only if functions H, K are independent in some open dense subset of M (or in a region under consideration). Let p be a singular point of X_H. Without loss of generality we assume $H(p) = K(p) = 0$. Henceforth we consider eigenvalues of p to be simple. In this case the functions H, K in some coordinate frame have the form

$$H = \lambda_1\xi + \lambda_2\eta + \cdots, \qquad K = \nu_1\xi + \nu_2\eta + \cdots \tag{1}$$

where dots mean terms of order greater than second in (x_1, x_2, y_1, y_2) and

$$\begin{array}{ll}
\xi = (x_1^2 + y_1^2)/2,\ \eta = (x_2^2 + y_2^2)/2 & \text{(elliptic point)}\\
\xi = x_1y_1,\ \eta = (x_2^2 + y_2^2)/2 & \text{(saddle-centre)}\\
\xi = x_1y_1,\ \eta = x_2y_2 & \text{(saddle)}\\
\xi = x_1y_1 + x_2y_2,\ \eta = x_1y_2 - x_2y_1 & \text{(saddle-focus)}
\end{array}$$

A singular point of IHVF is called *simple* if and only if the inequality $\Delta = \lambda_1 \cdot \nu_2 - \lambda_2 \cdot \nu_1 \neq 0$ is fulfilled. If it is the case then there exists a symplectic cordinate frame in which functions H and K may be written in a form $H = h(\xi, \eta)$, $K = k(\xi, \eta)$ [1].

Let now γ be a periodic orbit of X_H and $H(\gamma) = 0$. Such an orbit is called *specific* (SPO) if vector fields X_H and X_K are collinear along γ. Let us make a reduction of X_H by means of integral H (since $X_H \neq 0$) [2]. Then we obtain a family of Hamiltonian systems with one degree of freedom depending on a parameter $h(H = h$ determines a level of Hamiltonian $H)$. If $h = 0$ this system has a singular point which corresponds to γ. In general case a family of reduced Hamiltonians has the following versal forms:

$$1)\ h + x^2 + y^2, \qquad 2)\ h + x^2 - y^2, \qquad 3)\ hx - y^2 + x^3$$

We call SPO *simple* if and only if the corresponding versal family has one of these forms. An orbit will be called elliptic, hyperbolic or parabolic for cases 1), 2) or 3), respectively. A hyperbolic SPO itself may be orientable or nonorientable depending on types of its stable or unstable manifolds (cylinders or Möbius bands).

Throughout the paper we consider IHVF possessing the following properties:

1. The closure of any orbit is compact.
2. The invariant set V in question has only one simple singular point.
3. All SPOs are simple, the set of parabolic SPOs is finite.

To study a structure of IHVF we need some equivalence relation. Usual definition of topological equivalence of two vector fields is too rigid for our purposes because it leads to continuous invariants of a type of rotation numbers on Liouville tori. So we introduce the following defininion.

Definition. Two IHVFs (X_H, K) and $(X_{H'}, K')$ defined on M are isoenergetically equivalent if and only if there exists a homeomrphism $g : M \to M$ which maps each connected component of a level of Hamiltonian H onto that of H', and it maps each component of common levels of functions H and K onto that of H', K'.

Any IHVF (X_H, K) generates Poisson action of the group $\mathbb{R}^2$ on M. On the other hand, if we have a Poisson action of $\mathbb{R}^2$ on M one may select two independent one-parameter subgroups in $\mathbb{R}^2$ which two commuting Hamiltonian vector fields X_H, X_K correspond to. So we obtain IHVF (X_H, K) (and (X_K, H) as well). This allows us to study the structure of action simultaneously with the structure of IHVF.

Below we consider the class of actions which generate IHVF satisfying conditions 1–3, we shall use the usual definition of the topological equivalency of actions.

Let us pass to our main results. Let (X_H, K), $(X_{H'}, K')$ be two IHVFs, p and p' be their singular points of the same type. Throughout below we denote $V_\epsilon = V \cap \{H = \epsilon\}$.

I. Elliptic singular point. In this case the invariant set V is merely a four dimensional ball small enough and containing a singular point, because there are no orbits of IHVF which have a point p in their limit set.

Theorem 1. *There exist variant neighborhoods V and V' for singular points p, p', respectively, such that (X_H, K) is isoenergetically equivalent to $(X_{H'}, K')$ if and only if* $\mathrm{sgn}\lambda_1\lambda_2 = \mathrm{sgn}\lambda_1'\lambda_2'$ *where λ_i, λ_i' are coefficients in* (1).

Proposition 1. *The sets V_ϵ are diffeomorphic to: a) a 3-sphere if $\epsilon \neq 0$ and $V_0 = \{p\}$ for $\lambda_1\lambda_2 > 0$; b) a solid torus if $\epsilon \neq 0$ and a cone over a torus*[1] *if $\epsilon = 0$ for $\lambda_1\lambda_2 < 0$.*

The structure of flow X_H on levels V_ϵ is very simple. In case a) each sphere contains two elliptic SPOs linked with link coefficient 1. Remaining orbits belong to Liouville tori which foliate 3-sphere. In case *b)a* solid torus contains one elliptic SPO (axial circle) remaining set is foliated by Liouville tori. For $\epsilon = 0$ the set V_0 is obtained from V_ϵ by identifying the axial circle in a solid torus with p.

Theorem 2. *Two actions Φ_1, Φ_2 with elliptic singular points are always topologically equivalent in some invariant neigbourhoods of its singular points.*

II. Saddle–centre. In this case there exist only two orbits containing singular point p in their closure. These orbits are homoclinic to p and form two loops. Suppose $H(p) = 0$ then $H = 0$ on each loop.

Proposition 2. *For $\mid \epsilon \mid$ small enough there exist two symplectic two-dimensional submanifolds Σ_1, Σ_2 which intersect transversally at p, and contain all SPOs passing near p. Submanifold Σ_2 is a disk foliated by hyperbolic SPOs which lay in levels $H = h$ for $h \geq 0$ only (or $h \leq 0$ only). Submanifold Σ_1 is diffeomorphic to a disk with two disks removed (two holes). Σ_1 contains two loops, each loop surrounds one hole. Two loops divide Σ_2 into two parts corresponding to $H > 0$ and $H < 0$, respectively. One part is diffeomorphic to an annulus foliated with elliptic SPOs ("long" SPOs). Another part is diffeomrphic to disjoined union of two annuli foliated with elliptic SPOs which lie by pairsin each level of H ("short" SPOs).*

Let Hamiltonian H be positive at Σ_2 for definiteness. So for $\mid \epsilon \mid$ small enough we have two cases:

A. The level $H = \epsilon$, $\epsilon > 0$, contains one hyperbolic SPO and one long elliptic SPO.

B. The level $H = \epsilon$, $\epsilon > 0$, contains one hyperbolic and two short elliptic SPOs.

Theorem 3. *There exist invariant neighborhoods V, V' containing each their own loops such that IHVFs (X_H, K) and $(X_{H'}, K')$ are isoenergetically equivalent if and only if they correspond to the same case* A *or* B *takes place.*

Proposition 3. *In the case* A *the sets V_ϵ are diffeomorphic to:* 1) *connected sum of two solid tori for $\epsilon > 0$;* 2) *bouquet of two solid tori (glued by their inner points) for $\epsilon = 0$;* 3) *a union of two disjoint solid tori for $\epsilon < 0$. In the case* B *the sets V_ϵ are diffeomorphic to:* 1) *a connected sum of solid torus and $S^2 \times S^1$ (S^n being n-sphere) for $\epsilon > 0$;* 2) *a solid torus with two inner*

[1]It means that a set $T^2 \times I$ in which a boundary $T^2 \times \{1\}$ is identifyed to a point.

points identified for $\epsilon = 0$; 3) a solid torus for $\epsilon < 0$. The boundary ∂V of V is homeomorphic to a connected sum of two $S^2 \times S^1$.

Theorem 4. *Two actions Φ_1, Φ_2 with saddle-centre singular points are always topologically equivalent in some invariant neighborhoods of their loops.*

III. Saddle. Let p be a saddle singular point. From conditions 1–3 it follows that all orbits which belong to the stable manifold of p simultaneously lie in its unstable manifold, i.e. they are homoclinic ones. The closure W of the stable manifold is two-dimensional cellular complex. Among homoclinic orbits on W there exist exactly four orbits $\gamma_1, \dots, \gamma_4$ such that the fields X_H and X_K are collinear along these orbits. We call such orbits *loops*. As it is proved in [3], stable and unstable manifolds of p intersect transversally along loops within the three-dimensional level $H = 0$. This allows us to introduce the notion of orientability and nonorientability of a loop.

Proposition 4. *There exist exactly two 2-dimensional symplectic manifolds Σ_1, Σ_2 intersecting transversally at p. These Σ_1, Σ_2 contain four loops and all SPOs passing near p. Two loops belong to Σ_1 and two others belong to Σ_2. Another orbits in Σ_1, Σ_2 are hyperbolic SPOs and the orbit structure of the field X_H is the same as for the manifold Σ_1 in Proposition 2.*

Proposition 5. *Only four cases may occur: 1) all loops are orientable; 2) all loops are nonorientable; 3) three loops are orientable and one loop is nonorientable; 4) two loops in Σ_i are orientable and another two loops lying in Σ_j are nonorientable, $i \neq j$.*

The set of loops is not a full invariant of isoenergetical equivalency. Nevertheless the following statement is valid.

Theorem 5. *Two Poisson action Φ_1, Φ_2 with saddle singular points are topologically equivalent in some invariant neighborhood of W, W', respectively, if and only if they correspond to the same case of Proposition 5.*

To find conditions of isoenergetical equivalence we need to know more about the structure of orbits of X_H in the levels $H = \epsilon$. As it follows from Proposition 4 only two possibilities may occur:

A. The level $H = \epsilon \neq 0$ contains four short SPOs then level $H = -\epsilon$ contains two long SPOs.

B. Both levels $H = \epsilon$ and $H = -\epsilon$ contain three SPOs (two shorts and one long).

Thus, talking into account Proposition 5, we have 8 possible cases nA, nB, $n = \overline{1,4}$.

Theorem 6. *There exist invariant neighborhoods $V \supset W$, $V' \supset W'$ such that IHVFs (X_H, K) and $(X_{H'}, K')$ are isoenergetically equivalent if and only if they correspond to the same case nA or nB.*

To describe the topology of V_ϵ and its foliations by the level surfaces of the function K we shall present the following construction. Let N be a smooth two-dimensional manifold, f be a smooth function on N and Q be a connected compact component of the level line $f = 0$. We denote B the connected submanifold of N which is determined by the inequality $\mid f \mid \leq C$ for C small enough and such that $Q \subset B$. Additionally we assume that some smooth involution G ($G^2 = id$) acts on B. Let us define a three-dimensional manifold P with boundary which is a bundle with the base S^1 (a circle), a leaf B and with group $\{id, G\}$ acting on B as the structural group of a bundle (if $G = id$ then P is the direct product $S^1 \times B$). This manifold P posseses a foliation generated by the function F which is a natural continuation of f to P. Henceforth the manifold P with its foliation will be called the *model manifold.*

Let $k = k_i(\epsilon)$, $i = 1, 2$, be smooth functions which define the bifurcation diagram, i.e. the image of Σ_i under the mapping $z \to (\epsilon, k) \to (H(z), K(z))$, $z \in V$. Then the curve $k = k_m(\epsilon) = (k_1(\epsilon) + k_2(\epsilon))/2$ in the plane (ϵ, k) is situated between the graphs of $k = k_1(\epsilon)$ and $k = k_2(\epsilon)$. It is readily to check that V_ϵ is divided into two pieces V_ϵ^1, V_ϵ^2 by the level $K = k_m(\epsilon)$. For each piece V_ϵ^i we build the model manifold and point out how to glue these manifolds. For $\epsilon \neq 0$ this construction is close to that of [4]. The connected component of V_ϵ^i, $\epsilon \neq 0$, may be represented by means of the following 5 model manifolds.

$$P_1 : N = \mathbb{R}^2,\ f = y^2 - x^2(1 - x^2),\ C = 1/4,\ G = id$$
$$P_2 : N = \mathbb{R}^2,\ f = y^2 - (1 - x^2)^2(4 - x^2),\ C = 1,\ G = id$$
$$P_3 : N = S^2 = \{(x, y, z) \mid x^2 + y^2 + z^2 = 1\},\ f = yz,\ C = 1/2,\ G = id$$
$$P_4 : N = \mathbb{R}^2,\ f = y^2 - x^2(1 - x^2),\ C = 1/4,\ G : (x, y) \mapsto (-x, -y)$$
$$P_5 : N = S^2 = \{(x, y, z) \mid x^2 + y^2 + z^2 = 1\},\ f = yz,\ C = 1/2,$$
$$G : (x, y, z) \mapsto (x, -y, -z)$$

Each manifold P_i will be symbolically depicted by a graph (see Fig.1). The vertices of that graph correspond to boundary tori $F = \pm C$. Two vertices are joined with an edge if there is a trajectory of the vector field $-\text{grad}\ F$ passing through the corresponding tori. Under such an agreement P_4 and P_5 would have the same graph. To distinguish them we use two edges for P_5.

Wholly the manifold V_ϵ is built with gluing the model manifolds along their boundary tori in accordance with Fig.2. This gluing is rigidly defined by a behaviour of trajectories of the vector field $Y = -\text{grad}\ K$ on V_ϵ. The set V_0 is a submanifold with a singularity at the point p which is a singular point for the field Y. All the points of loops $\gamma_1 - \gamma_4$ are singular points of Y and the stable manifolds of the loops intersect each level $K = k > 0$ along a set of smooth closed curves. If $k \to +0$ these curves tend to $\cup\gamma_i$ and corresponding Liouville tori $K = k$, $H = 0$ turn into W. For $k < 0$ a similar deformation occurs along unstable manifolds of loops $\gamma_1 - \gamma_4$.

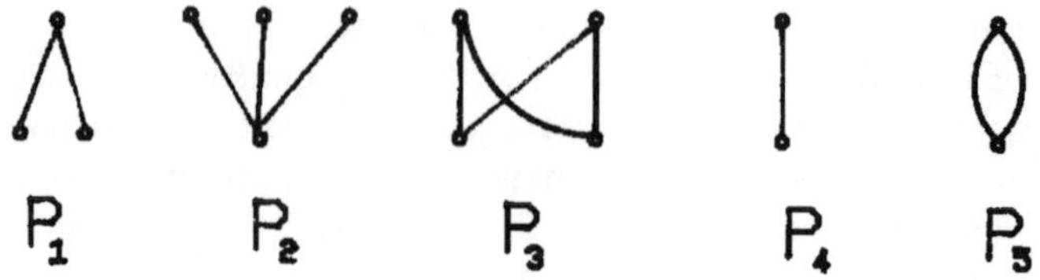

Fig. 1

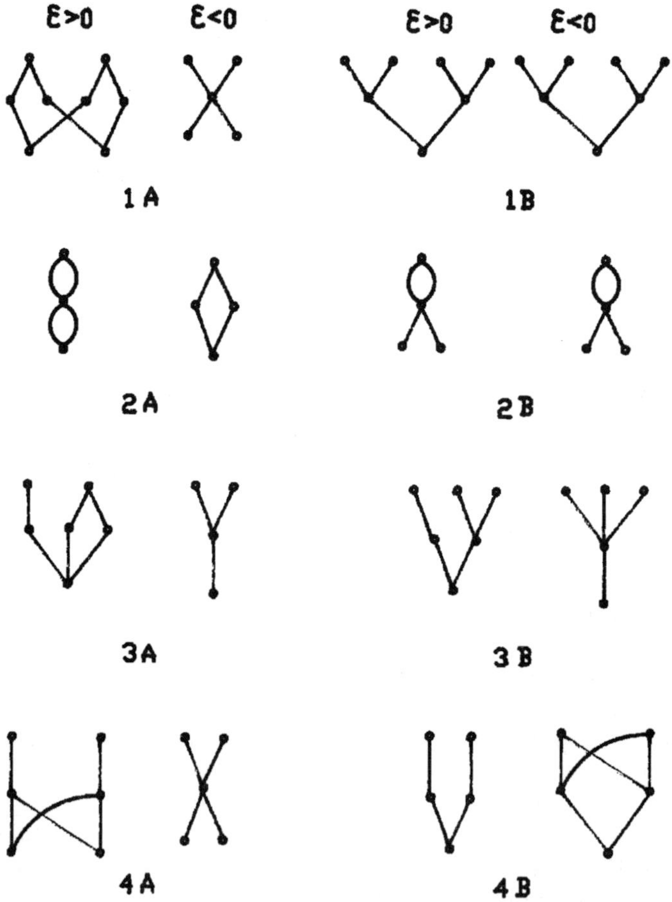

Fig. 2

IV. Saddle-focus. It follows from (1) that there exists a neighborhood U of p where fields X_H and X_K are linear independent (excepting point p). Within U all orbits of X_H, which contain p in their limit set, belong to the stable manifold W^s or the unstable manifold W^u of the point p. Under the prolongation along orbits the manifold W^u can merge with W^s or with a part of the stable manifold $W^s(\gamma)$ for some SPO γ lying out of U in the same level of Hamiltonian. Such an SPO must be hyperbolic or parabolic. According to these possibilities we shall consider the following cases:

1. W^u merges with W^s.
2. W^u merges with a component of the set $W^s(\gamma)\backslash\gamma$ of a hyperbolic orientable SPO γ.
3. W^u merges with $W^s(\gamma)$ of a hyperbolic nonorientable SPO γ.
4. W^u merges with $W^s(\gamma)$ of a parabolic SPO γ.

For the sake of simplicity we assume further that unstable manifold of γ merges with W^s in cases 3 and 4. As for case 2 we suppose W^s merges with a component of $W^u(\gamma)\backslash\gamma$ and another component of $W^u(\gamma)\backslash\gamma$ merges with a free component of $W^s(\gamma)\backslash\gamma$. Let W be the closure of the set $W^u(\gamma)$ (case 1) or the set $W^u(\gamma)\cup W^s(\gamma)\cup W^u\cup W^s$(cases 2–4).

Theorem 7. *There are invariant neighborhoods $V\supset W$, $V'\supset W'$ such that IHVFs (X_H,K) and $(X_{H'},K')$ are isoenergetically equivalent if and only if they correspond to the same case 1–4.*

The same assertions are valid for two Poisson actions with saddle-focus singular points.

Topology of sets V_ϵ and its foliation by levels of the function K will be described by means of its model manifolds for each case 1–4 (see construction in Sec.3). Denote P/l the factor-space of a manifold P obtained by shrinking a smooth closed curve $l\in\mathrm{int}P$ to a point. If P is a model manifold and l belongs to some level surface F=const then F is defined naturally in P/l. We also denote this function F.

Case 1. i) $\epsilon=0$. Here we take the model manifold P_4. Then $V_0=P_4/l$ where l corresponds to a circle which is determined by a point $(0,0)\in B$. ii) $\epsilon\neq 0$. Here the model manifold is defined by fixing $f(x,y)=x^2+y^2-1$, $c=1/2$, G=*id*.

Case 2. i). $\epsilon=0$. Here $f(x,y)=y^2-x^2(1-x^2)^2(4-x^2)$, $c=1/10$, $G(x,y)=(-x,-y)$. Thus we obtain the model manifold P. Then $V_0=P/l$ where l corresponds to a circle which is determined by the point $(0,0)\in B$. ii) $\epsilon\neq 0$. Here V_ϵ is diffeomorphic to the model manifold P_1.

Case 3. i) $\epsilon=0$. Here the model manifold is P_5. Then $V_0=P_5/l$ where l is the circle given by the singular point (1,0,0) of the function f. ii) $\epsilon\neq 0$. Here V_ϵ is diffeomorphic to the model manifold P_4.

Case 4. Topology of V_0 and V_ϵ is the same as in Case 1 but the function f is different. Namely $f(x,y)=y^2-x^2(1-x^2)^3$, $G:(x,y)\to(-x,-y)$, for $\epsilon=0$. Let assume for defineteness that hyperbolic and elliptic SPOs emerge from parabolic one for $\epsilon > 0$. Then we can take $f = y^2 - x^2(1-x)(1/2+x)$ for c small enough, G=*id*. For $\epsilon < 0$ let us choose $f = x^2 + y^2 - 1, \quad c = 1/2, \quad G$=*id.*

References

1. Elliasson L. H., *Normal forms for Hamiltonian systems with Poisson commuting integrals — elliptic case*, Comment. Math. Helv. **65** (1990), 4–35.
2. Marsden J. R., Weinstein A., *Reduction of symplectic manifolds with symmetry*, Repts Math. Phys. **5** (1974), no. 14, 121–130.
3. Lerman L. M., Umanskii Ya. L., *Integrable Hamiltonian systems and Poisson actions*, Selecta Math. Sovietica **9** (1990), no. 1, 59–67, (transl. from Russian text of 1984).
4. Fomenko A. T., *Topology of surfaces of constant energy of integrable Hamiltonian systems and obstacles to integrability*, USSR Math. Izvestiya **50** (1986), no. 6, 67–75. (in Russian)

THE PERIODIC POINTS AND SYMBOLIC DYNAMICS

G. Osipenko

1. Introduction

At present the methods of symbolic dynamics have wide applications. One of the variants of the junctions of the symbolic dynamics and the numerical methods of differential equations is presented. Usually the constructions of periodic trajectories of dynamical systems are based on the theory of perturbations. A general method of their construction is the following. Assuming a periodic orbit of an unperturbed system to be known one constructs a sequence of approximate periodic orbits which tend to a periodic one of perturbed system. Thus knowledge of a periodic orbit of unperturbed system is a necessary condition for the construction of such a sequence. The aim of present paper is to give an algorithm for the determination of periodic trajectory without any preliminary information about a system. A proposed construction is based on the methods of symbolic dynamics. The common scheme of our method is the following. At first, we associate to a dynamical system an oriented graph which is called symbolic image of the system. It can be said that the symbolic image is a finite approximation of the dynamical system. The investigation of the symbolic image gives an opportunity to separate the points which periodic trajectories may pass through from those which periodic trajectories may not pass through. To be more precise the method gives a possibility to locate a chain recurrent set which includes returning trajectories of all types. During the process of localization of chain recurrent points we obtain the approximate periodic trajectories. While choosing one of them we find a periodic trajectory using some method similar to one of the perturbations theory. The proposed construction is close to Cell-Mapping [1].

2. Localization of the chain recurrent trajectories set

Let M be a compact Riemannian manifold and f be a C^1 vector field on M which does not vanish. On M we have a smooth dynamical system

$$\dot{x} = f(x). \tag{1}$$

Denote by $X(t,x)$ the solution of this system. We use the usual convention $X(0,x) = x$. Let us fix some positive t_0 and set $X(x) = X(t_0, x)$. Obviously, $X : M \to M$ is diffeomorphism.

Definition 1. An infinite sequence $\{x_k\}$ is called a ε-trajectory of X if for any k the distance between the image $X(x_k)$ and x_{k+1} is less than ε:

$$\rho\big(X(x_k), x_{k+1}\big) < \varepsilon.$$

If the sequence $\{x_k\}$ is periodic then it is called a periodic ε-trajectory and points x_k are called ε-periodic.

In the majority of cases an exact trajectory of the system is seldom known, and in fact we find only ε-trajectory for sufficiently small positive ε. Denote the set of ε-periodic points by $Q(\varepsilon)$. It is clear that if $\varepsilon_1 > \varepsilon_2 > 0$ then every ε_2-trajectory is ε_1-trajectory, hence $Q(\varepsilon_2) \subset Q(\varepsilon_1)$. It can be shown that the set $Q(\varepsilon)$ is open.

Definition 2. A point x is called chain recurrent if x is ε-periodic for every positive ε, i.e. there exists a periodic ε-trajectiry passing through x.

The set of chain recurrent points is called a chain recurrent set and is denoted by Q. It is not difficult to show that the chain recurrent set is invariant, closed and contains periodic trajectories, almost-periodic trajectories, recurrent trajectories and other singular trajectories. It should be remarked that if a chain recurrent point is not periodic then there exists a ε-perturbation of homeomorphism X in C^0-topology for which this point is periodic. One may say that a chain recurrent point becomes periodic under small C^0-perturbation of the mapping X. From definition of the chain recurrent set it follows that

$$Q = \lim_{\varepsilon \to 0} Q(\varepsilon) = \cap_{\varepsilon > 0} Q(\varepsilon).$$

The construction of the symbolic image [4].

Let $C = \{M(1), ..., M(n)\}$ be a finite covering of the domain M by the closed sets. The set $M(i)$ is called a cell of the covering. For any i we define a covering $C(i)$ of the image $X(M(i))$ consisting of cells $M(j)$ from C whose intersections with $X(M(i))$ are non-empty, i.e.

$$C(i) = \{M(j) : M(j) \cap X(M(i)) \neq \varnothing\}.$$

The cells of the covering $C(i)$ are called the image cells of cell $M(i)$ under the mapping X. Let us construct the oriented graph G, associating to each cell $M(i)$ the vertex i. The vertexes i and j are connected by an oriented edge $i \to j$ only in case if the cell $M(j)$ is included in the covering $C(i)$, i.e. the cell $M(j)$ is the image cell of $M(i)$.

Definition 3. The graph G is called a symbolic image of X with respect to the covering C.

It is easily seen that the symbolic image depends on the covering C. Varying the covering C we can change the symbolic image as a finite appromaximation of the mapping X. This approximation is more precise if the mesh of the covering is smaller. Let

$$\text{diam} M(i) = \max\left(\rho(x, y) : x, y \in M(i)\right)$$

be a diameter of cell $M(i)$, where $\rho(x, y)$ is a distance between points x and y on M. Let d be the largest diameter of the cells $M(i)$ of the covering C. Denote by

$$R_i = \{\cup M(j) : M(j) \in C(i)\}$$

a union of the cells $M(j)$ belonging to the covering $C(i)$. By definition R_i contains the image $X(M(i))$ of the cell $M(i)$ and itself is contained in the closed d-neighborhood of the image $X\,(M(i))$:

$$X(M(i)) \subset R_i \subset cl\,\{\text{d-neighborhood of} \quad X(M(i))\} \\ = \{x : \min(\rho(x, y), y \in X(M(i))) \leq d\}\,.$$

Let q be the largest diameter of the images $X(M(i))$. We define the number r as follows. If a cell $M(k)$ does not belong to the covering $C(i)$ then the distance

$$r_{ik} = \rho(X(M(i)), M(k)) = \min(\rho(x, y) : x \in X(M(i)), y \in M(k)))$$

between the cell $M(k)$ and the image $X(M(i))$ is positive. Let r be minimum of such r_{ik}. Since the number of the pairs (i, k) described above is finite then $r > 0$. Clearly, the number r is the smallest distance between the image $X(M(i))$ and the cells $M(k)$ for which $M(k) \cap X(M(i)) = \varnothing$. The number r is called a lower bound of the symbolic image G. It is clear that the lower bound depends on the covering C. Changing the covering C we can construct a covering for which the lower bound r is arbitrarily small.

Proposition 1. *If a point x belongs to a cell $M(j)$ and the distance between x and the image $X(M(i))$ is less than r then the cell $M(j)$ belongs to the covering $C(i)$.*

Proposition 2. *The lower bound satisfies the inequality $r \leq d$.*

The structure of the symbolic image.

Definition 4. The sequence $\{z_k\}$ of the vertexes of the graph G is called an admissible path or simply a path if for any k the graph G contains the edge $z_k \rightarrow z_{k+1}$.

Proposition 3. *If a sequence $\{z_k\}$ is a path on the symbolic image G and $x_k \in M(z_k)$ then the sequence $\{x_k\}$ is ε-trajectory of the diffeomorphism X for any $\varepsilon > q + d$.*

Corollary 4. *If a sequence* $\{z_1, z_2, ..., z_m\}$ *of vertexes is periodic path and* $x_k \in M(z_k)$ *then the sequence* $\{x_1, x_2, ..., x_m\}$ *is* ε*-periodic trajectory for any* $\varepsilon > d + q$.

Proposition 5. *If a sequence* $\{x_k\}$ *is a* ε*-trajectory of the diffeomorphism* X, $\varepsilon < r$ *and* $x_k \in M(z_k)$ *then the sequence* $\{z_k\}$ *is an admissible path on the symbolic image* G.

Corollary 6. *If a sequence* $\{x_1, x_2, ...x_m\}$ *is* ε*-periodic trajectory,* $\varepsilon < r$ *and* $x_k \in M(z_k)$ *then the sequence* $\{z_1, z_2, ..., z_m\}$ *is a periodic path on the symbolic image* G.

Definition 5. A vertex of the symbolic image is called recurrent if a periodic path passes through it.

Let us denote by $P(d)$ the union of cells $M(i)$ for which the vertexes i are recurrent, i.e.

$$P(d) = \{\cup M(i) : i \quad \text{are recurrent}\},$$

where d is the largest diameter of the cells $M(i)$. It should be noted that in fact the set P depends on the covering C. However, in what follows we need only to consider the dependence of P on the largest diameter d. Let us denote by T the union of the cells $M(k)$ for which the vertexes k are not recurrent:

$$T = \{\cup M(k) : k \quad \text{are not recurrent}\}.$$

Theorem 7. *1) The set* $P(d)$ *is a closed neighborhood of the chain recurrent set. Moreover, if the maximum diameter* d *is small enough this neighborhood is sufficiently small.*

2) The chain recurrent set Q *coincides with an intersection of the sets* $P(d)$ *for all positive* d*:*

$$Q = \cap_{d>0} P(d).$$

3) The points of T *are not chain recurrent. Moreover, if* $\varepsilon < r$ *there is no period* ε*-trajectory passing through the point* x *from* T*, i.e.*

$$Q(\varepsilon) \cap T = 0, \qquad \varepsilon < r.$$

Notice that Theorem 7 and Corollary 6 lead to the following inclusions

$$Q \subset Q(\varepsilon_1) \subset M \setminus T = P(d) \setminus T \subset P(d) \subset Q(\varepsilon_2),$$

where $\varepsilon_1 < r < q + d < \varepsilon_2$. The set T is closed by construction. Hence the set $P(d) \setminus T$ is an open neighborhood of the chain recurrent set Q.

Theorem 7 makes it possible to realize localization of the chain recurrent set without preliminary information.

The algorithm of localization of chain recurrent set.

1) We start with an initial covering C. For the covering C the symbolic image G of the map X is found. Notice that the cells of the initial covering C may have sufficiently big diameter d_0.

2) The recurrent vertexes $\{i_k\}$ of the constructed graph G are recognized. The closed neighborhood P of the chain recurrent set is constructed using the recurrent vertexes.

3) The cells corresponding to the recurrent vertexes $\{M(i_k)\}$ are exposed to a partition. For example, the largest diameter d may be divided by 2. Thus the new covering is found.

4) The symbolic image G is constructed for new covering. It must be remarked that the new symbolic image may be constructed on the set $P = \{\cup M(i_k) : i_k \text{ are recurrent}\}$. In other words, the cells corresponding to non-recurrent vertexes do not participate in the construction of the new symbolic image G.

5) Then one must go back to the second step.

Repeating this process of the partition we obtain the sequence of the neighborhoods $P_0, P_1, P_2, \ldots$ of the chain recurrent set Q with the largest diameters $d_0, d_1, d_2, \ldots$.

Theorem 8. *1) The described algorithm defines the sequence of imbedded neighborhoods $P_0 \subset P_1 \subset P_2 \subset \ldots$ of the chain recurrent set Q.*

2) If the largest diameters $d_k \to 0$ as k becomes infinite then

$$\lim_{k\to\infty} P_k = \cap_k P_k = Q.$$

3 Construction of periodic trajectory

The preceding discussion of symbolic image of dynamical system gives the possibility to construct the periodic ε-trajectories for any sufficiently small ε without preliminary information about a system. Let the sequence of points $\{x_k\}$ be a periodic ε-trajectory. Then two problems arise.

1. Does a periodic trajectory of the diffeomorphism X exist near the periodic ε-trajectory $\{x_k\}$?

2. If the answer to the first question is positive can the periodic trajectory of X be obtained in a constructive manner? To solve these problems we introduce notion of linear extension of the symbolic image.

Linear extension over the synbolic image.

For an oriented edge $i \to j$ of the symbolic image G there exists a point $x(i,j)$ such that $x(i,j) \in M(i)$ and the image $X(x(i,j)) \in M(j)$. We say that the pair $x(i,j) \to X(x(i,j))$ realizes the oriented edge $i \to$j. It is easily seen that the point $x(i,j)$ is not determined uniquely. Any point from the set $M(i) \cap X^{-1}(M(j))$ can be taken as $x(i,j)$. Let

$$dX(x_{ij}) : TM(x_{ij}) \to TM(X(x_{ij}))$$

be a differential of the diffeomorphism X from the tangent space TM at the point $x(i,j)$ to the tangent space TM at the image $X(x(i,j))$. In the tangent space $TM(x)$ it is convenient to select a coordinate system with the first vector v_1 equal to $f(x)$. Others vectors $\{v_2, ...v_m\}$ form a basis in the plane orthogonal to v_1. In this basis the differential is of a form

$$dX(x(i,j)) = \begin{pmatrix} 1 & \cdots \\ 0 & A(j,i) \end{pmatrix},$$

where $A(j,i)$ is a liner mapping. Let us associate to each oriented edge $i \to j$ the linear mapping $A(j,i)$. The linear mapping $A(j,i)$ is not defined uniquely by the construction. The non-uniqueness is caused by the selection of the point $x(i,j)$. The further development requires the consideration of the covering with sufficiently small cells. Namely, the largest diameter d ought to be small enough to ensure the identification of the tangent spaces in different points of a cell. This allows us to associate to each vertex i the linear space $T(i)$ which is a copy of the tangent space $TM(x(i,j))$.

Definition 6. The oriented graph G together with the linear spaces $\{T(i)\}$ and the linear mappings $\{A(j,i)\}$ is called a linear extension of symbolic image.

The linear extension is denoted by LG. The linear extension of symbolic image can be regarded as a finite approximation of the differential dX. Consider a periodic path $w = \{z_1, z_2, ..., z_k\}$ on the symbolic image G, where k is its smallest period. For this periodic path let us construct the linear operator

$$A(w) = A(z_1, z_k)A(z_k, z_{k-1})...A(z_2, z_1).$$

Definition 7. The periodic path w is called nondegenerate if eigenvalues of the linear operator $A(w)$ are different from 1.

One can show that there exists a function F (natural for this problem) depending on C^1 norm $\|X\|$, the largest diameter d, the module of continuity α of dX, a norm of the matrix $(I - A(w))^{-1}$ and a period k such that if a periodic path w is nondegenerate and the largest diameter d is small enough to ensure

$$F(\|X\|, d, \alpha(d), |\ (I - A(w))^{-1}\ |, k) < 1,$$

then the system of differential equations (1) has periodic trajectory near periodic ε-trajectory

$$\{X([0, t_0], x(z_j, z_{j+1}))\ |\ j = 1, ..., k\}.$$

The computer programs realizing the above stated algorithm have been created by the author. The method proposed here permits also to check the transversality condition on the chain recurrent trajectories [5].

References

[1] C. S. Hsu, *Cell-to-sell Mapping*, Springer-Verlag, N.Y., 1987.
[2] P. Hartman, *Ordinary Differential Equations*, N.Y., 1964.
[3] Z. Nitecki, *Differential Dynamics*, London, 1971.
[4] G. S. Osipenko, *On the symbolical image of the dynamic system*, Boundary value problems, Perm, 1983, pp. 101–105 (In Russian).
[5] G. S. Osipenko, *Test of the transversality condition by the methods of symbolical dynamics*, Differential Equations, n.**9** (1990), pp. 1528–1536 (In Russian).

State Technical University, St.Petersburg, Russia

ON THE PERTURBATION OF INVARIANT MANIFOLDS

EUGENY ERSHOV, GEORGE OSIPENKO

1. INTRODUCTION

Let us consider an autonomous system of ordinary differential equations of class C^1

$$\frac{dx}{dt} = F(x), \tag{1.1}$$

where x is n-dimensional vector. Let $f_t(x)$, $x \in \mathbb{R}^n$, be the flow generated by system (1.1). Suppose that system (1.1) has a compact C^1 submanifold $M \subset \mathbb{R}^n$ without boundary invariant under f_t (i.e. $f_t(M) = M$ for all $t \in \mathbb{R}$). For the sake of simplicity in what follows such a submanifold is called an invariant manifold of system (1.1) or of the vector field F.

Several authors [1–4] have studied necessary and sufficient conditions under which for every vector field G nearby F there exists a submanifold M_G nearby M satisfying $g_t(M_G) = M_G$, where g_t is the flow generated by vector field G. Usually an invariant manifold is assumed to be locally unique in the following sense.

Definition 1.1. We say that the invariant manifold M of system (1.1) is *locally unique* if there exist a neighborhood U of M in $\mathbb{R}^n$ and a neighborhood V of F in $C^1(\mathbb{R}^n, \mathbb{R}^n)$ such that for all $G \in V$ the maximal contained in U invariant set

$$M_G = \bigcap_{t \in \mathbb{R}} g_t(U)$$

of the perturbed system

$$\frac{dx}{dt} = G(x), \tag{1.2}$$

is a C^1 submanifold diffeomorphic to M and $M_F = M$.

The following concept of preservation of invariant manifold is generally accepted [4].

Definition 1.2. Invariant manifold M of system (1.1) is called *persistent* if
(a) it is locally unique,
(b) M_G is C^1 near to M if G is C^1 near to F.

Let us denote by W a neighborhood of M in the space of C^1 submanifolds of $\mathbb{R}^n$ endowed with C^1 topology.

Notice that if M is persistent then there exists the map $H : V \to W$ associating to every $G \in V$ invariant manifold M_G of perturbed system (1.2), i.e. $H(G) = M_G$. If M is persistent, then H is uniquely determined and continuous at F. In fact one may show that H is continuous in the whole neighborhood V.

Persistent manifolds admit a nice description. The next result was obtained by R. Sacker [2], Yu. Neimark [3] and R. Mañé [4].

Theorem 1.1. *Invariant manifold M of system (1.1) is persistent if and only if it is normally hyperbolic.*

The normal hyperbolicity of M means that there exist a continuous splitting

$$T\mathbb{R}^n|_M = TM \oplus E^s \oplus E^u, \tag{1.3}$$

invariant with respect to the tangent map Df_t, and constants $K, \lambda > 0$ such that for all $x \in M$ the following inequalities take place:

$$\|Df_t^s\| \leq Ke^{-\lambda t}, \qquad \|Df_t^s\| \quad \|(Df_t^0)^{-1}\| \leq Ke^{-\lambda t}$$

for $t \geq 0$;

$$\|Df_t^u\| \leq Ke^{\lambda t}, \qquad \|Df_t^u\| \quad \|(Df_t^s)^{-1}\| \leq Ke^{\lambda t}$$

for $t \leq 0$, where

$$Df_t^s = Df_t\,|_{E^s}, \quad Df_t^u = Df_t\,|_{E^u}, \quad Df_t^0 = Df_t^0\,|_{TM}\,.$$

Notice that the sum in (1.3) is direct.

The aim of the present article is to consider the perturbation of invariant manifolds, which are not locally unique and therefore are not persistent. We examine the various phenomena arising under the perturbation of such manifolds. In Section 2 we give the necessary definitions and formulate the main results. In Section 3 we consider the dynamical systems illustrating the results of Section 2. The construction of examples of dynamical systems is based on two principles: their simplicity and the illustration of wide variety of phenomena.

2. Definitions and some results

First of all we introduce a weaker type of preservation of invariant manifold than its persistence [5].

Definition 2.1. Invariant manifold M of system (1.1) is called *indestructible* if

(a) there exist a neighborhood U of M in $\mathbb{R}^n$ and a neighborhood V of F in $C^1(\mathbb{R}^n, \mathbb{R}^n)$ such that for all $G \in V$ system (1.2) has at least one invariant (not necessarily maximal invariant) manifold $M_G \subset U$ diffeomorphic to M,

(b) there exists a continuous at F map $H : V \to W$ such that $H(G) = M_G$, $H(F) = M$.

It should be noted that in general the map H is not uniquely determined and cannot be chosen continuous in the whole neighborhood V.

Obviously, persistent manifold is indestructible. The following example shows that the converse is not true.

Example 2.1. On the real line $\mathbb{R}^1$ consider a differential equation

$$\frac{dx}{dt} = F(x) = x^3. \tag{2.1}$$

Equation (2.1) has an invariant manifold M, which is an equilibrium point $x = 0$. M is indestructible since the index of O is distinct from zero and therefore, every equation C^1 near to (2.1) has at least one equilibrium point near to O. But M is not persistent since the maximal invariant set of a perturbed equation lying in some neighborhood of O may contain more than one point. Clearly, the map H is not uniquely determined.

Equation (2.1) gives also an example of a system for which H cannot be chosen continuous in V entirely. To prove this consider the C^1 function

$$G(x) = \begin{cases} (x+\alpha)^3, & x < -\alpha \\ 0, & -\alpha < x < \alpha \\ (x-\alpha)^3, & x > \alpha \end{cases} .$$

It is easy to see that H is not continuous at G. In fact, the equation

$$\frac{dx}{dt} = G(x) + \delta$$

for $\delta > 0$ has the unique equilibrium point O_1 with x-coordinate $\alpha_1(\delta) < -\alpha$ and for $\delta < 0$ the unique equilibrium point O_2 with x-coordinate $\alpha_2(\delta) > \alpha$. Hence, $H(G+\delta) = \alpha_1(\delta)$ for $\delta > 0$ and $H(G+\delta) = \alpha_2(\delta)$ for $\delta < 0$. It follows from this that

$$\lim_{\delta \to +0} H(G+\delta) = -\alpha, \qquad \lim_{\delta \to -0} H(G+\delta) = \alpha.$$

Since the left and the right limits do not coincide then H is not continuous at G independently of the choice of $H(G)$.

This example makes natural the following definitions.

Definition 2.2. Invariant manifold M of system (1.1) is called *strongly indestructible* if it is indestructible and there exists the continuous map $H : V \to$

W $(H(G) = M_G)$ such that if M is an invariant manifold of perturbed system (1.2) then $H(G) = M$.

Definition 2.3. Invariant manifold M of system (1.1) is called *weakly indestructible* if it is indestructible and for every neighborhood V of F there exist $G \in V$ such that M is an invariant manifold of system (1.2), but it is not indestructible manifold of this system.

It is not difficult to verify that the invariant manifold $M = \{O\}$ of Equation (2.1) gives an example of a weakly indestructible manifold.

In practice the dynamical systems are known with some degree of inaccuracy. Therefore, it is important to investigate namely the class of strongly indestructible manifolds, since a small perturbation of $G \in V$ involves a small change of M_G.

The next results were recently obtained by one of the authors [5]. To give the precise statements define the linear subspaces

$$E_x^s = \{v \in T_x\mathbb{R}^n : \|Df_t(x)v\| \to 0, \\ \|Df_t(x)v\| \cdot \|(Df_t^0(x))^{-1}\| \to 0 \quad \text{as} \quad t \to +\infty\},$$

$$E_x^u = \{v \in T_x\mathbb{R}^n : \|Df_t(x)v\| \to 0, \\ \|Df_t(x)v\| \cdot \|(Df_t^0(x))^{-1}\| \to 0 \quad \text{as} \quad t \to -\infty\}.$$

Here $x \in M$, $T_x\mathbb{R}^n$ is the tangent space to $\mathbb{R}^n$ at x.

Definition 2.4. We say that the transversality condition holds at $x \in M$ if

$$T_x\mathbb{R}^n = T_xM + E_x^s + E_x^u. \tag{2.1}$$

Observe that if the sum in (2.1) is direct for all $x \subset M$ then M is normally hyperbolic.

Now we shall give the notion of a strong sink (source). At first we consider the case of an equilibrium point. Let $O \in M$ be an equilibrium point of system (1.1). For μ, ν $(\mu < \nu)$ denote by

$$I(\mu, \nu) = \{\lambda \in \mathbb{C} : \mu \leq \text{Re}\lambda \leq \nu\}$$

the strip of the complex plane $\mathbb{C}$.

Definition 2.5. We say that the condition of spectral separation holds at O if in some local coordinates the Jacobian matrix $DF(O)$ of F at O takes the form $DF(O) = \text{diag}(D_1, D_2)$, where $D_1 = DF(O)\mid_{TM}$, and there exist μ, ν such that

$$\text{Spect}(D_1) \subset I(\mu, \nu), \qquad \text{Spect}(D_2) \subset \mathbb{C}\backslash I(\mu, \nu).$$

If in addition $\mu \leq 0 \leq \nu$ then O is normally hyperbolic. If $\nu < 0$ (resp. $\mu > 0$) then O is called a *strong sink* (resp. *strong source*).

If O is normally hyperbolic then in the direction transversal to M $Df_t(O)$ contracts (expands) greater than in the direction of M. If O is a strong sink (resp. strong source) then O is a sink (resp. source) of the restriction of F on M and the contraction (resp. expansion) in the direction of M may be greater than in the transversal direction.

Definition 2.6. O is called non-degenerate if $0 \notin \mathrm{Spect}(DF(O))$.

In a similar way one can define a strong non-degenerate source (sink) in the case of periodic orbit lying on M. For this one needs to consider the Poincare map near a periodic orbit.

Theorem 2.1. [5]. *Invariant manifold M of system (1.1) is strongly indestructible if and only if the transversality condition holds on M except possibly for the non-degenerate strong sinks and the non-degenerate strong sources.*

Remark 2.1. It is evident from Definition 2.2 that if M is a strongly indestructible invariant manifold of the vector field F then there exists a neighborhood V of F in $C^1(\mathbb{R}^n, \mathbb{R}^n)$ such that for every vector field $G \in V$ for which M is invariant, the manifold M is strongly indestructible and, hence, indestructible. Such is the case since the conditions of Definition 2.2 hold for G with the same map H.

The analysis of the proof of Theorem 2.1 in a part of necessity shows that the converse is also true. Thus, we obtain

Proposition 2.1. *Invariant manifold M of the vector field F is strongly indestructible if and only if there exists a neighborhood V of F in $C^1(\mathbb{R}^n, \mathbb{R}^n)$ such that for every $G \in V$ for which M is invariant, the manifold M is indestructible.*

Let $M \subset \mathbb{R}^n$ be a smooth compact boundaryless manifold. Denote the space of vector fields $F \in C^1(\mathbb{R}^n, \mathbb{R}^n)$ for which the manifold M is invariant by Ω_M. Assume that Ω_M is equipped with C^1 topology. Let Σ, Σ_S, Σ_W be the subsets of Ω_M consisting of vector fields for which the manifold M is respectively indestructible, strongly indestructible and weakly indestructible. By virtue of Remark 2.1 and Proposition 2.1 we have

Proposition 2.2.

1) the sets Σ_S, Σ_W form a decomposition of Σ, i.e.

$$\Sigma = \Sigma_S \cup \Sigma_W, \qquad \Sigma_S \cap \Sigma_W = 0;$$

2) Σ_S is open in Ω_M.

As for the conditions of a weakly indestructibility at present it is known only the sufficient ones.

Theorem 2.2 [5]. *If the transversality condition holds on M except possibly for the strong sinks and the strong sources whose index is different from zero and there exists a degenerate strong sink (source) then M is weakly indestructible.*

3. Examples

Example 3.1. Strongly indestructible locally unique invariant manifold (persistent manifold).

In the plane consider a system having the invariant unit circle S. Assume that the system has two equilibrium points disposed on S: the saddle A and the sink B (see Fig. 1a). Let the linear part of the system at A be of the form $\frac{dx}{dt} = x$, $\frac{dy}{dt} = -(y-1)$ and at B of the form $\frac{dx}{dt} = -x$, $\frac{dy}{dt} = -2(y+1)$. It can be easily verified that S is normally hyperbolic: for all $z \in S$ $E^u_z = \{0\}$, E^s_z is a straight line transversal to S at Z, e.g. E^s_A, E^s_B are the vertical straight lines. By Theorem 1.1 S is persistent.

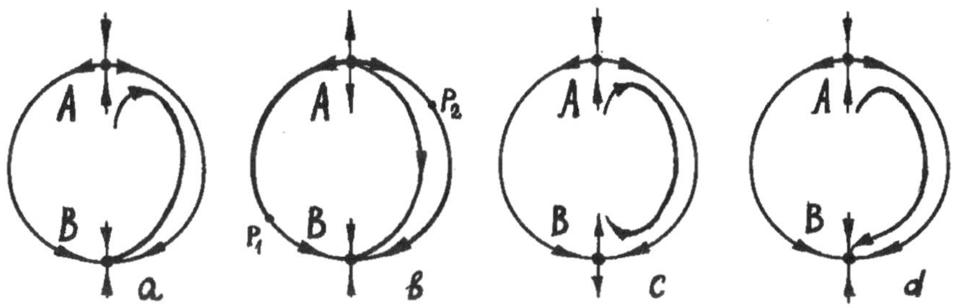

Figure 1.

Notice that in this case the map H is uniquely determined since in some neighborhood of S every perturbed vector field G C^1 close to the original one has a unique invariant manifold S_G diffeomorphic to S. S_G consists of two equilibrium points (the saddle A_G near to A and the sink B_G near to B) and two separatrices from A_G to B_G. Hence, the map H must be of the form $H(G) = S_G$.

Example 3.2. Locally non-unique strongly indestructible manifold on which the transversality condition is fulfilled.

Similarly to Example 3.1. consider a system in the plane having the invariant unit circle S and two equilibrium points disposed on S: the source A and the sink B (see Fig. 1b). Let the linear part of the system at A be of the form $\frac{dx}{dt} = x$, $\frac{dy}{dt} = 2(y-1)$ and that at B of the form $\frac{dx}{dt} = -x$, $\frac{dy}{dt} = -2(y+1)$. The transversality condition holds on S entirely since it is easily seen that $E^s_A = E^u_B = \{0\}$, E^u_A, E^s_B are the vertical straight lines, for $z \neq A, B$ E^u_z, E^s_z

are two straight lines transversal to S at z. By Theorem 2.1 S is strongly indestructible. Notice that in every neighborhood of S there is an infinite number of smooth invariant manifolds which are tangent to the horizontal direction at A and B.

In some neighborhood of S every perturbed vector field G C^1 close to the original one has two equilibrium points (the source A_G near to A and the sink B_G near to B) and an infinite number of trajectories going from A_G to B_G and tangent to each other at these points. To construct the map H let us choose two points p_1, p_2 on the left and the right parts of the circle S other than A, B. Assume the perturbation small enough to ensure that $p_1, p_2 \neq A_G, B_G$ and the trajectories $\gamma_G(p_1), \gamma_G(p_2)$ passing through p_1, p_2 tend to A_G, B_G as $t \to \mp\infty$. Clearly, $S_G(p_1, p_2) = A_G \cup B_G \cup \gamma_G(p_1) \cup \gamma_G(p_2)$ is an invariant manifold of G C^1 close to S. It remains to set $H(G) = S_G(p_1, p_2)$. It can be verified at once that H satisfies Definition 2.2. Notice that the construction of H depends on the choice of points p_1, p_2. By choosing the other points we obtain a map different from the constructed one.

Example 3.3. Destruction of an invariant manifold in the case when the transversality condition does not hold at a wandering point.

In $\mathbb{R}^2$ let us consider a system having the invariant unit circle and two saddle points A, B (see Fig. 1c). Let the linearized system at A be of the form $\frac{dx}{dt} = x$, $\frac{dy}{dt} = -(y-1)$ and that at B of the form $\frac{dx}{dt} = -x$, $\frac{dy}{dt} = (y+1)$. It is easily seen that A, B are normally hyperbolic: $E^s_B = E^u_A = \{0\}, E^s_A, E^u_B$ are the vertical straight lines. If $z \in S, z \neq A, B$ then $E^s_z = E^u_z = \{0\}$. Hence, the transversality condition is violated at Z . Since the arc $AB \subset S$ is a separatrix joining two saddles one can construct a perturbed system having nearby S no invariant manifold homeomorphic to S.

Example 3.4. Destruction of the C^1 structure of invariant manifold in the case when the transversality condition does not hold at a wandering point.

As in Example 3.1 consider a system defined in the plane and having the invariant unit circle S. Assume also that $A, B \in S$ are its equilibrium points. Let the linear part of system at A be the same as in Example 3.1 and that at B be of the form $\frac{dx}{dt} = -x$, $\frac{dy}{dt} = -(y+1)/2$. The behavior of the trajectories is represented in Fig. 1d. As above the transversality condition holds at A. B is a strong sink. If $z \in S, z \neq A$ then $E^s_z = E^u_z = \{0\}$. Thus, the transversality condition is violated at z. Perturbing the system in a neighborhood of some point $z \in S, z \neq A, B$ one can obtain a system whose saddle A has the unstable separatrix, which is tangent to the vertical direction at B. Thus, the perturbed system nearby S has no invariant C^1 submanifold diffeomorphic to S. Observe that there exists nevertheless an invariant C^0 manifold homeomorphic to S.

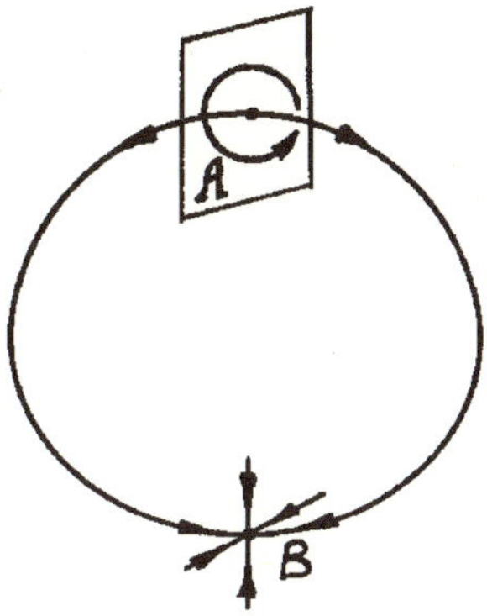

Figure 2.

Example 3.5. Strongly indestructible manifold in the case when the transversality condition is violated at a strong source.

In $\mathbb{R}^3$ consider a system having in the plane $x = 0$ the invariant unit circle S and two equilibrium points $A(0, 0, 1), B(0, 0, -1) \in S$ (see Fig. 2). Suppose that in some neighborhood of A the plane $y = 0$ is invariant for the system. Let in this plane the system be of the form $\frac{dx}{dt} = z - 1$, $\frac{dz}{dt} = -x$, i.e. the equilibrium is of the center type in this plane. Let in some neighborhood of A the linear part of the system on S be of the form $\frac{dx}{dt} = y$. It is clear that A is a non-degenerate strong source and the transversality condition does not hold at A. At B the linear part of the system is of the form $\frac{dx}{dt} = -2x$, $\frac{dy}{dt} = -y$, $\frac{dz}{dt} = -2(z + 1)$. The transversality condition is obviously fulfilled on $S \backslash A$. For $z \in S \backslash A$ $E^u_z = \{0\}, E^s_z$ is a plane transversal to S at z. By Theorem 2.1 S is strongly indestructible.

The map H is determined, in this case, uniquely and can be easily constructed. Obviously, every vector field G C^1 close to the original one has two equilibrium points A_G, B_G nearby A, B. By the Center Manifold Theorem [1] there exists a locally invariant surface P_G containing A_G and C^1 close to the plane $y = 0$. Every trajectory of G passing through a point near to P_G tends to P_G as $t \to -\infty$. On the surface P_G the equilibrium A_G is of a center, focus or center-focus type. It is not difficult to see that in either case there are only two trajectories γ^1_G, γ^2_G tending to A_G as $t \to -\infty$ and C^1 close to S. Since $\gamma^1_G, \gamma^2_G \to B_G$ as $t \to +\infty$ and are tangent to each other at A_G, B_G it remains to set $H(G) = M_G = A_G \cup B_G \cup \gamma^1_G \cup \gamma^1_G$. Easily seen that $H(G)$ depends continuously on G in C^1 topology and $H(G) = S$ is invariant for G.

References

[1] Hirsch M., Pugh C., Shub M., *Invariant manifolds*, Lect.Notes in Math. **583** (1977), pp. 1–150.

[2] Sacker R., *A perturbation theorem for invariant Riemannian manifolds*, Differential Equations and Dynamical Systems, Proc. Symp. Diff. Equation and Dyn. Syst., 1965, pp. 43-54, Academic Press, New York, 1967.

[3] Neimark Yu.I., *Integral manifolds of differential equations*, Izv. Vuzov, Radiophisics **10** (1967), pp. 321–334 (In Russian).

[4] Mañé R., *Persistent manifolds are normally hyperbolic*, Trans. Amer. Math. Soc. **246** (1978), pp. 261–280.

[5] Osipenko G.S., *Perturbation of invariant manifolds*, I,II,III,IV Differential Equations **21** (1985), pp. 406–412; **21** (1985), pp. 908–914; **23** (1987), pp. 556–561; **24** (1988), pp. 647-652.

State Technical University, St.Petersburg, Russia

Civil Engineering Institute, St.Petersburg, Russia

COMPLEX GEOMETRY OF THE BILLIARD ON THE ELLIPSOID AND QUASICRYSTALLIC CURVES

ALEXANDER P. VESELOV

This paper can be considered as a remark to the old Jacobi paper [1] about the quadruple periodic functions. The reason to come back to Jacobi has appeared in connection with the following integrable dynamical system.

Let E be the ellipsoid in $\mathbb{R}^3$:

$$\frac{x_1^2}{a_1} + \frac{x_2^2}{a_2} + \frac{x_3^2}{a_3} = 1, \tag{1}$$

where $a_1 > a_2 > a_3 > 0$, H be the hyperboloid, confocal with E,

$$\frac{x_1^2}{a_1 - b} + \frac{x_2^2}{a_2 - b} + \frac{x_3^2}{a_3 - b} = 1, \quad a_2 > b > a_3. \tag{2}$$

We are interested in the billiard dynamics in the domain Ω of the ellipsoid E, bounded by the intersection $\Gamma = E \cap H$ (see Fig. 1). It is easy to investigate this problem in the elliptic coordinates $\lambda_1, \lambda_2, \lambda_3$ $(\lambda_1 \geq \lambda_2 \geq \lambda_3)$, which are the roots of the following equation

$$\frac{x_1^2}{a_1 - \lambda} + \frac{x_2^2}{a_2 - \lambda} + \frac{x_3^2}{a_3 - \lambda} = 1. \tag{3}$$

In this coordinate system the ellipsoid E has the equation $\lambda_3 = 0$, the boundary $\Gamma - \lambda_2 = b$, and the geodesics on E can be found by the method of separation of variables, as it was demonstrated by Jacobi in [2]. As a result we have the following equations for the geodesics

$$F(\lambda_1) + F(\lambda_2) = \text{const}, \tag{4}$$

where F is the abelian integral:

$$F(z) = \int_0^z \frac{z}{\sqrt{R(z)}}\, dz \tag{5}$$
$$R(z) = z(z - \mu)(a_1 - z)(a_2 - z)(a_3 - z).$$

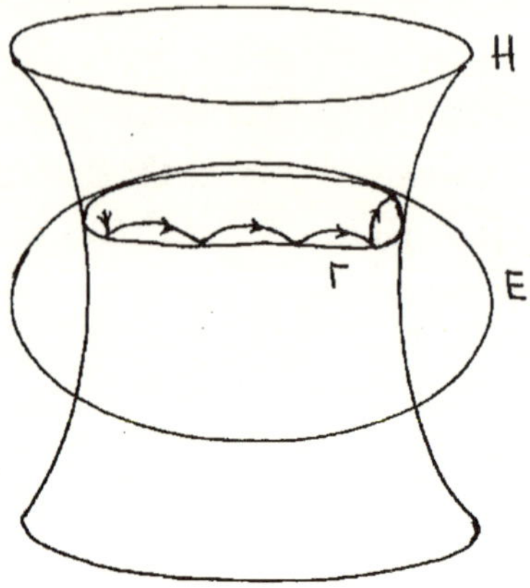

Figure 1.

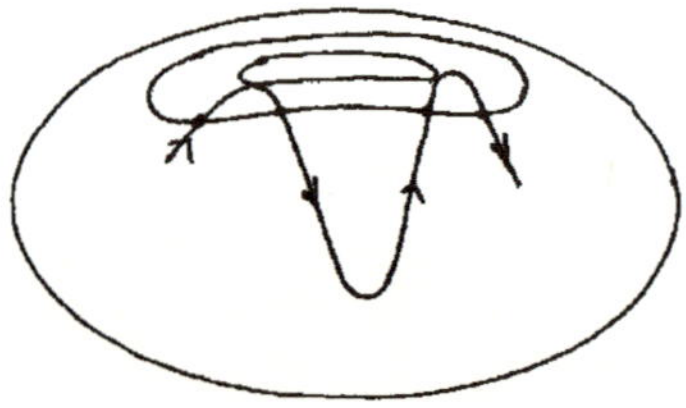

Figure 2.

The parameter μ, which is the integral of this system, has the following geometrical meaning: the geodesic is tangent to the confocal hyperboloid with the parameter μ (see Fig. 2).

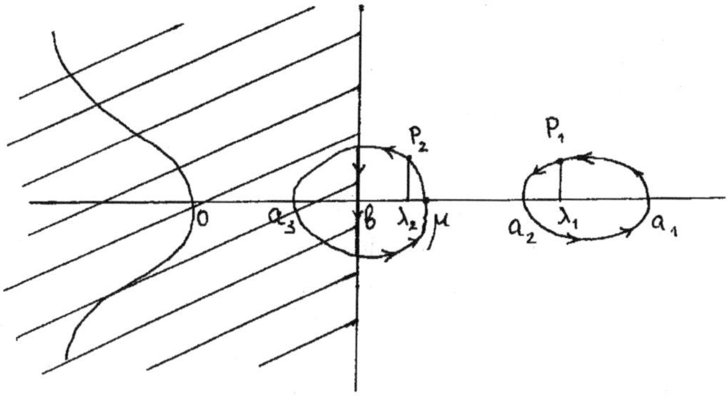

Figure 3.

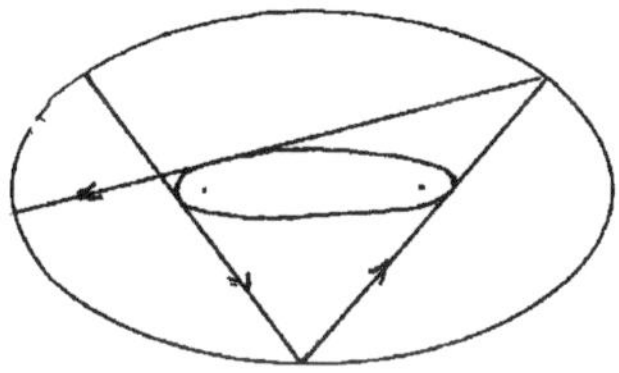

Figure 4.

On the hyperelliptic curve C, given by the equation $y^2 = R(z)$, we have the following picture (Fig. 3). The change of sheet in the moment of the reflection follows from the orthogonality of the elliptical coordinate system (see e.g. [3]).

In the angle variable on Γ, defined by the abelian integral F, our billiard mapping becomes the shift, so the number $\frac{\Delta}{\omega}$,

$$\Delta = 2\int_b^{\mu} \alpha, \quad \omega = 2\int_{a_2}^{a_1} \alpha, \qquad \alpha = \frac{zdz}{y} = \frac{zdz}{\sqrt{R(z)}},$$

completely determines the dynamical properties of the corresponding billiard trajectories.

Up to now the situation was completely analogous to the elliptical billiard on the plane (Fig. 4). The differences begin at the complex level. The idea to consider the dynamics in the complex domain goes back to S. Kowalevskaya and Painleve and now is again very popular (see e.g. [4]). The principial difference of the planar and ellipsoidal billiards is that in the second case the geodesic intersects the boundary in the *infinitely many points* (see Fig. 2). On the reals we have the possibility to determine the dynamics by considering the first of such points, but for the complex dynamics it has no sense.

Therefore we consider the dynamics on the set G_μ of all geodesics (w ithout the parametrization) on E, which are tangent to the given hyperboloid H_μ.

Theorem 1. *The set G_μ in the complex domain has the following structure: $G_\mu = Q/\mathbb{Z}_2$, where $Q = \mathbb{C}/\mathbb{Z}^4$ is the quotient of $\mathbb{C}$ by the subgroup $\mathbb{Z}^4$, generated by 4 shifts. The billiard dynamics on G_μ is described by following commutative diagram*

$$\begin{array}{ccc} Q & \xrightarrow{z \to z \pm \Delta} & Q \\ \mathbb{Z}_2 \downarrow & & \downarrow \mathbb{Z}_2 \\ G_\mu & \longrightarrow & G_\mu \end{array}$$

The quotients of $\mathbb{C}$ by the finite generated group of shifts ("quasilattices") we will call as *quasicrystallic curves*. So the theorem says that G_μ is the quotient of the quasicrystallic curve by the involution $z \to -z$. The proof follows from the equations of the geodesics (4). Indeed, the values of the abelian integral F are determined only modulo 4 periods ω_i on the abelian differential α:

$$\omega_i = \oint_{\gamma_i} \alpha \qquad (i = 1, 2, 3, 4),$$

where γ_i $(i = 1, ..., 4)$ form the basis of cycles on the hyperelliptic curve C. The hyperelliptic involution $\tau\colon C \to C$ changes the sign of F, but does not change the geodesic.

It is useful to compare this picture with the planar billiard inside the ellipse. There we also have the commutative diagram

$$\begin{array}{ccc} \mathcal{E} & \xrightarrow{z \to z \pm \Delta} & \mathcal{E} \\ \downarrow & & \downarrow \\ G_\mu & \longrightarrow & G_\mu, \end{array}$$

but $\mathcal{E} = \mathbb{C}/\mathbb{Z}^2$ now is an elliptic curve and G_μ consists of the tangents to the confocal ellipse $C_\mu : G_\mu = C_\mu^*$ (for the details see e.g. [5, 6]). The projection $\mathcal{E} \to G_\mu \approx \mathbb{C}P^1$ is given by the elliptic $\wp$-function, in terms of which the dynamics can be completely described.

Returning to the ellipsoid we have instead of $\wp(z)$ the inversion of the hyperelliptic integral F, whose analytical properties not so nice like that of $\wp$-function. Jacobi [1] was the first to discuss this question and proved that F^{-1} has four periods. It was not so evident in his time because there was no general conception of the riemannian surfaces.

In the same paper [1] Jacobi has proved that a "good" analitical function on $\mathbb{C}$ with four periods must be constant and posed the new problem, which now is well-known as Jacobi inversion problem. It is very surprising but to the author's knowledge after Jacobi and Riemann there were no serious investigations of the functions with many periods. The billiard dynamics on the ellipsoid leads us in a natural way to this problem and the results we present now can be considered as some steps in this direction.

First of all we want to make more clear the following connection:

Quasicrystallic curves $Q = \mathbb{C}/\mathbb{Z}^m$ and the functions on them	$\longleftrightarrow$	Algebraic curves $C\colon P(x,y) = 0$ and abelian integrals

In one direction this connection was explained by Jacobi and Riemann: the inversions of the abelian integrals leads to the functions on some quasicrystallic curves. We explain now the way back from the quasicrystallic to the algebraic curves.

Let $\Pi(x)$ be a multiplevalued function of the complex variable x, $x \in \mathbb{C}$, with the following properties:

1) $\Pi(x + \omega_i) \equiv \Pi(x), \qquad i = 1, ..., m;$
2) $\Pi(-x) \equiv \Pi(x);$
3) $\Pi(x)$ has the singularities only in the points of quasilattice

$$\mathcal{L}_Q = \sum_{i=1}^{m} k_i \omega_i, \qquad k_i \in \mathbb{Z}.$$

In particular, when $x \approx 0$ $\Pi(x)$ is supposed to have the behaviour

$$\Pi(x) = Cx^{-\beta} \left(1 + o(x)\right),$$

where β is some rational number.

4) The sheets of Π differ each from another only by the action of the group $G = \mathbb{Z}^m \ltimes \mathbb{Z}_2$, generated by $x \to x + \omega_i$, $x \to -x$. Such functions we will call as *quasicrystallic* Π*-functions*. In the "crystallic" case $m = 2$ we have Weierstrass

$\wp$-function. The last property is the correct generalization of the fact that $\wp$ takes all its values twice: in x and in $-x$. The absense of good fundamental domain is the main difficulty of the general quasicrystallic case.

Let's consider the inverse function $F = \Pi^{-1}$. It is defined only up to the transformations

$$F(z) \to \pm F(z) + \sum_{i=1}^{m} k_i \omega_i.$$

The ratio $R(z) = F''(z)/F'(z)$ is already well-defined rational function of the form

$$R(z) = \sum_{i=1}^{N} \frac{\alpha_i}{z - z_i}.$$

The equation $x'' = R(z)x'$ has the general solution

$$x = F(z) = C \int^{z} \prod_{i=1}^{N} (z - z_i)^{\alpha_i} dz.$$

It is easy to show that such function has the inversion, which has the proprties 2)–4) of Π-function, only if $2\alpha_i \in \mathbb{Z}$ and $\frac{1}{\alpha_i + 1} \in \mathbb{Z}_+$, what implies $\alpha_i = -\frac{1}{2}$ for all $i = 1, ..., N$ and

$$F = \int_{\infty}^{z} \frac{dz}{\sqrt{P(z)}}, \qquad P(z) = a_N z^N + ... + a_0. \tag{6}$$

Theorem 2. *The quasicrystallic* Π*-functions are nothing but the inversions of certain hyperelliptic integrals of the special type* (6).

Remark. One can consider the functions, which are invariant under the groups $\mathbb{Z}^m \ltimes \mathbb{Z}_n$ ("quasicrystallic" in the sense of S. P. Novikov). The theory of such functions also leads to the algebraic curves and abelian integrals. The most general approach concerns the arbitrary nondiscrete subgroup of $SL_2(\mathbb{C})$ and the corresponding automorphic functions.

Leaving the further investigation for the future we discuss now only the case $m = 4$ and the inversions of the hyperelliptic integrals

$$F = \int_{\infty}^{z} \alpha, \qquad \alpha = \frac{c_1 dz}{\sqrt{z(z-1)(z-c_2)(z-c_3)(z-c_4)}}.$$

The natural question: do the Π-functions exist on arbitrary quasicrystallic curve?—is closely connected with the properties of *period mapping* p : $(c_1, c_2, c_3, c_4) \to (\omega_1, \omega_2, \omega_3, \omega_4)$, $\omega_i = \oint_{\gamma_i} \alpha$; where γ_i is some basis of cycles on the corresponding hyperelliptic curve C.

The following results show that under certain assumptions the answer is positive.

Theorem 3. *For the nondegenerated curve C the period mapping is also nondegenerated:*

$$\det \left\| \frac{\partial p}{\partial c} \right\| \neq 0.$$

Theorem 4. *For the real ω_1, ω_2 and pure imaginary ω_3, ω_4 there exists the real hyperelliptic curve C (i.e. real c_1, c_2, c_3, c_4) such that $p(c) = \omega$.*

Theorem 3 follows from some calculations, Theorem 4—from Christoffel-Schwarz formula for the conformal mapping and Riemann theorem about such mappings.

Acknowledgements. I am thankfull to R. Perline and V. Roganov for the discussions of the billiard problem on the ellipsoid and to S. P. Novikov, who stimulated my interest to the quasicrystallic theme.

References

[1] C. G. Jacobi, *De functionibus duarum variabilum quadrupliciter periodicis quibus theoria transcendentium Abelinarium innititur*, Crelle J., b.**13** (1835).

[2] C. G. Jacobi, *"Forlesungen über Dynamik"*, Berlin, 1884.

[3] Chang S.-J., Shi K.J., *Billiard system on qudratic surfaces and the Poncelet theorem*, J. Math. Phys., n.**1** (1989), pp. 788–804.

[4] M. Adler, P. van Moerbeke, *Algebraic integrable system. A systematic approach*, Perspectives in Math.-Boston, AP, 1989.

[5] P. Griffiths, *A variation on the theorem of Abel*, Invent. Math., vol. **35** (1976), pp. 321–390.

[6] A. P. Veselov, *Integrable mappings*, Russ.Math.Surv., vol. **46**, n.**5** (1991), pp. 3–45 (In Russian).

Moscow State University, 119899 Moscow, Russia

DYNAMICAL SYSTEMS

PROGRAMME

14–25 OCTOBER

Monday, October 14

Moser J. (Zurich, Swizerland) An unusual variational problem connected with Mather's theory.

Nekhoroshev N. N. (State University, Moscow) A stability of the resonant zones of the systems with quasiconvex nonperturbed Hamiltonians.

Fel'shtin A. L. (St. Petersburg, USSR) The Reidemeister torsion in dynamical system.

Turchetti G. (Bologna, Italy) Numerical results on normal forms for sympletic maps.

Veselov A. P. (State University, Moscow) Complex geometry of the billiard on the ellipsoid.

Tuesday, October 15

Arnol'd V. I. (Steklov Math. Inst., Moscow) Asymptotics of complexity of intersections and of bifurcations in dynamical systems.

Simó C. (Barcelona, Spain) Quasiperiodic perturbations of equilibrum points.

Wednesday, October 16

Pöschel Ju. (Bonn, Germany) Infinite-dimensional KAM-Theory and nonlinear Anderson localisation.

Sharkovskii A. N. (Kiev, USSR) Ideal turbulence.

Rüssman H. (Mainz, Germany) On the frequencies in quasi-periodic solutions of analytic nearly integrable Hamiltonian systems.

Khanin K. M. (Moscow) Mixing for special flows with logarithmic singularities.

Thursday, October 17

Palis J. (Rio de Janeiro, Brazil) Sensitive-chaotic dynamics: new approach.

Simó C. (Barselona, Spain) On the Bogdanov-Takens bifurcation for diffeomorphisms.

Dovbysh S. A. (State University, Moscow) Transversal intersection of separetrices and nonexistance of additional integral in many-dimensional systems.

Martinez R. (Bellaterra, Spain) On the parabolic orbits of the elliptic restricted three body problem.

Treshchev D. V. (State University, Moscow) Trajectories of nearly singular discrete Lagrangian systems.

Friday, October 18

Sevrjuk M. B. (Moscow) New results in the reversible KAM-Theory.

Turchetti G. (Bologna, Italy) Analyticity domains of normalizing transformation in area-preserving maps.

Monday, October 21

Il'jashenko Yu. S. (State University, Moscow) Normal forms of local families, nonlocal bifurcations and Hilbert-Arnol'd problem for elementary complicates cycles.

Lochak P. (Paris, France) Finite time perturbations of convex integrable Hamiltonians.

Tuesday, October 22

Herman M. (Palaiseau, France) Topological stability of conservative dynamical systems.

Voronin S. M. (State University, Cheljabinsk) Orbital analitical classification of germs of vector field in $(C^3, 0)$ with a line of singular points.

Karasev M. V., Vorobjev Yu. M. (Moscow) Linear connections, integrability and index for Hamiltonian dynamics over an isotropic torus.

Wednesday, October 23

Bikbaev R., Kuksin S. (Moscow) Periodic boundary value problem for Sine-Gordon equation and its Hamiltonian perturbations.

Pöschel J. (Bonn, Germany) On exponential stability times in nearly integrable Hamiltonian systems.

Suris Yu. B. (St. Petersburg) Schroedinger equation with quasi-periodic potential: small divisors and irredusibility.

Zhidkov P. E. (Dubna) On the stability of some solutions and the existance of the invariant measure for some infinite-dimensional dynamical systems defined by non-linear evolution equations of mathematical physics.

Herman M. (Palaiseau, France) Counterexamples to the C^{inf} closing lemma for Hamiltonian vector fields.

Thursday, October 24

Bazzani G. (Bologna, Italy) Stability and diffusion in modulated area-preserving maps.

Vershik A. M. (State University, St. Petersburg) Isoholonomic problems and nonholonomic geodesic flows.

Neishtadt A. I. (State University, Moscow) On accuracy of the conservation of the adiabatic invariant.

Gelfreich V. G. (St. Petersburg) The separatrices splitting for the rapidly forced pendulum.

Lazutkin V. F. (St. Petersburg) Resurgent approach to separatrices splitting.

Friday, October 25

Douady R. (Paris, France) Stability in non-autonomous dynamical systems.

Vasiliev N. N. (St. Petersburg) Sympletic methods for numerical integration of Hamiltonian systems.

18 NOVEMBER — 1 DECEMBER

Monday, November 18

Lacomba E. (Mexico-City, Mexico) Poincaré Compactification for the collinear Three-Body Problem.

Kuksin S. B. (Moscow, USSR) On the Constructive Interpolation of Analytical Symplectomorphism by Hamiltonian Flows.

Dovbysh S. A. (Moscow, USSR) Some New Qualitative Phenomena in Dynamics near Separatrices for Hamiltonian Systems with One and a Half Degrees of Freedom.

Ershov E. K., Osipenko G. S. (St.Petersburg, USSR) The Examples of Indestructible Invariant Manyfolds which are not Persistent.

Osipenko G. S. (St.Petersburg, USSR) The Periodic Points and the Symbolic Dynamics.

Tuesday, November 19

Lerman L. M., Umanskii Ya. L. (Nizhnii Novgorod, USSR) Isoenergetical Classification of Integrable Hamiltonian Systems with Two Degrees of Freedom within an Extended Neighbourhood of a simple Singular Point.

Troubetzkoy S. E., Krueger T. (Bielefeld, Germany) Markov Partitions and Shadowing for Non-Uniformly Hyperbolic Systems with Singularities.

Wednesday, November 20

Bikbaev R. F. (St.Petersburg, USSR) Finite-Dimensional Attractors in Infinite-Dimensional Integrable Systems of KdV Type.

Chiercia L. (Roma, Italy) Maximal Almost-Periodic Solutions for Second Order Hamilton Equations on Infinite-Dimensional Tori.

Denzler J. (Zurich, Switzerland) Breather Solutions to Non-linear Wave Equations and Perturbations of The Sine-Gordon Equation.

Vakulenko S. A. (St.Petersburg, USSR) Asymptotical Transition from Parabolic Non-linear Systems to Finite-Dimensional Dynamic Systems.

Thursday, November 21

Pöschel J. (Bonn, Germany) Infinite-Dimensional KAM-Theory and Nonlinear Anderson Localization.

Tarkhov D. A. (St.Petersburg, USSR) Problems with Small Denominators in the Case of Infinite Basis.

Round Table

"Infinite-Dimensional Hamiltonian Systems"

Moderator Kuksin S.

Friday, November 22

Elskens Y. (Marseille, France) Perturbative Construction of a Significant Piece of Homoclinic Trellis in 1.5 Degree-of-Freedom Hamiltonian Systems.

Neishdadt A. I. (Moscow, USSR) Capture into resonances and Surfatron Acceleration of Particles.

Lerman L. M., Shil'nikov L. P. (Nizhnii Novgorod, USSR) Homoclinic Chaos in Hamiltonian Systems.

Bakhtin V. I. (Minsk, USSR) Random Processes Generated by Expanding Maps.

Monday, November 25

Burago D. Yu. (St.Petersburg, USSR) Geodesics on Periodic Metrics.

Viana M. (Rio de Janeiro, Brazil) Henon-like Strangle Attractors in Higher Dimensions.

Bakaleinikov L. A. (St.Petersburg, USSR) On Applicability of the Approximate Poincaré Map on ODE-Systems with Homoclinic Trajectory.

Delshams A. (Barselona, Spain) Exponentially Small Expressions for Separatrix Splittings.

Tuesday, November 26

Bruno A. D. (Moscow, USSR) Local Analysis of the Hamiltonian Systems.

Galgani L. (Milano, Italy) Recent Progress in the Fermi Pasta Ulam Problem and in Classical Electrodynamics.

Douady R. (Paris, France) Arnol'd Diffusion.

Galeeva R. F. (Dubna, USSR) Two-Parameter Family of Bimodal Maps with Simple Properties of Monotonicity.

Zhidkov P. E. (Dubna, USSR) On Some Non-linear Boudary Value Problems Arising in Physics.

Round Table

"Stability in Hamiltonian Systems"

Moderator Bruno A.

Wednesday, November 27

Delshams A. (Barselona, Spain) First Steps towards Locating Arnol'd Diffusion in Hamiltonian Systems.

Chierchia L. (Roma, Italy) Towards an Analytic Theory of Arnol'd Diffusion.

Round Table

"Arnol'd Diffusion: Does It Exist?"

Moderator Lazutkin V.

Thursday, November 28

Pöschel J. (Bonn, Germany) On Nekhoroshev Estimates.

Pilyugin S. Yu. (St.Petersburg, USSR) Limit Sets for Domains: Arnol'd Conjecture.

Meiss J. (Boulder, USA) Resonances and Escape in Symplectic Maps.

Benettin G. (Padova, Italy) Adiabatic Invariants and Equilibrium Times in Models of Classical Gases.

Friday, November 29

Giorgilli A. (Milano, Italy) Realistic Nekhoroshev Estimates for the Lagrangian Triangular Equilibria.

Suris Yu. B. (St.Petersburg, USSR) Phase Volume and Symplectic Structure Preserving Runge-Kutta Methods.

Chaikovsky D. K. (Moscow, USSR) Anomalous Diffusion under Adiabatic Chaos Condition.

Progress in Nonlinear Differential Equations and Their Applications

Editor
Haim Brezis
Département de Mathématiques
Université P. et M. Curie
4, Place Jussieu
75252 Paris Cedex 05
France
and
Department of Mathematics
Rutgers University
New Brunswick, NJ 08903
U.S.A.

Progress in Nonlinear and Differential Equations and Their Applications is a book series that lies at the interface of pure and applied mathematics. Many differential equations are motivated by problems arising in such diversified fields as Mechanics, Physics, Differential Geometry, Engineering, Control Theory, Biology, and Economics. This series is open to both the theoretical and applied aspects, hopefully stimulating a fruitful interaction between the two sides. It will publish monographs, polished notes arising from lectures and seminars, graduate level texts, and proceedings of focused and refereed conferences.

We encourage preparation of manuscripts in some form of TeX for delivery in camera-ready copy, which leads to rapid publication, or in electronic form for interfacing with laser printers or typesetters.

Proposals should be sent directly to the editor or to: Birkhäuser Boston, 675 Massachusetts Avenue, Cambridge, MA 02139

PNLDE 1 Partial Differential Equations and the Calculus of Variations, Volume I
Essays in Honor of Ennio De Giorgi
F. Colombini, A. Marino, L. Modica, and S. Spagnolo, editors

PNLDE 2 Partial Differential Equations and the Calculus of Variations, Volume II
Essays in Honor of Ennio De Giorgi
F. Colombini, A. Marino, L. Modica, and S. Spagnolo, editors

PNLDE 3 Propagation and Interaction of Singularities in Nonlinear Hyperbolic Problems
Michael Beals

PNLDE 4 Variational Methods
Henri Berestycki, Jean-Michel Coron, and Ivar Ekeland, editors

PNLDE 5 Composite Media and Homogenization Theory
Gianni Dal Maso and Gian Fausto Dell'Antonio, editors

PNLDE 6 Infinite Dimensional Morse Theory and Multiple Solution Problems
Kung-ching Chang

PNLDE 7 Nonlinear Differential Equations and their Equilibrium States, 3
N.G. Lloyd, W.M. Ni, L.A. Peletier, J. Serrin, editors

PNLDE 8 An Introduction to Γ–Convergence
Gianni Dal Maso

PNLDE 9 Differential Inclusions in Nonsmooth Mechanical Problems. Shocks and Dry Friction
Manuel D.P. Monteiro Marques

PNLDE10 Periodic Solutions of Singular Lagrangian Systems
Antonio Ambrosetti and Vittorio Coti Zelati

PNLDE11 Nonlinear Waves and Weak Turbulence with Applications in Oceanography and Condensed Matter Physics
N. Fitzmaurice, D. Gurarie, F. McCaughan and W.A. Woyczynski, editors

PNLDE12 Semester on Dynamical Systems
S. Kuksin, V. Lazutkin and J. Pöschel, editors